2.99   C4
43

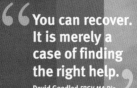

"You can recover. It is merely a case of finding the right help."

David Goodlad *FRSH MA Dip. MBACP (Snr. Accred) UKRC NCAC CADC*

CW00734804

About DryOutNow.com™

Call 0800 160 1020
E-mail: freeadvice@dryoutnow.com

dryoutnow.com

DryOutNow.com, a division of Triage Healthcare, was formed in 2005 by Consultant Addiction Psychiatrist Dr Bruce Trathen MBBS MRCPsych, and Addictions Therapist David Goodlad FRSH MA Dip. MBACP (Snr. Accred) NCAC CADC. Created in the knowledge of the imbalance between availability of addiction treatment in the NHS and the demand in the community, the aim of the company is to deliver high quality, best value treatment to people throughout the UK.

Concerned individuals and carers receive an initial confidential telephone assessment from an experienced professional (psychologist, nurse, doctor) leading to the development of a baseline care plan. Further assessment is then arranged at your request with the DryOutNow. com team in your locality of the UK – this usually involves a home visit from the local nurse or senior counsellor in your area. Alternatively, for those who wish to travel, assessment is available with our senior medical team in Harley Street, London.

The care plan developed from these assessments may involve provision of one or more of a number of modalities of treatment, including detoxification (at home or residentially), out-patient care and counselling, various forms of group support, medical and psychiatric care, and residential rehabilitation (rehab). The plan is matched to the needs, circumstances and wishes of the individual, and where funding is limited, referrals are made to the relevant local NHS and voluntary services.

Your local DryOutNow.com team continues to work with you, through the plan, and into the future until such time as you are safe from relapse.

Our network

DryOutNow.com™ consists of highly experienced teams of professionals working around the UK. Our call centre and Harley Street offices are staffed by nurses, doctors, psychologists and counsellors working under the supervision of a consultant psychiatrist. Our teams working locally throughout the UK consist of specialist addictions counsellors and nurses, trained to bring you the highest standards of effective care.

Information and advice services

DryOutNow.com provides a range of free information and advice services.

Call centre immediate response service:
Our call centre is staffed by psychology graduates (enquiry handlers) who have received specialist training in the field. Enquiry handlers are supported and supervised by specialist nurses, as well as having immediate access to advice from senior addiction counsellors and addiction psychiatrists. Overall medical responsibility falls on our medical director, Dr Bruce Trathen, consultant addiction psychiatrist.

Call 0800 160 1020 now or E-mail freeadvice@dryoutnow.com

dryoutnow.com
A division TRIAGE HEALTHCA

Individuals and professionals with technical queries are supported through the call centre with personal or technical advice and provision of practical advice such as contact details for local, free and private addiction services. The full immediate response service is available from 8am to 9pm seven days weekly.

Websites:

Our frontline websites – www.dryoutnow.com and www.addictionadvisor.co.uk, contain downloadable books aimed at individuals with an addiction problem, their friends and relatives, best practice guidelines for professionals working in the field, self-assessment tools, user-friendly access to find local free services from our postcode searchable databases (NHS community drug and alcohol teams, voluntary sector services, AA and NA meetings), information on locating and contacting private help of various kinds including residential rehabilitation centres.

Hardcopy materials:

We have a range of hardcopy books and information leaflets available at cost price to individuals with an addiction problem, their friends and relatives and professionals working in the field.

Patient Services

Assessment and care planning

Standard initial assessment and care planning is provided in the patient's home environment (when risk assessment allows), by the local care coordinator (either specialist nurse or counsellor). A care plan is developed providing choice of use of local free services or private services, for both the patient and involved family members. With the patient's consent, the GP is approached for information and provided with the assessment and care plan.

Enhanced assessment is available in Harley Street, London with specialist consultant psychiatrist or nurse consultant, where indicated.

Community care coordination

If a private option is chosen as the route forward, the foundation of private service provision is community care coordination. The care coordinator is a professional with expertise in addiction treatment, usually a specialist nurse or counsellor, and is tasked with developing an in-depth understanding of the individual's needs. Risk assessment allowing, the care coordinator will provide routine visits to the patient's home for a number of years, with the frequency increasing or decreasing dependent on the presentation and risk of relapse at a particular point in time. The care coordinator is responsible for all liaison and for advice on the provision of services below according to the needs of the patient at a particular point in time.

Outpatient treatment

Outpatient treatment is often suitable for individuals with a lesser degree of problem, such as those who are drinking heavily but are not physically addicted to alcohol. Elements of outpatient treatment may include addictions counselling, attendance of AA or NA meetings, relapse prevention prescribing, psychiatric review, specific psychological therapies such as relapse prevention therapy. All such treatment is provided accessibly in the local area of the patient.

Residential rehabilitation

Residential rehabilitation is probably the form of intervention most likely to bring positive, sustainable results, for those with more serious addictive illness. The evidence-based 'golden rules' of 'rehab' are i) to match the individual to the programme most likely to result in retention in treatment; ii) to commit to at least one month and as long as possible thereafter; iii) to complete the chosen programme duration.

DryOutNow.com works with a large number of treatment centres in the UK and abroad, and has developed expertise in matching to programme type, whilst catering to the needs of an individual's budget.

Aftercare
Equally important is aftercare. Aftercare on return home from a period of residential treatment has proven efficacy in improving outcomes. Typically aftercare will consist of ongoing community care coordination, with a home visit on the day of discharge, local face-to-face counselling and attendance of AA or NA meetings.

Detoxification
Medicated detoxification is necessary if an individual has developed a physical dependency. Detoxification can take place in the home if screening indicates its appropriateness, or residentially. Most residential rehabilitation centres offer detoxification at the beginning of their programmes. DryOutNow.com offers a range of home detoxification services, followed by aftercare, as well as residential detoxification where appropriate.

Other prescribing interventions
Prescribing to prevent relapse is often useful as an adjunct to psychologically-based aftercare treatments. The use of disulfiram, acamprosate and/or naltrexone has been shown to improve outcomes in certain circumstances. DryOutNow.com offers relapse prevention and other prescribing interventions through its network of specialist doctors and nurse prescribers.

Treatment of psychiatric complications
Psychiatric complications are commonly associated with substance misuse (dual diagnosis). Consultant psychiatric assessment, review and prescribing is available both locally and in our Harley Street clinical offices.

Support for Relatives and Carers
Relatives and carers are often depressed or otherwise affected by the addictive behaviour of their spouse or close other. Counselling, general supportive psychotherapy and attendance of Al-Anon meetings can help directly, and also through education as to their future interactions with the patient. DryOutNow.com routinely refers relatives to local Al-Anon meetings, provides a routine initial session of free counselling, and further services where required.

Conclusion

Whatever your budget (and this includes those who have no money for private alcohol treatment) we will provide you with expert advice and meaningful contact information to move forward. If you are able to invest in treatment we will support you in finding the most effective treatment for the money you have to spend. At DryOutNow.com we believe in Ethics, Experience, Expertise and Effectiveness.

We believe in your right to a successful recovery, and we believe in ourselves to deliver that for you.

Make sure you start your journey with the best advice by calling us on **0800 160 102**0 between 8am and 9pm seven days weekly. All calls are dealt with in the strictest confidence.

10 Harley Street, London W1G 9PF
Tel: 0800 160 1020
E-mail: freeadvice@dryoutnow.com
Web: www.dryoutnow.com

* DryOutNow.com™ is a trading name for Triage Healthcare Limited which is registered in England & Wales: No 5584516. Registered office: 14 & 15 Craven Street, London WC2N 5AD.

> Residential rehabilitation from DryOutNow.com is one of a variety of treatment options available to move forwards into recovery from addiction

Residential Rehabilitation

Call 0800 160 1020
E-mail: freeadvice@dryoutnow.com

dryoutnow.com

What is residential rehabilitation?

Residential rehabilitation refers to a period of stay in a residential addictions treatment centre. There are various types of addictions rehabilitation programmes – twelve-step programmes (taken from the Alcoholics-Anonymous model of treatment), religious-based programmes, so called 'therapeutic communities' based on psychotherapeutic models of treatment, and cognitive-behavioural programmes. The large majority of rehabilitation centres in the UK operate using the 12-step model, although increasingly, new centres are opening which use the cognitive-behavioural model of treatment.

What does residential rehabilitation involve?

All treatment centres tend to share a number of key features. Many provide alcohol or drug detoxification in-house at the beginning of the programme. Residents must be drug and alcohol free (apart from tobacco) by the completion of detoxification. A structured programme of psychological, educational and social therapy is provided, which aims at preparing the patient to better manage a drug or alcohol free life back in society. Programmes vary in duration from one week to nine months or longer.

What are the advantages of residential treatment over community-based treatment?

In general, residential treatments appear to present a higher probability of successful outcome than do community based treatments. A 1996 study, conducted as part of the National Treatment Outcome Research Study (NTORS) indicated the following: When compared to community services, residential services achieved comparable outcomes, but were treating clients with more severe patterns of addiction, thus indicating greater effectiveness of residential as compared to community rehabilitation. Treatment centres which actively engage with the client, provide supportive environments and well structured programmes, which are clear about their policies and therapies, and which tailor their activities to individual needs of the client, produce better outcomes.

What is the ideal duration of residential treatment?

The NTORS study (see above) found that, compared to early leavers from residential treatment, those retained in treatment at least 28 days in shorter programmes, and 90 days in longer programmes were four times more likely to maintain abstinence than others. It is generally accepted that retention in residential rehabilitation is central to effectiveness, and can be seen as a function of how the service relates to its clients. There are many examples of studies which show a relationship between duration of stay in residential treatment and successful outcomes in the longer term. In short, standard advice is to commit to as long as possible in treatment.

Call 0800 160 1020 now or E-mail
freeadvice@dryoutnow.com

dryoutnow.com

A division o
TRIAGE HEALTHCAR

What are the other important points?

It is generally accepted that it is essential for clients to engage in a period of 'aftercare' on completion of residential rehabilitation. Aftercare should comprise ongoing psychological and medical support as indicated, and will usually consist of a combination of counselling, group-work, AA or NA meeting attendance. In some cases prescribing of medication to prevent or reduce the chances of relapse may be beneficial, as may the treatment of on-going psychiatric problems such as depression. For practical reasons, it is imperative that 'aftercare' treatment is provided in the home locality of the patient; reliance on 'aftercare' programmes provided by residential treatment centres is impractical if they are distant from the patient's home locality.

Differences between various treatment centres

- Apart from the model of treatment used (see above), treatment centres vary in several important areas all of which may impact on the likelihood of successful outcomes for the patient:

- Duration of programme: Some centres are completely flexible in the duration of treatment provided, whilst others only provide treatment of a specific programme duration. The minimum programme duration possible to arrange is one week, a typical period of stay is one to three months, and treatment can be arranged for durations of one year or longer.

- Medical and psychiatric complications: Treatment centres vary in the quantity and quality of medical cover they provide. The mainstay of treatment in residential rehabilitation is psychological treatment, delivered by counsellors and therapists. However, medical and psychiatric concerns (typically detoxification needs and illnesses such as depression) may require medical input. It is important to match the individual to a treatment centre which has medical staffing adequate to deal with the individual's medical and psychiatric needs.

- Accommodation standards: Standards of accommodation vary from bed-and-breakfast style to luxury hotel accommodation. Whilst this has little if any direct impact on the quality of treatment delivered, the environment provided can be key in retaining the individual in treatment.

- Geographical location: Experience shows that for those who travel overseas for residential rehabilitation, retention rates are superior to UK-based rehabilitation. This is most likely a factor of environment and the practical hurdles faced by an individual who wishes to leave treatment early when abroad, rather than the quality of treatment provided. Nevertheless, retention in treatment for the total duration of the planned programme is a well recognised predictor of good outcomes in the longer term, and as such travel far from home for residential treatment should always be given serious consideration.

- Price: Rehabilitation centres vary hugely in price with programmes varying from £500 per week to £10,000 per week or more. Price tends to be linked more to standards of accommodation and medical cover, than it is to the quality of psychological treatment provided, and good quality treatment can be accessed at the lower end of the price range for most patients. It should be noted that lower end rates tend to be available only in longer programmes, and as such, the minimum total budget required for meaningful treatment tends to be in the region of several thousand pounds. Residential rehabilitation can sometimes be accessed through local NHS and social services, although waiting lists are typically many months long, if the treatment is available at all.

Further information on residential treatment for addiction.

Details of the technical side and best practice for residential rehabilitation can be found in the DryOutNow.com professional guidelines. These can be viewed online at www.dryoutnow.com, or a hard copy book requested by telephoning 0800 160 1020.

Conclusion

Dryoutnow.com provides access to over 200 residential treatment programmes in the UK and abroad, covering the whole spectrum of programme types and prices.

Telephone 0800 160 1020 between 8am and 9pm seven days weekly, or email freeadvice@dryoutnow.com, for further details.

10 Harley Street, London W1G 9PF
Tel: 0800 160 1020
E-mail: freeadvice@dryoutnow.com
Web: www.dryoutnow.com

* DryOutNow.com™ is a trading name for Triage Healthcare Limited which is registered in England & Wales: No 5584516. Registered office: 14 & 15 Craven Street, London WC2N 5AD.

> *Access to treatment options in stunning locations including South Africa and Thailand*

Overseas Rehabilitation Centres

Overseas clinics advice line: 0845 1300 757
E-mail: overseasclinics@dryoutnow.com

dryoutnow.com

DryOutNow.com offers options of residential treatment in various stunning overseas locations including South Africa and Thailand. Medical and psychological care in these treatment centres is recognised as being of the highest standard available worldwide, whilst prices offer excellent value compared to those payable for similar treatment in the UK.

There are many advantages in travelling to these beautiful countries for treatment, not least a clear break from one's usual surroundings and drug or alcohol using network. Some say just experiencing the natural surroundings is enough to help make that vital first step all the more possible.

Working with partner treatment centres, DryOutNow.com assists you in developing the ideal plan of treatment, given your particular needs. Vitally, DryOutNow.com is based here in the UK so as to support you on your return from treatment when the risk of relapse can be at its highest.

Our aims are simply to find you the best quality treatment, deal with all the practical problems involved in accessing that treatment, and to provide you with ongoing support (aftercare) on your return to the UK.

Treatment Centres

Programmes from 1 week to 5 months duration are provided in locations such as Cape Town, The Indian Ocean Coast, the beautiful Garden Route (South-East coast of South Africa) and Johannesburg. In Thailand, luxury accommodation is provided in a setting adjacent to the River Kwai.

All treatment centres meet local regulatory standards and have been reviewed for good practice by our own senior medical team. Quoted costs always include all standard treatment (detoxification, counselling and education), as well as accommodation and food for the duration of the programme.

Call 0800 160 1020 now or E-mail
freeadvice@dryoutnow.com

dryoutnow.con
A division
TRIAGE HEALTHCA

Pre-admission and ongoing services

- Expert Addictions Counsellor, Nurse Consultant, or Consultant Addiction Psychiatrist preadmission assessment in Harley Street, or your home locality
- Toxicology testing
- Pre-treatment preparation
- Care management and all liaison with your chosen treatment centre
- Protection of patient confidentiality
- Transfer of (patient approved) documentation to the treatment centre
- Pre-admission prescribing as indicated
- Coordination and arrangement of all travel needs
- Application for and arrangement of medical visas where appropriate
- Arrangement of pick up and transportation to treatment centre from airport
- Provision of expert nurse, or experienced lay-person chaperone as required for travel
- On-going, UK-based independent emergency medical advice throughout the duration of your treatment programme
- On-going, UK-based care coordination throughout the duration of your treatment programme to deal with any practical or financial difficulties as they arise
- Management of your treatment fees from the UK, enabling you to claim refunds within the UK in case of early discontinuation of treatment (see our refunds policy)
- On-going aftercare on return to the UK
- All relevant administration

Other services

- When medically necessary arrangements can be made for the patient to be accompanied by a nurse or doctor from their home to the treatment centre
- If indicated, pre-flight detoxification in the UK can be arranged, with seamless transportation for the overseas programme immediately on completion of detoxification
- Appropriate travel insurance can be arranged on request

Aftercare

Aftercare on return to the UK is essential to prevent relapse during the first high-risk period when the patient is settling back into their new life at home.

There are various elements including the following:

- Care coordination

- Emergency medical advice

- Relapse prevention counselling

- Other forms of counselling

- Medical review of associated illness and progress in physical health

- Support with attendance at self-help Alcoholics Anonymous/Narcotics Anonymous meetings

- Psychiatric review and treatment

- Supportive advice for family members

10 Harley Street, London W1G 9PF
Tel: 0800 160 1020
E-mail: freeadvice@dryoutnow.com
Web: www.dryoutnow.com

* DryOutNow.com™ is a trading name for Triage Healthcare Limited which is registered in England & Wales: No 5584516. Registered office: 14 & 15 Craven Street, London WC2N 5AD.

> "Home detoxification from DryOutNow.com is one of a variety of treatment options available to move forewards into recovery from addiction"

Home Detoxification from DryOutNow.com

Advice line: 0800 160 1020
E-mail: freeadvice@dryoutnow.com

dryoutnow.com

What is detoxification?

Detoxification is the use of prescribed medication to minimize or prevent the occurrence of drug or alcohol withdrawal symptoms. In the case of alcohol or some other sedative drugs such as diazepam, uncontrolled withdrawal can cause damage and may even be fatal in some circumstances. In these instances, detoxification is absolutely essential for medical reasons. For other substances such as heroin, although withdrawal is not life-threatening, it is usually so uncomfortable that detoxification is necessary to successfully cease use of the substance.

What does detoxification involve?

Detoxification involves the prescription of medication to prevent the occurrence of withdrawal symptoms. Usually a relatively large starting dose of medication is prescribed at the beginning of the detox, and the dose is then slowly reduced over a number of days, down to zero. In the case of alcohol detoxification, the usual first choice of medication is chlordiazepoxide (Librium) or diazepam (Valium). In the case of heroin (opiate) detoxification, a number of different medications may be used, but common ones are buprenorphine (Subutex) or lofexidine (Britlofex).

Apart from these main detox medications, additional medicines may be prescribed during the course of the detox to prevent specific symptoms occurring (such as nausea and vomiting, or sleeplessness).

What are the advantages of home detox?

People choose detox at home over residential detox for a number of reasons. The common reasons are privacy, lower costs and convenience.

What are the disadvantages of home detox as compared to residential detox?

Residential detox is preferable to home detox for a number of reasons. Firstly residential detox is usually considered safer (medically) than home detox for substances where serious complications can occur (alcohol, benzodiazepines, heroin) – simply because more qualified staff are likely to be on hand to deal with complications as they occur.

Secondly, in general, people are more likely to complete a residential detox than a home detox, as alcohol or drugs are less easily accessible in a specialist residential unit as compared to the home environment. Finally, residential detox in a specialist unit will usually involve some counselling as well as the medical treatment – this acts to reduce the chances of relapse.

What are the other important points?

The most important point to stress is that detox is all about stopping alcohol or drug use – but it has nothing whatsoever to do with 'staying stopped'. Detox on its own, with no follow-up care usually leads to relapse in due course. It is essential that ongoing psychological care is provided to continue immediately following the completion of detox if relapse is to be prevented.

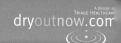

The Programme:

Assessment – Detoxification – Aftercare.

DryOutNow.com™ home detox programmes involve 3 stages – assessment, detoxification and aftercare.

Assessment

Assessment involves ascertaining your suitability for home detox. Withdrawal from some substances (including alcohol) can be life-threatening in some circumstances, and the assessment procedure aims to exclude those for whom the risk of performing detox at home is too high.

In general, those who have any history of withdrawal seizures, confusion or hallucinations when withdrawing from alcohol or other substances are advised against home detoxification. Equally those with a history of serious medical or psychiatric illness are strongly advised to consider residential detox as a preferable alternative.

The assessment process commences with a telephone assessment by a specialist nurse, and continues with a face-to-face assessment in your home. If all seems right at this point, the detox can proceed immediately during the first home nursing visit.

Detoxification

An expert DryOutNow.comTM nurse visits the patient and carer on a daily basis for the first seven days of detoxification, as standard. During the first visit, the assessment is completed, and a full explanation of how and when to take medication is provided to both patient and carer.

The nurse provides the medication, which is left in the care of the carer. Explanation is also provided as to what to expect during the detoxification, any warning signs of complications to look out for, and what actions to take if complications do seem to be occurring.

Often, the detoxification will be completed by the seventh day, but in difficult cases this may need to be extended by a few days. Additional nursing visits, home doctor review, and live-in professional carers can also be arranged on request and/or when necessary.

Aftercare

All DryOutNow.com home detox programmes include 3 months of weekly counseling with a specialist addictions counsellor, to continue on from the detox. The counsellor is provided within reasonable traveling distance from the patient's home (we work with over 200 counsellors throughout the UK – so we can usually find a counsellor near to your home). As a routine, attendance of local AA or NA meetings is advisable, and details of the nearest meetings are provided. In some circumstances, additional help to prevent relapse can be provided by the prescription of specialist medications – these options will be explained by the detox nurse, and for those who wish to receive such medication (to prevent relapse) a specialist doctor or nursing appointment is arranged.

Call 0800 160 1020 now or E-mail
freeadvice@dryoutnow.com

A division of
TRIAGE HEALTHCARE
dryoutnow.com

Further information on detoxification

Details of the technical side and best practice for detoxification can be found in the DryOutNow. com professional guidelines. These can be viewed online at www.dryoutnow.com, or a hard copy book requested by telephoning 0800 160 1020

Conclusion

Home detoxification can provide a more comfortable and convenient option than residential detoxification. For further details or to arrange home detoxification, contact us on 0800 160 1020.

10 Harley Street, London W1G 9PF
Tel: 0800 160 1020
E-mail: freeadvice@dryoutnow.com
Web: www.dryoutnow.com

* DryOutNow.com™ is a trading name for Triage Healthcare Limited which is registered in England & Wales: No 5584516. Registered office: 14 & 15 Craven Street, London WC2N 5AD.

Aftercare Services

Call 0800 160 1020
E-mail: freeadvice@dryoutnow.com

dryoutnow.com

DryOutNow.com prides itself in offering you the most extensive network of expert addiction treatment providers available in the UK today. Aftercare programmes are delivered within easy travelling distance of your home by the DryOutNow.com team based in your locality; and for those who prefer, appointments can be made with our senior medical team in Harley Street, London. DryOutNow.com Aftercare Services maximise the effectiveness of a period of residential treatment or home detox by preventing relapse following the patient's return home.

What Is Aftercare?

Simply, this is on-going care provided for someone following their completion of residential treatment for addiction, or following home detox. For obvious practical reasons, DryOutNow. com supports provision of a full programme of aftercare in the patient's home locality.

Is It Necessary To Get On-Going Care?

Addiction is a disease of the Central Nervous System for which various treatments are of proven effectiveness. Residential treatment is probably the most effective of these for many individuals. However, it is also the case that any individual who has become afflicted by the disease of addiction will remain at risk of relapse for the rest of his or her life, even if they have completed a period of residential treatment. The highest risk period for relapse is the first year following completion of treatment, and it is highly advisable for an individual to engage in a full package of on-going care for at least this period of time.

What Does Aftercare Involve?

Care Coordination
Care coordination involves the overall management of the individual's recovery plan when they are back at home. The care coordinator is a professional who is tasked with keeping an in-depth knowledge of the individual's circumstances and treatment history. The coordinator acts as a point of contact for practical advice and support, to put into place the various aspects of the plan, and to monitor and develop this plan as the newly abstinent person progresses.

Emergency Advice – 8am to 9pm 7 days per week
Alcohol and drug misuse is associated with a number of potentially life-threatening consequences. Sometimes these can occur with no or very little notice.

Equally, relapse after a period of abstinence can occur suddenly with no or very little warning. Access to immediate expert advice can act to save lives and prevent relapse.

Call 0800 160 1020 now or E-mail
freeadvice@dryoutnow.com

dryoutnow.cor

Relapse Prevention Counselling

This is a form of cognitive-behavioural therapy that focuses on developing coping strategies to deal with high-risk times for relapse such as episodic cravings, depression and poor self view. Specific planning involves the use of the 'Personal Recovery Plan'.

Other forms of Counselling

The underlying causes of addictive behaviour are multiple and non-specific. The counselling is aimed at providing caring support for the individual, the building of improved relationships and insight into personal development.

Medical Review

A review of associated illness and progress in physical health. Addictive behaviour is associated with a number of physical illnesses including hepatitis, cirrhosis, pancreatitis, diabetes, stomach ulceration, high blood pressure to name but a few. On-going medical assessment and review can improve general health, as well as helping to motivate the individual through witnessing improvement in various things such as improving liver function and reducing blood pressure.

Alcoholics Anonymous/Narcotics Anonymous Meetings Location of nearest 10 meetings

These are often considered unpopular in modern society, probably because of their religious overtones and the stigma felt by some in attending them. However, attendance of these meetings can be especially helpful for those who are aiming at abstinence rather than controlled drinking or controlled drug use. AA/NA's principles dictate that AA/NA is NOT allied to any sect, organisation OR religion. The research shows that those that attend AA/NA meetings on a regular basis are less likely to relapse than others.

Psychiatric review and treatment with Consultant Psychiatrist (Addictions)

Depression, anxiety and difficulties with sleep commonly accompany addictive illnesses. More often than not they are directly caused by misuse of the substance, but this is not always the case. Sometimes, severe psychiatric illness such as manic-depression (bipolar disorder) or schizophrenic symptoms may be associated with a pattern of heavy drinking or drug use. Psychiatric review and treatment can be vital in many cases to treat these conditions, and minimise their chances of causing a relapse to the addictive behaviour.

Supportive advice for family members with Triage specialist family advisor

It is often the case that those who are closest to an individual with an addiction problem have become depressed, or are finding it difficult to cope under extremely stressful circumstances. Supportive advice for those family members or carers closest to the individual with the addiction problem can be vital for all involved, if the progress made is to be maintained into the future.

Call 0800 160 1020 now or E-mail
freeadvice@dryoutnow.com

How can DryOutNow.Com help?

If you wish to take up aftercare, you will be allocated a 'care coordinator'. The care coordinator is there to help answer any questions during your residential treatment or home detox, both on your behalf and on behalf of your loved ones (with your permission of course). They will also be available to help sort out any practical or other difficulties that may arise. At the point of discharge from residential care, your care coordinator will set up your ongoing aftercare package, and continue to support you until you have settled back into normal life.

10 Harley Street, London W1G 9PF
Tel: 0800 160 1020
E-mail: freeadvice@dryoutnow.com
Web: www.dryoutnow.com

* DryOutNow.com™ is a trading name for Triage Healthcare Limited which is registered in England & Wales: No 5584516. Registered office: 14 & 15 Craven Street, London WC2N 5AD.

Out-patient Services

Phone 0800 160 1020
E-mail: freeadvice@dryoutnow.com

dryoutnow.com

DryOutNow.com prides itself in offering you the most extensive network of expert addiction treatment providers available in the UK today. Out-patient programmes are delivered within easy travelling distance of your home by the DryOutNow.com team based in your locality; and for those who prefer, appointments can be made with our senior medical team in Harley Street, London. DryOutNow.com Out-Patient Services maximise effectiveness by providing a programme of specialist addictions counselling and personal care coordination, with additional medical, psychiatric and emergency advice services as required.

What Is Out-patient Treatment?

Simply this is addiction treatment provided for someone while they remain living at home, rather than in a residential treatment centre.

Is it necessary to get Out-patient Treatment?

Addiction is a disease of the Central Nervous System which tends towards increasing severity in time, rather than resolving by itself. Various treatments are of proven effectiveness and professional treatment is usually required once a habitual (rather than recreational) pattern of use has become established. For those individuals who use drugs or alcohol harmfully, but who have not yet progressed to daily or physically dependent use, out-patient treatment should usually be the starting point.

What does Out-patient Treatment involve?

Care Coordination
Care coordination involves the overall management of the individual's recovery plan. The care coordinator is a professional who is tasked with keeping an in-depth knowledge of the individual's circumstances and treatment history. The coordinator acts as a point of contact for practical advice and support, to put into place the various aspects of the plan, and to monitor and develop this plan as the newly abstinent person progresses.

Emergency Advice – 8am to 9pm 7 days per week
Alcohol and drug misuse is associated with a number of potentially life-threatening consequences. Sometimes these can occur with no or very little notice. Equally, relapse after a period of abstinence can occur suddenly with no or very little warning. Access to immediate expert advice can act to save lives and prevent relapse.

Relapse Prevention Counselling with your Personal Counsellor
This is a form of cognitive-behavioural therapy that focuses on developing coping strategies to deal with high-risk times for relapse such as episodic cravings, depression and poor self view. Specific planning involves the use of the 'Personal Recovery Plan'.

Call 0800 160 1020 now or E-mail
freeadvice@dryoutnow.com

A division
TRIAGE HEALTHCA
dryoutnow.con

Other forms of Counselling – With your Personal Counsellor
The underlying causes of addictive behaviour are multiple and non-specific. The counselling is aimed at providing caring support for the individual, the building of improved relationships and insight into personal development.

Medical Review
A review of associated illness and progress in physical health. Addictive behaviour is associated with a number of physical illnesses including hepatitis, cirrhosis, pancreatitis, diabetes, stomach ulceration, high blood pressure to name but a few. On-going medical assessment and review can improve general health, as well as helping to motivate the individual through witnessing improvement in various things such as improving liver function and reducing blood pressure.

Alcoholics Anonymous/Narcotics Anonymous Meetings Location of nearest 10 meetings
These are often considered unpopular in modern society, probably because of their religious overtones and the stigma felt by some in attending them. However, attendance of these meetings can be especially helpful for those who are aiming at abstinence rather than controlled drinking or controlled drug use. AA/NA's principles dictate that AA/NA is NOT allied to any sect, organisation OR religion. The research shows that those that attend AA/NA meetings on a regular basis are less likely to relapse than others.

Psychiatric review and treatment with Consultant Psychiatrist (Addictions)
Depression, anxiety and difficulties with sleep commonly accompany addictive illnesses. More often than not they are directly caused by misuse of the substance, but this is not always the case. Sometimes, severe psychiatric illness such as manic-depression (bipolar disorder) or schizophrenic symptoms may be associated with a pattern of heavy drinking or drug use. Psychiatric review and treatment can be vital in many cases to treat these conditions, and minimise their chances of causing a relapse to the addictive behaviour.

Supportive advice for family members with Triage specialist family advisor
It is often the case that those who are closest to an individual with an addiction problem have become depressed, or are finding it difficult to cope under extremely stressful circumstances. Supportive advice for those family members or carers closest to the individual with the addiction problem can be vital for all involved, if the progress made is to be maintained into the future.

Call 0800 160 1020 now or E-mail
freeadvice@dryoutnow.com

A division of:
TRIAGE HEALTHCARE
dryoutnow.com
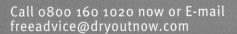

How can DryOutNow.Com help?

If you wish to take up out-patient treatment you will be immediately allocated a 'Care Coordinator'. Your Care Coordinator will set up your counselling and medical appointments, locate your local AA/NA meetings and will continue to help you sort out any practical or other difficulties that may arise during your treatment.

10 Harley Street, London W1G 9PF
Tel: 0800 160 1020
E-mail: freeadvice@dryoutnow.com
Web: www.dryoutnow.com

* DryOutNow.com™ is a trading name for Triage Healthcare Limited which is registered in England & Wales: No 5584516. Registered office: 14 & 15 Craven Street, London WC2N 5AD.

How To Enjoy Life Without Alcohol:

Routes to a Healthier Existence

By Dr Bruce Trathen MBBS MRCPsych, Consultant in Addiction Psychiatry

If at any time you require urgent access to treatment, or need an immediate response for any other reason, do not hesitate to telephone the DryOutNow.com Immediate Response Service (IRS) on:

0800 160 1020
(8am-9pm, seven days weekly)

dryoutnow.com

DryOutNow.com is a division of

FOREWORD

In my work as an addiction specialist over the years I have become increasingly frustrated by the sad state of affairs that exists for most people trying to find help for alcohol problems. While the Government has made major headway in improving services for drug addicts, they have done very little (if anything at all) to improve services for alcoholism. The number of people suffering from alcoholism is at least three times that of drug addiction, and is increasing dramatically. Could this Government's lack of action be something to do with profits from taxation on alcohol, or possibly the poor potential for headlines and publicity as compared to illicit drugs?

1. "To cut a long story short when we arrived in casualty the doctor that Ben saw was just horrible. He said to him "Why are you here? What do you want me to do for you? You're just wasting valuable resources"."

2. "When I complained to the GP that this had been going on for ages now, and nothing seemed to be happening, he got really abusive to me and said "You're lucky I'm seeing you at all – most doctors will have nothing to do with alcoholics"."

3. "He made an appointment with the doctor to discuss the problem and ask for support in the way of something to help him through this intense period. She refused to give him anything – why would she refuse to help him? I feel terrible as he is really committed and doing what everyone is telling him, but there is no help to get him through this."

The comments above (all made by people I have helped through this service) are representative of the kind of problems suffered by people trying to get help for the disease of alcoholism. The first two comments exemplify one of the most unpleasant features – abuse and stigmatisation from people employed by The State as 'caring' professionals.

And then the stigma creates another problem – the need to deny there is a problem, to keep it quiet, to hide it. Even if you are (or the person you are trying to help is) not concerned about the views of others, you may feel unable to approach available services in the first place for fear of lack of confidentiality and the effects this may have on employment, driving licences, life insurance etc. etc.. And so the problem is compounded.

The third comment underlines a different problem – the difficulty most people have in finding and accessing help even when they are fully committed to finding it and sorting out their problems. In my view, this is the major failing of this Government – they cannot directly control the attitudes of their citizens; they cannot directly control the flow of confidential information, BUT THEY COULD provide the financial resources to allow access to good quality care for the millions of people in the UK who suffer from this disease... they have not done so.

In providing you with this information and advice pack, I will do my utmost to enable you to:

- Find the help you need and deserve.

- Plan your route through the system you choose.

- Stay in charge of the treatment you are getting.

- Keep it totally, 100% confidential.

- Get alcohol detox and treatment for free or get the best price privately.

- And most importantly – find out how to stay dry so you don't have to do it all again.

Wishing you health and happiness,

Signed,

Dr Bruce Trathen MBBS MRCPsych, Consultant in Addiction Psychiatry.

CONTENTS

INTRODUCTION:
HOW TO USE THIS BOOK

- This book is divided into three main parts.

- The first part helps you to make the decisions you will need to make in order to plan your route through treatment for your alcohol problem.

- The second part consists of a number of chapters which describe the best route through treatment for you (according to the research evidence), and tells you how to find all local help contacts (generated from your postcode). You should read only one of the chapters in Part II; you will know which one to read after you have finished Part I, and read the Introduction to Part II.

- The third part tells you how to increase your chances of success to the absolute maximum.

- Whatever you do, do not read through the whole of Part II. The chapters in Part II are similar, but also contain vital differences which depend on things like whether or not you are physically addicted to alcohol, and whether you plan to continue to drink in the long term or to stop drinking forever. Part I will help you to make these decisions.

- And one final thing... try to make this book your own. The notes on these pages at the front, and the tables inside and in the appendix are for you to use. Write down your ideas, contacts, and use the tick boxes in the tables. If you need to start again, dryoutnow.com will just send you another book.

Now, have a look at the next page before you start reading
– this should help you find your way through the book

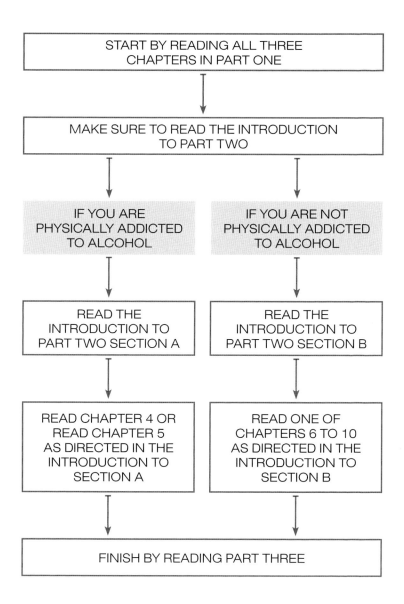

START BY READING ALL THREE CHAPTERS IN PART ONE

MAKE SURE TO READ THE INTRODUCTION TO PART TWO

IF YOU ARE PHYSICALLY ADDICTED TO ALCOHOL

IF YOU ARE NOT PHYSICALLY ADDICTED TO ALCOHOL

READ THE INTRODUCTION TO PART TWO SECTION A

READ THE INTRODUCTION TO PART TWO SECTION B

READ CHAPTER 4 OR READ CHAPTER 5 AS DIRECTED IN THE INTRODUCTION TO SECTION A

READ ONE OF CHAPTERS 6 TO 10 AS DIRECTED IN THE INTRODUCTION TO SECTION B

FINISH BY READING PART THREE

PART ONE

MAKING DECISIONS

If at any time you require urgent access to treatment, or need an
immediate response for any other reason, do not hesitate to telephone
the DryOutNow.com Immediate Response Service (IRS) on:

0800 160 1020
(8am-9pm, seven days weekly)

INTRODUCTION TO PART ONE

Part 1 of this book is aimed at helping you to make three vital decisions. When you are clear in your own mind about these decisions, you will be in the best position to plan your route to a healthier life, either through abstinence from alcohol, or by controlling your drinking within healthy limits. Of course, you may choose to skip this section and proceed straight to Part II, but if you do, please be very sure indeed that you are certain of the facts as they are relevant to you.

The three decisions you will need to make in advance of planning your route to health are:

> ### 1. AM I PHYSICALLY ADDICTED TO ALCOHOL, OR DO I JUST DRINK TOO HEAVILY?

> ### 1. AM I GOING TO TRY TO STOP DRINKING COMPLETELY FOREVER, OR DO I PLAN JUST TO CUT DOWN MY DRINKING?

> ### 1. AM I REALLY READY TO DO SOMETHING ABOUT MY DRINKING, OR DO I NEED TO THINK ABOUT THIS A LITTLE MORE BEFORE DOING SOMETHING ABOUT IT?

The first three chapters of this book address each of these questions one by one. If you have any doubts or questions when you have finished one of the chapters, or at any other time, you can access free, confidential expert advice by telephoning:

DryOutNow.com Immediate Response Service on 0800 160 1020 or by email: freeadvice@dryoutnow.com

GOOD LUCK

CHAPTER ONE

ARE YOU PHYSICALLY ADDICTED TO ALCOHOL?

If at any time you require urgent access to treatment, or need an
immediate response for any other reason, do not hesitate to telephone
the DryOutNow.com Immediate Response Service (IRS) on:

0800 160 1020
(8am-9pm, seven days weekly)

CHAPTER ONE

ARE YOU PHYSICALLY ADDICTED TO ALCOHOL?

MAIN QUESTION: ARE YOU PHYSICALLY ADDICTED TO ALCOHOL?

There are many different forms of help for people with alcoholism. We can break these down into four categories:

- **Medical help**

- **Psychological help**

- **Social help**

- **Spiritual help**

When you are planning your route to a life free from the disease of alcoholism, you will need to make a judgment about which kinds of help you need, and in which order you get them. Making a good decision about this depends on a number of different factors, and I will help you to make these good decisions in later sections.

For the moment, it is vital to make a single, central decision, by answering a question which will set the basic course towards your recovery:

- **Am I physically addicted to alcohol?**

If you are physically addicted to alcohol, then this means two things:

1. **At some point you will require a medicated detoxification in order to cease drinking safely.**

2. The research evidence shows that **you are highly unlikely to ever be able to drink any alcohol again,** without relapsing to alcoholic levels of drinking. In other words, your aim should almost definitely be to become tee-total/ abstinent/permanently dry. (More on this in Chapter Two).

Now this may well come as disappointing news, but these are the hard facts of the matter:

Let's consider point 1 – the need for a medicated detox:

- **To cease drinking suddenly without a medicated detox if you are physically addicted can be fatal.**

- **To cease drinking suddenly without a medicated detox if you are physically addicted may lead to permanent brain damage, and permanent memory loss.**

....

- **To cease drinking suddenly without a medicated detox if you are physically addicted to alcohol may lead to epilepsy and fits.**

....

- **Approximately 50% of all alcoholics have evidence of brain damage, and this has probably been mostly caused by trying to stop drinking suddenly on occasions during their lives.**

....

- **The provision of a medicated detox reduces the risks of all these things happening to almost zero.**

....

WHY DO ALL THESE PROBLEMS OCCUR, JUST BECAUSE I'VE BECOME PHYSICALLY ADDICTED ALCOHOL?

In alcohol withdrawal the brain is in an overactive state which results in the whole body (including the brain) being triggered into a state of emergency - similar to that which occurs if you have a great fright - sweating, trembling and tremor, high heart rate, high blood pressure, nausea, vomiting, diarrhoea etc. When the person is heavily alcohol dependent, the overactive brain state may be so severe that epileptic fits occur (discharged electricity in the brain). Fits can sometimes lead directly to death, and in other cases cause fatal injuries. Apart from fits, the overactive state may become so severe that the brain is no longer able to understand properly what is going on around it, and delusions (e.g. paranoid thoughts), and hallucinations (seeing things that aren't there) may occur. If this syndrome occurs (Delirium Tremens), then death occurs in 10% of cases that go untreated. Additionally, the overactive state of the whole body results in more energy being burned up; this in turn can use up vital supplies of vitamins which are essential for brain functioning. In some cases, loss of these vitamin supplies can lead to death, and in other cases to devastating permanent memory loss (Wernicke-Korsakoff syndrome).

Now, there is a medically safe alternative to detox, which would prevent all these problems and risks. That alternative is – to cut your drinking down slowly but surely over a period of several weeks. The problem is that you are highly unlikely to manage to do this, if you've already become physically addicted to alcohol. That's the Catch 22. It is in the very nature of addiction, that you will probably not be able to cease drinking in this manner, if you have already become physically addicted to alcohol.

In my NHS practice, I do not advise people who are physically addicted to alcohol to try this (slow but sure cut down of drinking over several weeks) unless they are very determined that they wish to give it a go. And simply because I know that we'll all be back to square one in several weeks time; I routinely include a medicated detoxification as part of the plan, as long as the patient is prepared to go along with this (most are).

Having said that, as a doctor, I do not advise you against trying this (slow but sure cut down over a period of at least several weeks) – it IS a medically safe alternative to a detoxification – if you want to, then give it a go – a few of you will succeed, but the large majority will not. If you choose this route to dry out, and you succeed, then I congratulate you. If you find after several weeks that you have made no progress, then please start reading this book again at that point.

But please remember this – do NOT attempt to stop drinking suddenly without a medicated detoxification – to do so will almost definitely fail (you will start drinking again), and may cause you irreversible damage in the meantime.

AM I PHYSICALLY ADDICTED TO ALCOHOL?

In this modern day world of theory and technological advance, many specialists seem to have forgotten the central importance of a vital distinction in addiction – that of psychological addiction versus physical addiction. For people with alcoholism this distinction has huge practical implications – if you are physically addicted to alcohol to cease its use suddenly may be fatal. If you are not physically addicted, but are psychologically addicted it would be safe for you to stop drinking suddenly, and you are also more likely to be able to achieve on-going 'controlled drinking' in the future – more on this later.

The presence of physical addiction to alcohol is ascertained by the occurrence of 'withdrawal symptoms' when you have not had a drink for a period of time. If you suffer from ANY of the following when you have not had a drink for a period of time, then you are likely to be physically addicted to alcohol:

If you can answer yes to ANY of the following then you are likely to be physically addicted to alcohol:

....

• **I get sweaty if I go without a drink for too long.**

....

• **I get a tremor, or shake if I go without a drink for too long.**

....

• **I feel sick or vomit if I go without a drink for too long.**

....

• **I feel panicky, anxious and agitated if I go without a drink for too long.**

....

WHAT DOES 'WITHOUT A DRINK FOR TOO LONG' MEAN'?

Withdrawal symptoms typically commence somewhere between 6 and 24 hours after the last drink.

Some people who are physically addicted may have their last drink at say midnight, and then be able to go the whole of the next working day without drinking. By the time they get home they are feeling agitated and in need of a drink. If they do not drink, their levels of agitation increase. Within 15 minutes or so of their first drink the levels of agitation decrease and they will then continue to drink for the rest of the evening until they go to bed. The pattern will be repeated the next day… and the next day... This pattern of physically addicted drinking is typical of those with a relatively minor level of physical addiction – however, such a person will probably NOT be able to cease drinking without a detox, and to do so would place them at risk of memory loss and other damage. Equally, in time, their level of drinking is likely to slowly but surely increase, gradually increasing the degree of their physical dependency to alcohol.

At the other end of the spectrum, a person might have their last drink at midnight and then be awake by 6am sweating profusely. If they haven't had a drink by 8am, their hands will start to shake and they will feel nauseous. If they haven't had a drink by 10am they may be vomiting, and by 3pm they will be starting to have hallucinations of insects walking on the walls. By 5pm they will have lost touch with reality, and by 7pm they may have suffered an epileptic seizure. If at any time during these events they find a supply of alcohol and start to drink, then all the above symptoms will calm down and disappear within an hour or so of continued alcohol use. This pattern is typical of people who are severely physically addicted to alcohol.

OTHER WAYS OF ESTABLISHING WHETHER OR NOT YOU ARE PHYSICALLY ADDICTED TO ALCOHOL

Now, if you remain uncertain whether or not you are physically addicted to alcohol there are two further means of attempting to establish this:

ALTERNATIVE 1: THE SEVERITY OF ALCOHOL DEPENDENCE QUESTIONNAIRE (SADQ):

Completing this questionnaire results in a score delivered on its completion. Scores above 4 indicate likely physical dependence to alcohol, scores above 10 indicate definite physical dependence to alcohol and scores above 30 indicate severe physical dependence to alcohol. Any total score above 4 should lead you to include a medicated detoxification as part of your plan to cease alcohol use. You can use the table below, or complete this online when your score will be calculated for you automatically. To complete on line go to this web-page:

http://www.dryoutnow.com/self-assessment/

Q1: Please indicate below the physical symptoms that you have experienced first thing in the morning during typical periods of heavy drinking.

ZERO POINTS	ONE POINT	TWO POINTS	THREE POINTS

I wake up feeling sweaty:
Almost Never ☐ (0)   Sometimes ☐ (1)   Often o (2)   Nearly Always ☐ (3)

My hands shake first thing in the morning:
Almost Never ☐ (0)   Sometimes ☐ (1)   Often ☐ (2)   Nearly Always ☐ (3)

My whole body shakes violently first thing in the morning if I don't have a drink:
Almost Never ☐ (0)   Sometimes ☐ (1)   Often ☐ (2)   Nearly Always ☐ (3)

I wake up absolutely drenched in sweat:
Almost Never ☐ (0)   Sometimes ☐ (1)   Often ☐ (2)   Nearly Always ☐ (3)

TOTAL SCORE for Q1:
....

Q2: The following statements refer to moods and states of mind you may have experienced during these periods of heavy drinking.

ZERO POINTS	**ONE POINT**	**TWO POINTS**	**THREE POINTS**

I dread waking up in the morning:
Almost Never ☐ (0) Sometimes ☐ (1) Often ☐ (2) Nearly Always ☐ (3)

I am afraid of meeting people first thing in the morning.
Almost Never ☐ (0) Sometimes ☐ (1) Often ☐ (2) Nearly Always ☐ (3)

I feel at the edge of despair when I first wake up.
Almost Never ☐ (0) Sometimes ☐ (1) Often ☐ (2) Nearly Always ☐ (3)

I feel very frightened when I wake up.
Almost Never ☐ (0) Sometimes ☐ (1) Often ☐ (2) Nearly Always ☐ (3)

TOTAL SCORE for Q2: ....

Q3: The following statements refer to morning drinking habits during any recent period when you were drinking heavily, and periods like it.

ZERO POINTS	**ONE POINT**	**TWO POINTS**	**THREE POINTS**

I like to have a morning drink:
Almost Never ☐ (0) Sometimes ☐ (1) Often ☐ (2) Nearly Always ☐ (3)

I always gulp my first few morning drinks down as quickly as possible:
Almost Never ☐ (0) Sometimes ☐ (1) Often ☐ (2) Nearly Always ☐ (3)

I drink in the morning to get rid of the shakes.
Almost Never ☐ (0) Sometimes ☐ (1) Often ☐ (2) Nearly Always ☐ (3)

I have a very strong craving for a drink when I wake up.
Almost Never ☐ (0) Sometimes ☐ (1) Often ☐ (2) Nearly Always ☐ (3)

TOTAL SCORE for Q3: ....

Q4: The following statements refer to a degree of alcohol consumption during any recent period of heavy drinking and periods like it.

ZERO POINTS   **ONE POINT**   **TWO POINTS**   **THREE POINTS**

I drink more than a quarter of a bottle of spirits per day i.e. 4 doubles or 1 bottle of wine or 4 pints of beer/lager.
Almost Never ☐ (0)   Sometimes ☐ (1)   Often ☐ (2)   Nearly Always ☐ (3)

I drink more than half a bottle of spirits per day or 2 bottles of wine or 8 pints of beer/lager.
Almost Never ☐ (0)   Sometimes ☐ (1)   Often ☐ (2)   Nearly Always ☐ (3)

I drink more than one bottle of spirits per day or 4 bottles of wine or 15 pints of beer/lager.
Almost Never ☐ (0)   Sometimes ☐ (1)   Often ☐ (2)   Nearly Always ☐ (3)

I drink more than two bottles of spirits per day or 8 bottles of wine or 30 pints of beer/lager.
Almost Never ☐ (0)   Sometimes ☐ (1)   Often ☐ (2)   Nearly Always ☐ (3)

TOTAL SCORE for Q4:
....

Q5: Imagine the following situation. You have been completely off drink for a few weeks and you then drink very heavily for two days. How would you feel the morning after those two days of heavy drinking?

ZERO POINTS   **ONE POINT**   **TWO POINTS**   **THREE POINTS**

I would start to sweat:
Almost Never ☐ (0)   Sometimes ☐ (1)   Often ☐ (2)   Nearly Always ☐ (3)

My hands would shake:
Almost Never ☐ (0)   Sometimes ☐ (1)   Often ☐ (2)   Nearly Always ☐ (3)

My body would shake:
Almost Never ☐ (0)   Sometimes ☐ (1)   Often ☐ (2)   Nearly Always ☐ (3)

I would be craving for a drink:
Almost Never ☐ (0)   Sometimes ☐ (1)   Often ☐ (2)   Nearly Always ☐ (3)

TOTAL SCORE for Q5:
....

Now, add up the total scores from questions 1, 2, 3, 4 and 5. The maximum possible score is 60. Scores above 4 indicate probable physical dependence to alcohol, scores above 10 indicate definite physical addiction and scores above 30 indicate severe physical dependence to alcohol. Any total score above 4 should lead you to include a medicated detoxification as part of your plan to cease alcohol use.

TOTAL SADQ SCORE

Q1 + Q2 + Q3 + Q4 + Q5 =

ALTERNATIVE 2: MAKING AN ESTIMATE BY CALCULATING THE NUMBER OF UNITS OF ALCOHOL YOU ARE DRINKING IN A TYPICAL WEEK:

Most people who are actively seeking help for their problems are nearer the milder end of the spectrum (i.e. the first example), or somewhere between the two. This is because such people still have their faculties about them and are able to actively seek help. Those who have let things develop to the extent of the second example rarely seek help for themselves – by the time things have progressed this far the mind is only able to focus on one thing – finding a supply of alcohol to stay OK for the next few hours. Occasionally I will see such patients in casualty when they have turned up in 'crisis'. Usually they are severely depressed and suicidal at such times, and it is such feelings of desperation that have led them to turn up.

Of course, those lucky enough to have concerned relatives (or relatives that can no longer tolerate their behaviour), may be referred for help at any time in the progression of this disease. It is usually the case that others recognise the existence of a problem developing before the individual themselves. The important point to take away is that wherever you are along the spectrum of development of addiction to alcohol, it is ONLY LIKELY TO GET WORSE. This again is part of the addictive process – one slowly drinks more and more to get the same effect (an effect known as 'tolerance') – levels of drinking slowly but surely build up. The only meaningful response to dealing with this situation is to SEEK HELP – and of course, if you are still reading by this time then that is exactly what you are doing, right now.

This is a relatively unreliable way to determine whether or not you are physically addicted to alcohol. However, it can provide further confirmation for you if you remain a little uncertain regarding your need for detoxification. The reason it is a little unreliable is because people's bodies vary so much from one to another. One person may be able to deal with less alcohol than another, just because of the way they have been born. In particular, there is no doubt, that on average, women more easily suffer

from the adverse effects of alcohol use than do men – including becoming physically addicted more quickly and with less regular alcohol use than men.

As a rule of thumb, a man drinking more than 100 units of alcohol weekly is likely to become physically addicted in good time, and a woman drinking more than 70 units of alcohol weekly is likely to become physically addicted in time.

You can work out your daily units of alcohol consumption by using the following calculation:

(Litres of drink consumed in a day) TIMES ('% abv') of the particular drink EQUALS (units of alcohol).

The % abv is the alcohol content of the particular drink you are consuming – it is always recorded on the label of the can or bottle of the drink – have a look. 'abv' stands for 'Alcohol-by-Volume'. To work out how many units of alcohol you are drinking you may need to convert pints to litres, and you will also need to know the '% abv' of the different types of alcohol you are drinking.

As a rough approximation, 2 pints = just over 1 litre (1.13 litres to be precise).

- Beer varies from 3% abv to 16% abv.

- Wine is typically 12% abv.

- Spirits are typically 40% abv.

- Liqueurs are usually in the region of 15 - 20% abv.

EXAMPLE 1:

So for example, if you are drinking 4 pints of Stella Artois daily, and nothing else, then your total units will be:

4 pints = 2 litres (plus a little extra). % abv of Stella = 5% (in fact 5.2% to be precise). Thus total daily units = 2 TIMES 5 EQUALS 10. Thus total weekly units = 70 units. As such you are unlikely to be physically addicted if you are male, although you will doubtless cause yourself damage if you continue to drink at these levels for a period of time.

EXAMPLE 2:

If you are drinking 1 bottle of spirits daily, and nothing else then your total units will be:

1 bottle EQUALS 3/4 litre. (Sometimes 1 litre). % abv of spirits usually equals 40%.

Thus, 3/4 TIMES 40 = 30 units daily. Thus total weekly units will be 210 units – you are highly likely to be physically addicted drinking at these levels.

There are two important points to take away when calculating units:

1. **As far as your physical health is concerned, there is no known difference between drinking spirits and drinking wine or beer.** It is nothing to do with the type of drink you use. It is everything to do with the total amount of actual alcohol that you consume – this is calculated by units. Don't fall into the trap of telling yourself that you "only drink beer/wine" and thus are not alcoholic – what kind of drink you use has absolutely nothing to do with it.

2. **Don't fall into the trap of underestimating your units by using the old fashioned estimates.** The old estimates of units – "one unit = half a pint of beer or one glass of wine" are completely out-of-date. The reasons for this are due to the 'drinks industry'. There has been a slow but sure increase in the amount of alcohol in commonly drunk beer and wine (% abv), and a slow but sure increase in the size of wine glasses in pubs and wine bars/restaurants. Whereas in times-gone-by a typical pint of bitter was 3% abv, it is now the case that commonly consumed lagers (Stella and Kronenberg) are in the region of 5% abv. Equally wine has increased from 8 or 9% abv to 12 or 13% abv. In the meantime, wine glasses have increased in size. If you go out these days and order a large glass of wine, you are probably drinking approximately 3 units per glass (a large difference from the old 1 unit per glass). In effect if you are female and are drinking more than 3 large glasses of wine per night, then you are at risk of becoming physically addicted to alcohol in due course. If you are male and are drinking more than 5 pints of Stella or Kronenberg per night, then you are at risk of developing physical addiction to alcohol in due course.

SO IN SUMMARY:

1. Determine whether or not you are physically addicted to alcohol by considering whether or not you suffer from alcohol withdrawal symptoms. If you are clear you suffer from such symptoms you will need a medicated detoxification.

2. If you remain in doubt, then complete the questionnaire above (SADQ) and calculate your score. Scores greater than 4 indicate probable physical addiction to alcohol and the need for a medicated detoxification.

3. If you need further convincing, then calculate your weekly alcohol consumption in units: greater than 70 units weekly for a woman, and 100 units weekly for a man, is likely to lead to physical addiction to alcohol in due course (remember this is a rough estimate only and varies from individual to individual).

4. Don't fall into the trap of under-estimating your units.

Chapter Two looks at another point raised above: If you have become physically addicted to alcohol you are unlikely to ever be able to drink again without relapsing to damaging levels of alcohol consumption. Bad news... but not to be ignored... if you wish to avoid ending up back at square one.

CONCLUSION

You have now reached the end of this chapter and should be able to answer the question:

'ARE YOU PHYSICALLY ADDICTED TO ALCOHOL?'

If you are, then you must plan for alcohol detoxification at some point in the future. Alcohol detoxification is NOT a cure for alcoholism in itself – it is a way of getting from drinking to NOT drinking safely and effectively. It is highly unlikely that you will achieve this safely without a detoxification. Once you have ascertained the need for a detoxification, there is more work to do. This work is mainly about 'how to stay stopped' rather than how to 'get stopped'. Some of the following chapters address this in more detail.

If you are NOT physically addicted to alcohol, then from a 'medical perspective' you do not need a detoxification to stop alcohol use. By this, I mean that you would be unlikely to cause yourself physical damage by ceasing alcohol use suddenly. However, you may choose to use detoxification as a way to stop alcohol use comfortably and effectively, especially if you have tried but failed to cut down your drinking.

If you have any questions about how this chapter applies to you, or simply want professional advice on a one-to-one basis, then I advise you to contact the DryOutNow.com Immediate Response Service. All advice is free, totally confidential, and is provided by an expert in the field of alcoholism.

Their telephone number is: 0800 160 1020.

Alternatively, you can email: freeadvice@dryoutnow.com

CHAPTER TWO

SHOULD YOU DRINK LESS OR STOP COMPLETELY?

If at any time you require urgent access to treatment, or need an immediate response for any other reason, do not hesitate to telephone the DryOutNow.com Immediate Response Service (IRS) on:

0800 160 1020
(8am-9pm, seven days weekly)

CHAPTER TWO

SHOULD YOU DRINK LESS OR STOP COMPLETELY?

"Doctor, I know I need a detox, but I'm sure I can have just an occasional drink afterwards – what harm could that do?"

Well none... if it was just the occasional drink. In fact, to drink a small amount on a few days per week may actually be healthier than drinking nothing at all. And this leads us on to the main question for this Chapter:

MAIN QUESTION TWO: DO YOU PLAN TO CONTINUE DRINKING (BUT LESS) OR TO CEASE DRINKING ALTOGETHER?

POSSIBLE ANSWER 1:
I PLAN TO CONTINUE DRINKING – BUT LESS.

OK – fair enough – but how much do you plan to drink?

The World Health Organization has published guidelines on what it considers to be the maximum levels of alcohol use that an individual can tolerate in the long term without causing damage to the body.

These guidelines state the following:

FOR MALES:

- A maximum of 21 units should be consumed in any one week.

- Within a period of one week there should be at least two drink-free days.

- No more than 4 units should be consumed in any one day.

Effectively this means the following:

- *You should drink no more than 2 pints of 3-4% lager/beer (Carlsberg/Heinekin) or 1½ pints of 5% lager/beer (like Stella/Kronenberg) or 1/3 bottle of wine or 1/9th bottle of spirits on any one night.*

- *You should have at least two days in the week when you drink no alcohol at all.*

- *You should drink no more than 9 pints of 3-4% lager/beer **per week** or no more than 7 pints of 5% lager/beer **per week** or no more than 2 bottles wine **per week** or no more than 2/3 bottle spirits **per week**.*

FOR FEMALES:

- A maximum of 14 units should be consumed in any one week.

- Within a period of one week there should be at least two drink-free days.

- No more than 3 units should be consumed in any one day.

Effectively this means the following:

- *You should drink no more than 1.5 pints of 3-4% lager/beer (Carlsberg/ Heinekin) or 1 pint of 5% lager/beer (like Stella/Kronenberg) or 1/4 bottle of wine or 1/10th bottle of spirits on any one night.*

- *You should have at least two days in the week when you drink no alcohol at all.*

- *You should drink no more than 6 pints of 3-4% lager/beer per week or no more than 4½ pints of 5% lager/beer per week or no more than 1½ bottles wine per week or no more than ½ bottle of spirits per week.*

Now, for someone who is used to drinking heavily, these **guidelines may seem rather mean.**

From one perspective, I agree; if you find drinking enjoyable then you may think it is acceptable to take some risks with your health in order to enjoy life more. Maybe you like to 'live for the moment' rather than spend all your time planning to stay alive as long as possible. After all (you might say to yourself), **"I could find myself walking across the road tomorrow and be knocked over – why not enjoy today for today?"**

In general, there is nothing wrong with that argument at all. **What is wrong with it in your case is that you are already experiencing problems caused by alcohol; if you weren't there is no way you would have read this far.**

SOME SOCIAL PROBLEMS CAUSED BY HEAVY DRINKING:

- **Relationship difficulties e.g. divorce/ separation, aggression & violence, lowered sex drive/impotence.**

- **Work difficulties e.g. redundancy, long-term unemployment, difficulty getting in on time, drinking whilst working, disciplinary procedures, generally poor performance, difficulty with reemployment. Financial difficulties arising from work difficulties e.g. meeting mortgage payments & repossession orders, maintenance payments, savings running low or running out, debts.**

- **Pleasure difficulties i.e. replacement of previous pleasurable activity (hobbies, exercise, EATING etc.) with drinking; inability to take pleasure from such activities even if you try.**

- **Legal difficulties e.g. drink-drive charges; assault charges.**

SOME PSYCHOLOGICAL PROBLEMS CAUSED BY HEAVY DRINKING:

- **Depression.**

- **Irritability.**

- **Anxiety & panic attacks.**

- **Paranoid feelings & ideas.**

- **Sleep problems.**

- **Memory loss.**

- **Difficulty with concentration.**

SOME PHYSICAL PROBLEMS CAUSED BY HEAVY DRINKING:

- **Permanent memory loss.**

- **Dementia.**

- **High blood pressure.**

- **Stomach ulcers.**

- **Strange sensations in feet and hands – typically pins and needles.**

- **Loss of all sensation in feet and hands.**

- **Wasting of thigh muscles.**

- **Skin complaints such as psoriasis and dermatitis.**

- **Impotence and erectile failure.**

- **Road traffic and other accidents (often fatal).**

- **Liver disease (sometimes fatal).**

- **Pancreatitis (sometimes fatal).**

....

- **Fertility problems and foetal malformations (often fatal for the foetus).**

....

- **Brain damage (sometimes fatal).**

....

- **Epilepsy and fits (sometimes fatal).**

....

- **Heart attacks (often fatal).**

....

- **Vascular disease and amputations (sometimes fatal).**

....

- **Vomiting blood (sometimes fatal).**

....

- **Bleeding from the rectum (sometimes fatal).**

....

Now that's a long list, and you will never experience all of these problems at any one time. Only you can decide how many risks you want to take. Remember only this: the more you drink, the more likely you are to experience an increasing number of these problems. The healthy drinking limits apply to all of us, whether or not we require detoxification. However, there is an additional problem for you over and above the immediate health risks if you have already become physically addicted to alcohol. This problem is known as:

"REINSTATEMENT AFTER ABSTINENCE".

"Reinstatement after abstinence" is the technical term for almost immediate relapse to drinking at the same old extremely damaging levels if you try to start drinking again. For the purposes of translation it means the following:

Situation: You have become physically addicted to alcohol, and then spend a period of time completely dry from alcohol:

- If you have just one drink again at any time in the future, you will automatically start to consume large amounts of alcohol, rather than small (healthy) amounts of alcohol.

- The large amounts of alcohol you consume will be similar in quantity to the amounts you were drinking before you stopped drinking.

- It will take only a matter of days to progress from drinking nothing to drinking at those same old damaging levels.

- This will be an automatic process beyond your control.

You may have spent over a year without drinking. One day, you are stressed, the sun is shining, and you see people relaxing and enjoying themselves in the pub garden. One drink cannot do any harm. In fact two drinks cannot do any harm. You are correct – they cannot. However, there is a problem here – your brain has at some time in the past become used to drinking at extremely high levels ("tolerance"). Your brain also has an extremely long memory.

All of us have a natural tendency to adapt to our environment. In this modern day world with its rapid changes, if we didn't have this natural tendency we would simply not survive. All animals have to adapt to their environment in order to survive, and human beings are no different. This ability to adapt is a good thing. Without it you and I would not be here today. But in some cases, this automatic ability to adapt can lead to unwanted side-effects. In the specific example we are talking about at the moment (an environment full of alcohol) this adaptation will lead to an automatic, subconsciously motivated, return to alcoholic levels of drinking.

Why? Because the very fact that you have become physically addicted in the past means that you have changed – permanently. All addictive drugs (including alcohol) interact with the brain in order to cause some kind of pleasurable experience (such as getting drunk). As you drink more and more, your brain re-sets itself so that you get less and less drunk at a particular level of alcohol use. Eventually, your brain accepts that this level of drinking is now what it can expect every day, day-in, day-out. The nerves in the brain alter their response to alcohol. Effectively they try to function as though you were not drunk, even though you may have drunk large amounts.

Now this is great in the short-term. You can drink more and more without making a fool of yourself – adaptation.

The problem occurs when you stop drinking – the nerves in your brain are no longer used to this, and now send messages to your body telling you that something is very wrong – an emergency message is sent, and the body reacts accordingly – it gets ready to respond to an emergency. Your heart rate goes up, your blood pressure goes up, you sweat in order to get rid of all the excess heat you will generate in fighting or fleeing, you tremor in fright etc.etc.. In the process of your body reacting to this, you experience alcohol withdrawal symptoms.

After several days, your body realises that in fact there is no emergency to deal with, and things return to normal – the withdrawal period is over.

However, your brain never forgets.

It has adapted to alcohol permanently.

> *However long you leave it (years in some cases), the next time you have a drink, your brain remembers the smell, the taste and the sensation of alcohol. Whereas before it took months and years for the adaptation to heavy alcohol use to occur,* **this time it immediately readjusts itself in less than a moment. As it readjusts, you will find yourself drinking more than you intended to. The next day your brain will send you messages to drink even more – simply because it remembers that this is how it was in the past. The brain never forgets addiction.**

Within several days, you will be drinking as you were before. You will not have planned or intended to do this; and you will almost definitely feel devastated that this has happened to you. But it is beyond your personal control.

At some point along the line, if you are to overcome alcoholism, you will accept that this disease (alcoholism) is more powerful than you are – except in one case – that is that you decide never to drink alcohol again – ever. If you truly decide this, then you have beaten alcoholism. If you hanker after the idea of being able to drink again in months or years to come then you will relapse.

Now this permanent change in the brain only occurs if you have become physically addicted to alcohol. If you do not experience withdrawal symptoms on cessation of drinking, then your brain has not reached this point of permanent change. But, if you have become physically addicted at some point in the past, then it is highly unlikely that you will ever be able to drink again without relapsing to damaging levels of alcohol use.

Of course many of you will give it a try – drinking again. And just a few will succeed in proving me wrong. I have known people who have done this – returned to healthy drinking when they have been physically addicted in the past.

Maybe you will need to try this out for yourself. After all someone has to win the lottery – it could be you. It really could be you, there is no way I can say it will not be. What I can say, without a doubt, is that the odds are stacked against you. Just as many people play the lottery, many alcoholics try having just that one drink.

CONCLUSION

You have now reached the end of this chapter and should be able to answer the question:

DO YOU PLAN TO CONTINUE DRINKING (BUT LESS) OR TO CEASE DRINKING ALTOGETHER?

If you DO plan to continue drinking at some point in the future, then this may be possible to achieve, especially if you have not yet become physically addicted to alcohol. It is certainly not my place to tell you that you will not manage to drink within healthy limits at some point in the future. That can only be your decision.

If you have any questions about how this chapter applies to you, or simply want professional advice on a one-to-one basis, then I advise you to contact the DryOutNow.com Immediate Response Service. All advice is free, totally confidential, and is provided by an expert in the field of alcoholism. Free home assessments are provided in certain circumstances.

Their telephone number is: 0800 160 1020

Alternatively, access advice by email: freeadvice@dryoutnow.com

CHAPTER THREE

ARE YOU READY TO ACT NOW?

If at any time you require urgent access to treatment, or need an immediate response for any other reason, do not hesitate to telephone the DryOutNow.com Immediate Response Service (IRS) on:

0800 160 1020
(8am-9pm, seven days weekly)

CHAPTER THREE

ARE YOU READY TO ACT NOW?

If you have read Chapters One and Two of this book and come to a conclusion about the main questions asked (1.Are you physically addicted alcohol? 2. Do you plan to become abstinent from alcohol or to continue to drink?) you will have made the necessary decisions in order to form a basic plan for how to proceed. I will discuss the various routes forward in later chapters.

However, for the moment, there is a final 3rd main question to ask:

MAIN QUESTION 3: ARE YOU READY TO ACT NOW?

Now that might seem like an obvious question with an obvious answer – **"Of course I am, I wouldn't be reading this if I wasn't ready to do something about it."** Well yes, you may well be ready, and the fact that you are still reading bodes well. To have found this book, and to still be reading by Chapter Three demonstrates that you are taking this seriously and have a commitment to addressing the problems you are experiencing.

Having said this, in my NHS practice, I see many patients who think they are ready, but who I know are 99.9% likely to relapse to drinking either immediately after detox or within a matter of weeks. How do I know this? Because I've seen it happen again and again and again. These are not people who are uncertain about whether or not they need help, and they are not people who are uncommitted. These are people who are honestly motivated to stop drinking – they are experiencing serious and multiple problems due to alcohol, and they want these problems to go away. So why do they return to drinking? Where does it all go wrong?

There are a multitude of technical explanations for relapse to alcohol occurring, and I will touch on some of these below. But for the moment, they can really be summarised in one simple statement. **You must remind yourself of this statement constantly, again and again and again:**

" THE DETOX IS THE EASY BIT – STAYING OFF IS MUCH HARDER"

And again:

" THE DETOX IS THE EASY BIT – STAYING OFF IS MUCH HARDER"

And again:

" THE DETOX IS THE EASY BIT – STAYING OFF IS MUCH HARDER"

The bad news is that its all too easy to convince yourself that all your problems will be over once you've managed to stop drinking. I'm sorry to bring you this news, but the truth is that to stay off the drink (or to stay drinking within healthy limits) is very hard work – and it's hard work for a long, long time. **By this I do NOT mean physically hard work** – the detox takes care of that – and if the detox is carried out professionally it will be a painless experience throughout. **I do mean mentally hard work.**

If you can answer yes to ALL of the 10 questions below, then you are most likely ready right now to go ahead and prepare to implement your plan. If you cannot honestly answer yes to all these questions, then I suggest that you think very hard indeed before progressing further at this stage*. Read the remainder of this chapter carefully, and then take some time out to think about it all a little more. Come back to this chapter and read it again when you think you may be ready. Now, if you don't follow this advice that's fine by me, and of course some people always prove me wrong; and when they do that's great – one – because they're leading healthy lives again, and – two – because they've beaten the odds that are stacked against them. And, in a way, this is all about beating the odds.

The more of these questions you can honestly tick off, the more likely I think you are to beat alcoholism in the long term.

Part of my role as a doctor specialising in alcoholism is to help people to lower those odds against them as much as possible before proceeding with their plan. That way more people succeed and less fail in the longer term. There are three main things I consider:

1. How determined is the person to follow this through in the long term?

2. How realistic is this person in terms of what it's going to involve?

3. How does the person relate to him/herself and others?

So, here are the questions I suggest that you should ask of yourself before continuing to read this book. If you can tick yes to all of them, then proceed further. If you cannot, please think hard before progressing.

---

* There are some circumstances when you should try to proceed straight to detox, even if you have not prepared for this. See Part III of this book for more information on this.

	Question	Tick here
Q1	Have you made a completely honest commitment to yourself to totally cease all alcohol use for at least a period of months after detox?	
Q2	Are you prepared to suffer disturbed sleep, feelings of agitation and to resist sometimes overwhelming cravings for alcohol for many months after your detox?	
Q3	Are you prepared to keep on working at staying dry or drinking at safe limits for the rest of your life?	
Q4	Do you honestly believe that the gains you will make by ceasing alcohol use by far outweigh the losses?	
Q5	Are you absolutely 100% convinced that your overall quality of life will be improved by stopping drinking?	
Q6	Are you aware that for the rest of your life you will remain at high risk of relapsing to damaging levels of alcohol consumption within a matter of days after taking your first drink?	
Q7	Are you prepared to be on guard for the rest of your life against the repetitive thought that will enter your head when most unexpected, saying: "Go on – just one drink can't hurt – how could it?"	
Q8	Are you prepared to do whatever it takes to stay off alcohol in the long term, and give this absolute priority over everything else in you life?	
Q9	Are you planning to stop drinking because you want to do this for yourself, and not solely for the benefit of another person?	
Q10	Do you take full, personal responsibility for all the problems in your life, whether or not you believe they are caused by drinking?	

So what's your score? If you ticked yes for all questions you may wish to skip the rest of this chapter and continue straight to Part II of this book. If it's less than 10 out of 10 I suggest you continue to read the rest of this chapter.

When you have finished reading this chapter, answer the questions again. If you still score less than 10 seriously think about taking a break from reading this book, and come back when you have reconsidered. As I said above, sometimes people will prove me wrong and that's fine by me – they've beaten the odds. **What is clear though, is that the more ticks you can put in the boxes above, the greater your chances of staying healthy and avoiding relapse.**

Let's take a more detailed look at each of the ten questions.

QUESTION ONE: HAVE YOU MADE A COMPLETELY HONEST COMMITMENT TO YOURSELF TO TOTALLY CEASE ALL ALCOHOL USE FOR AT LEAST A PERIOD OF MONTHS AFTER DETOX?

If you have become physically addicted to alcohol then the decision most likely to prevent a return to alcoholic levels of drinking is that of committing yourself to complete abstinence in the long term – for life. However, some people who have become physically addicted in the past will manage to control their drinking in the future without a return to previous damaging levels of drinking – these people are in the minority.

Whatever your decision and even if you are not physically addicted but are drinking at damaging levels, I recommend that you should make a commitment to at least six months completely dry following detoxification. Why is this?

Well firstly, statistically, the longer you are abstinent the less likely you are to start drinking again at damaging levels. That's the plain fact – a simple matter of observation by researchers who have observed people who have stopped drinking and have remained dry for up to a number of years. Those who start drinking again, shortly after detox has been completed, are more likely than those who don't, to relapse to alcoholic levels of drinking.

There are several ways of trying to understand why this occurs.

From the physical point-of-view this is explained by the gradual changes that take place in your brain both before and after you have given up drinking. The brain has a natural tendency to try to keep things stable for you, a natural tendency to adapt and change itself so that you continue to experience things normally despite changes in the world and the environment around you. A brain that has been bathed in alcohol every day for years-on-end slowly develops methods of trying to ward off the effects of this, so that you can continue to function as normally as possible. These methods involve the occurrence of long-term changes to the structure and functioning of the brain which enables it to become less responsive to the effects of alcohol over time – it does this in an attempt to keep everything normal despite the alcohol infusing it. One example of this occurring is the phenomenon of tolerance – whereby more and more alcohol has to be consumed before you get drunk. However, there are many other changes that occur in the brain in response to drinking heavily for a number of years.

When you stop drinking, the brain is unable to get used to this new world free of alcohol in a matter of days – after all it has taken it years to adapt to a world full of alcohol, and so it is likely to take a long time before it gets used to a world without alcohol. At first, your brain will tell you to carry on drinking because it thinks (incorrectly) this is the best way to keep things stable. Messages from the brain are sent to your consciousness in the form of thoughts and feelings and result in the experience of craving for alcohol. This is the brain's way of trying to make you drink again. If you continue to resist these cravings and do not relapse to drinking, the brain will slowly start to adapt to this 'new' world without alcohol; over the months it slowly gets used to the fact of the matter that it no longer has to deal with excessive alcohol use, and that the world is quite stable now without it. Slowly, the changes that occurred in its structure and function in the past start to reverse, and as this occurs the experience of craving diminishes in intensity and frequency.

However, if at any time within these early months you drink again, your brain receives urgent messages that it must readjust immediately back to its old state, the one which it became used to for so many years. Because of this, to have just one drink does not relax the craving you have felt, it intensifies it, and having had the one drink you will almost definitely progress to the next and to the next.....

Secondly, from the psychological point-of-view the tendency to return to drinking heavily can be understood in terms of habits. To develop the habit of drinking heavily on a regular basis probably took you a matter of years. The person who has their first taste of alcohol at the age of 10 or 11, very rarely continues to drink in increasing quantities from that day on. More usually, the habit of drinking develops over a number of months and years, until it starts to cause problems in all areas of your life. Equally, when you cease drinking, there is a new habit to learn – the habit of staying off alcohol. After one week of detox, there is no way that you will have developed the **habit of NOT drinking;** but you will easily recall the habit of drinking. After a matter of months, this new habit of not drinking will slowly start to become established. To start drinking before this time will almost definitely re-awaken the old pattern of drinking daily. Thinking about things from this perspective, for the habit of not drinking to become the predominant way of behaving, you will probably have to stay dry for as long as you were drinking heavily – how long were you drinking heavily for? I will wager with you that it has been at least five years. Are you prepared to stay completely abstinent for at least five years?

Thirdly, from a social point-of-view the longer you remain abstinent from drinking, the more likely you are to have replaced your drinking with an increasing number of other activities. If you persevere and choose the right kind of activities for you (something I discuss in Part II), you will eventually start to experience pleasure and satisfaction from these. Equally, other things will improve in time. Relationships may improve, finances may improve and your work situation may improve. None of these things will happen over night – the positive results of a cessation of drinking will only slowly become clear over a matter of months and years. When you have re-established the social side of your life, the benefits you experience from this will act to protect you from a return to drinking – you are more likely to think twice about what you have to lose, and if your time is full, you will tend to dwell less on the temptation of a return to drinking. Equally, the longer you stay dry the more situations you will have encountered where you have been tempted to drink but have succeeded in not doing so – you will learn from these situations and hopefully will be able to implement the same or improved tactics in the future when faced with a similar situation. Psychologists refer to these learned tactics of avoiding relapse as 'coping skills' – more on this later.

So, in short, the longer you stay dry, the better your chances of avoiding a return to alcoholic levels of drinking.

QUESTION TWO: ARE YOU PREPARED TO SUFFER DISTURBED SLEEP, FEELINGS OF AGITATION AND TO RESIST SOMETIMES OVERWHELMING CRAVINGS FOR ALCOHOL FOR MANY MONTHS AFTER YOUR DETOX?

Some doctors talk of two distinct phases of withdrawing from alcohol – 'early withdrawal' and 'protracted withdrawal'. Early alcohol withdrawal lasts a matter of days (at most two weeks) and is characterised by the symptoms of alcohol withdrawal discussed in Chapter One – i.e. sweating, tremor, nausea, vomiting, raised blood pressure and pulse etc.etc. Early alcohol withdrawal is potentially life threatening and requires treatment with a medicated detoxification. If detoxification is performed professionally it is a painless experience and the large majority of people will successfully complete detox and attain abstinence.

The phase of 'protracted alcohol withdrawal' commences following completion of detoxification, and may last for many months. This on-going low-grade alcohol withdrawal syndrome is not life-threatening and has no direct potential to cause damage to your body or brain. However, its unpleasant nature places you at high risk of relapse to alcohol, for the simple reason that drinking will relieve it immediately.

The 'symptoms' of protracted alcohol withdrawal include marked difficulty with sleeping, intense feelings of craving for alcohol, and a general feeling of restlessness and agitation. These symptoms may continue for many months in some people; however, some lucky individuals do not experience any of these effects. As you may not be one of the 'lucky ones' it is important to prepare yourself for the possibility that you will have to put up with poor sleep and an irritating feeling of restlessness for a long period of time after detoxification. In good time these feelings will diminish and then disappear - if you persevere without drinking. Don't underestimate the power of lack of sleep and frustration - together with strong cravings for alcohol they act to make the first few months after detox the highest risk time for relapse.

QUESTION THREE: ARE YOU PREPARED TO KEEP ON WORKING AT STAYING DRY OR DRINKING AT SAFE LIMITS FOR THE REST OF YOUR LIFE?

To stay dry or to control your drinking within healthy limits, and to keep this going will require you to change your outlook on the world. This is a long-term, life-long project, whether you choose abstinence or controlled drinking. People who have become addicted to alcohol (whether physically or psychologically addicted) have become used to the availability of 'the quick fix'. Whatever you use this 'quick fix' for (to feel high, to socialise better, to relieve feelings of depression, to relax, to quell boredom etc. etc.) it is simply not going to be available to you after you have given up drinking. (That is, unless you decide to replace alcohol use with the use of another addictive drug or destructive activity such as addictive gambling; this often occurs when someone has not prepared themselves adequately for how they are going to feel when they are dry.) In the modern day world there are very few healthy options that can completely replace the unhealthy quick fix of heavy alcohol or drug use. In times gone by, when human beings literally had to fight for survival on a daily basis, this 'fix or rush' may well have been supplied by activities necessary for survival such as hunting or escaping from a life-threatening situation. As our lives have become safer and more comfortable these natural activities have all but disappeared from our daily lives. Of course there are activities undertaken by some that provide the equivalent of this – mountain climbing, rally car driving, bunjee jumping and extreme sports such as snowboarding down dangerously steep mountainsides. The common theme with all these activities is their potential to produce an adrenaline rush due to the risk involved; it is also the case that heavy exercise causes the release of a natural (and healthy) form of heroin in the brain. So, it seems, there is some potential to replace addictive drinking or drug taking with other forms of healthy activity, and if you are interested in involving yourself in such activities then they really could help you to stay off the drink.

However, there are two main problems with this – firstly heavy exercise, high risk leisure activities neither appeal to nor are practical for many people who have a drinking problem. Secondly, there is a subtle difference between all these activities and drinking. That is, they all require some form of planning in order to implement them; they are not immediately available on demand. **The only planning necessary to take a drink is to plan to lift the bottle towards your mouth.**

The bottom line for most people reading this book is that you will need to readjust your expectations and desires. Everyone who drinks heavily has become reliant on the availability of an 'activity' that both makes them feel better (even if just for a short while) and that is available immediately. There are very few (if any) healthy activities that offer the potential to replace this exactly. In short, if you are to overcome your reliance on the immediate fix of a drink, you will have to replace your desire for short-term immediately available rewards with an acceptance of the long-term rewards that come from committed work on your life as an adequate replacement. You must aim for a sense of fulfillment and peace rather than a life of spontaneous fun and immediate relief.

For many people, the need to change their outlook and expectations in this way is the single most difficult part of staying dry. I will discuss ways of helping you to achieve this in Part II.

QUESTION FOUR: DO YOU HONESTLY BELIEVE THAT THE GAINS YOU WILL MAKE BY CEASING ALCOHOL USE BY FAR OUTWEIGH THE LOSSES?

If you are not completely convinced at the time of reading this sentence that the gains of giving up drinking will outweigh the losses, then you are almost definitely going to relapse shortly after detoxification. More about the reasons for this in the discussion of question five. For the meantime, if you have any lingering doubts there is a simple exercise you may wish to perform. This involves considering all the positive things about drinking as well as the negative things. In fact this exercise may be useful for three reasons. Firstly, to create a list of all the reasons you want to give up drinking may be helpful for you now, but also in the future after you have stopped drinking. The memory can be very short – to be able to look back at the reasons you wanted to stop drinking may be a useful reminder for you in the future of just how bad things had become. Secondly, by creating a list of all the things you enjoy about alcohol, or that you use it for, will be useful when it comes to planning how you are going to stay dry. When it comes to planning to stay dry, one important thing to do will be to plan to replace as many of these positive aspects of drinking with other healthy activities that will go at least some way towards offering similar pleasure or relief. **Thirdly,** you will be able to compare all the positives and negatives about drinking and see if you are clear that the negatives clearly outweigh the positives.

I've given you a start by including some of the common reasons people wish to continue drinking. But not all the reasons I have given are good reasons for continuing to drink. For example, drinking alcohol is only healthier than not drinking if you limit yourself to one unit of alcohol per day. Equally depression and anxiety are very often the long-term effects of heavy drinking – unfortunately both tend to be relieved in the short-term by drinking. But if you think these are good reasons you will probably continue to drink. **An important aspect of planning for detox or cessation of drinking is to get some of these basic facts sorted out before you go any further. The list of possible misunderstandings is so long that it would be impossible to address them all in this book. This is where it is important to get personal advice about your particular situation from a professional in the field.**

OK, let's start by considering the possible reasons that you find drinking an enjoyable or helpful activity. Tick off those things on this list that apply to you, and add items of your own as you think of them. If you wish to record this for the future, I have included an empty table for you in the appendix of this book.

POSSIBLE REASONS THAT YOU MAY WISH TO CONTINUE TO DRINK:

		Tick here
1	I enjoy the feeling of drinking and getting drunk.	
2	I've heard that drinking alcohol may actually be healthier for you than not drinking alcohol.	
3	Drinking stops me getting withdrawal symptoms.	
4	I have trouble getting to sleep – without a drink I cannot sleep well.	
	Psychological Reasons	
5	I tend to get depressed and drinking improves my mood.	
6	Drinking makes me less anxious.	
7	I tend to get a bit paranoid about going out. If I have a drink I can get out the house without worrying.	
8	I'm usually tense and stressed – drinking helps me to relax.	
	Social Reasons	
9	I have a much better time going out if I have a drink.	
10	I can't imagine going out without having a drink.	
11	I tend to be anxious in the company of other people; when I have a drink inside me I can talk more easily and get on with people better.	
12	I've become a bit of a loner over the years – the only time I ever get into a conversation is in the pub.	
	PUT YOUR OWN REASONS in the spaces below:	

POSSIBLE REASONS YOU MAY WISH TO CEASE DRINKING:

		Tick here
	Physical Health Reasons	
1	I'm feeling generally un-well most of the time.	
2	I never eat anything these days.	
3	I'm increasingly worried that I'm permanently damaging my physical health.	
4	I wake up early in the morning covered in sweat.	
	Psychological Reasons	
5	I feel horribly depressed when I wake up in the morning after drinking.	
6	My memory seems terrible these days.	
7	I seem so much more nervous than I used to be.	
8	I'm sick and tired of having this thing called alcohol in control of me. I want to get back in control of myself.	
	Social Reasons	
9	I want to be a better parent to my children.	
10	My relationship's a mess and I know it's because of my drinking.	
11	I've just been arrested for my second drink-drive offence – I might go to prison this time – I know I've got to do something about it.	
12	I'm finding it difficult to get into work on time – someone's going to say something soon.	
13	Of late my temper's got increasingly worse. I'm worried what I might do next time someone annoys me.	
	PUT YOUR OWN REASONS in the spaces below:	

Now, give one point for each reason for continuing to drink, and one point for each reason you would like to stop drinking. Tot-up the points for and against. Is your score in favour of stopping drinking at least twice that of your score for continuing to drink? If it's not, then you should think very hard before planning any further. Read on to question 5, and I'll tell you why. In the meantime, remember that some of the reasons you have given for continuing to drink may be there because of a misunderstanding about how alcohol works on your body and brain. To truly convince yourself of the need to give up drinking you should sort out the facts at an early stage. You can do this by talking to a professional in the field, and I will tell you how to do this in confidence and for free at the end of this chapter.

QUESTION FIVE: ARE YOU ABSOLUTELY 100% CONVINCED THAT YOUR OVERALL QUALITY OF LIFE WILL BE IMPROVED BY STOPPING DRINKING?

If you are not completely convinced at the time of reading this sentence that the gains of giving up drinking will outweigh the losses, then you are almost definitely going to relapse shortly after detoxification. Why? Because right now you are actively experiencing the negative effects of drinking; if you have doubts at the very time that you are actively experiencing these problems, then you will certainly have much stronger doubts when these problems start to recede and diminish. As the problems caused by drinking start to resolve, you will start to remember all the good things about drinking – how it helped you to relax, how it helped you to socialise etc. etc. In addition, for the period after detox, you will be experiencing the problems caused by NOT drinking such as sleeplessness, agitation, frustration, boredom and craving. The balance between gains and losses will seem to shift towards the overall advantage of a return to drinking.

If you do not believe that your overall quality of life will be improved by a cessation of drinking at this stage, when you are serious enough about giving up to be reading this book, then you will **never believe it at times of craving** after you have given up. At these times you will convince yourself that you'll be better off after all with a return to drinking. Now, in your present state this may seem unlikely to occur to you – you may not believe that it would be possible for you to start thinking in this way. But don't underestimate the power of your subconscious to overwhelm what may seem totally logical. It's an incredibly powerful force that you're fighting against – the force of the subconscious – the force of the more primeval parts of the brain that lead to craving. Most people happily lead their lives imagining that they are personally in control of all their thoughts and actions, and that when they do something it's because they have thought about it and made a decision to do it. In fact, at many times in life nothing could be further from the truth. Think about this – you can control the rate of your breathing by saying to yourself "I'm going to take a few deep breaths in rapid succession", or "I'm going to hold my breath for one minute". Does that mean that you are totally in control of your breathing?

Do you breathe by thinking about it? No – you don't – you probably haven't thought about your breathing all day until reading this. Moreover, if you did breathe by thinking about it what would happen when you go to sleep? – well, none of us would have made it past our first night on this earth. To give a harsher example, have you ever heard of anyone committing suicide by holding their breath? I doubt it, because it's impossible – if you tried it you would faint after several minutes and then start to breathe comfortably as the subconscious part of your brain took over. This is one simple demonstration of the power of the subconscious to overcome your conscious thoughts.

I was told about another example by a colleague of mine who works as a psychiatrist. His work at that time was on a general psychiatric ward looking after many seriously suicidal patients. His patients had all recently made very serious attempts on their lives, and some of them were being held in special padded rooms due to their continuing attempts to kill themselves. One such patient managed to start a small fire in the corner of his room. As the fire caught hold and grew he started to panic and banged on the door of his room to be let out. As the door was opened the rush of air into the room fanned the fire, and smoke started to fill the whole ward.

Now remember we are talking about a group of people who were very serious about wanting to kill themselves.

Not a single patient attempted to stay in the building as the smoke spread. Not a single patient attempted to harm themselves in any way as they left the ward. All patients gathered outside the building to wait for the fire brigade to arrive. Some of them rushed there in panic. No patient took the opportunity to 'escape 'from the hospital grounds once outside even though many were held there against their will under the Mental Health Act.

What is the explanation for this? Simply that the rudimentary, ingrained fear of fire caused the subconscious to take over and all the patients to save themselves, including the one that started the fire in the first place. For this short period of time the intensely depressive thoughts that led these patients to try to take their lives were overcome by a more primal need to escape and survive. If any of them had been able to think through the situation and control their behaviour by their thoughts, then some of them would have died that day. None did.

Now my point here is that the subconscious can be very powerful, and is quite capable of overcoming rational, conscious thought. So how is this related to alcoholism?

It is these same subconscious, primeval parts of the brain that have become all powerful in people who are addicted to alcohol (and other drugs). In particular there is one area of the brain that acts as a 'reward centre'. When you are healthy, this part of the brain provides you with feelings of satisfaction and pleasure when you do things that are necessary for survival, such as eating, or having sex (necessary for survival of the human race). In the process of addiction, the brain's reward centre literally gets hijacked by the addictive drug (alcohol in this case). After years of heavy drinking, the reward centre no longer responds well to activities such as eating, and sex; it increasingly responds only to drinking alcohol.

The problem when you cease to drink is that your brain has by now become convinced that you need to continue to drink alcohol in order to survive. It sends messages to you telling you to find alcohol at all costs. Imagine yourself without water in the desert for several days – how strong would your desire for water be? Is there anything that you would not do in order to get just one glass of pure, cold water? You may be prepared to do things that you would never do in any other situation. You may even be prepared to kill to get that glass of water. This is the power of the survival instinct. And this instinct is controlled by subconscious parts of the brain. This is my final example and for a good reason. The craving that the dying person in the desert feels when thinking of water is the same sensation that you will experience when you crave for alcohol. It is caused by the same brain mechanisms; in your case these brain mechanisms have been hijacked by alcohol. If you were that person in the desert and I placed a glass of water in front of you, could you refuse it? Probably not – but what if you had been given advance notice that the water was poisoned?

To refuse it you will have to be in no doubt that to drink it will actually be more damaging for you than to turn it away. To refuse that drink, especially in the early days following detox, your conscious thought processes will have to overcome the powerful drive of your subconscious. You will not achieve this unless you are completely, 100% convinced that the advantages of turning down the drink outweigh the disadvantages.

QUESTION SIX: ARE YOU AWARE THAT FOR THE REST OF YOUR LIFE YOU WILL REMAIN AT HIGH RISK OF RELAPSING TO DAMAGING LEVELS OF ALCOHOL CONSUMPTION WITHIN A MATTER OF DAYS AFTER TAKING YOUR FIRST DRINK?

Question one asked whether you were honestly committed to a total cessation of alcohol use for a period of months following detox. I noted that researchers have discovered that those who stay dry for longer are less likely to relapse to

damaging levels of alcohol use than those who have their first drink shortly after detox. Unfortunately, that's not the whole story. Now, I am not one of those doctors who say 'You absolutely have to stay off alcohol for ever, otherwise you will definitely return to drinking at alcoholic levels'. However, if you do have another drink at some point in the future, remember this – **you will always be much more likely than someone who has never had a drink problem to start drinking at dangerous and addictive levels.** I can say this with certainty for two reasons. Firstly there is a very simple rule of thumb that you can use when trying to predict what is going to happen to someone in the future; that is – 'The best predictor of the future is the past'. Someone who has become depressed in the past is statistically more likely than an 'average' member of the population to become depressed again in the future. Someone who has been divorced in the past is more likely than an 'average' member of the population to find their second marriage ending in divorce. Equally, someone who has had a drink problem in the past is much more likely than someone who has never had such a problem, to start drinking heavily again.

The second reason is due to the brain changes that occur following extended periods of heavy drinking. I talked above (Question 1) about the brain adapting to a world full of alcohol. I also mentioned that some of these brain changes will slowly but surely start to reverse in time. The problem is that they will never completely reverse – your brain will never be exactly the same as it was before you started to drink heavily. And because of this, it will always be more difficult for you than others who have never experienced a drink problem, to avoid a relapse to alcoholic drinking. Yes, this gets less likely to occur the longer you go without drinking, but it will always be more likely to occur to you than to others.

It is probably because of your permanent high risk of a return to heavy drinking that many doctors will tell you that you must never drink again. Personally, I prefer to give people the facts and then let them make their own decisions, and I would be lying to you if I said that you will 100% definitely return to alcoholic drinking if you ever have another drink again. So in summary here are the facts:

- The longer you go without drinking after detox, the less likely you are to relapse to heavy drinking.

- However, you will always (for the rest of your life) be much more likely to return to heavy drinking if you have a single drink, than someone who has never had a drinking problem.

- Probably only 25% of people who have been detoxed are still dry after one year.

- Many of those people who have relapsed have been through several detoxes already.

- **The only way to be sure that you will never return to heavy drinking is to commit yourself to never drinking again.**

QUESTION SEVEN: ARE YOU PREPARED TO BE ON GUARD FOR THE REST OF YOUR LIFE AGAINST THE LITTLE VOICE THAT WILL ENTER YOUR HEAD WHEN MOST UNEXPECTED SAYING: "GO ON – JUST ONE DRINK CAN'T HURT – HOW COULD IT?"

Under Question Five I talked about the power of the subconscious to overcome your determination. Craving (triggered by subconscious mechanisms) will remain a threat to you always. It will occur less frequently as time passes by, but in a way this makes it even more dangerous for you – you may have lowered your guard by then. When you are craving you will find yourself thinking "Go on – just one drink can't hurt – how could it?" Psychologists talk about 'cues and triggers' that in an instant lead to thoughts like this. There are probably an infinite number of possible triggers for craving, and they range from feelings such as depression and excitement, to thoughts such as the memory of a friend you used to drink with, to situations you find yourself in such as a wedding where there is drink readily available, or just walking past an off-license or pub. The things that cause craving in one person will not have the same effect in another.

You will learn the common causes of craving for you in time, as you experience them. Each time you stay dry and resist the temptation to drink, you will have the opportunity to see how you managed to do this, and to learn how to either avoid the same situation in the future, or how to deal with it if it occurs. Some forms of counselling for alcohol problems concentrate specifically on strengthening your skills in dealing with the situations, thoughts and feelings that trigger craving. I will tell you how to access such counselling in your area in Part II of this book.

In the meantime it is important to remember that craving may strike you completely unawares, even many years after you last had a drink. There are so many drinkers out there who will tell you their story – the story of how they hadn't had a drink for years and years, and then one day they found themselves in the pub on their sixth pint. **They found themselves there because they had let down their guard against the little voice.**

QUESTION EIGHT: ARE YOU PREPARED TO DO WHATEVER IT TAKES TO STAY OFF ALCOHOL (OR CONTROL IT) IN THE LONG TERM, AND GIVE THIS ABSOLUTE PRIORITY OVER EVERYTHING ELSE IN YOUR LIFE?

If you have read the comments beneath the previous seven questions, you will see that I personally think that you are going to have to be very determined indeed if you are going to avoid a relapse to heavy drinking. Maybe you will be lucky and find it a breeze, but if you do, you will be in a very small minority of those that go through detox and try to remain abstinent. Sometimes being determined to achieve something involves making difficult choices. None of us can do everything, and none of us can keep everyone pleased, all at the same time. For example, you may have decided that you are interested in education of some kind, and this may involve having to sit an exam. You know the exam is going to involve a lot of preparation and study if you are going to pass it, and you may need to pay for the course which involves doing extra hours at work as well as studying. You know that you don't stand a chance of passing the exam unless you put in the required amount of study, and you can't even start the course unless you work harder to pay for it. On the other hand you may have other responsibilities in your life such as children, and you may have friends that expect to see you on a regular basis. You know that if you carry on giving as much time to your children and friends, there's no way you will be able to afford the course and pass the exam. Equally, you know that if you want to pass the exam your children and friends will have to see you less. What are you going to do? Pass the exam or give as much time as usual to your children and friends?

Now this is a difficult decision, and different people will make different choices in this situation. If you choose to do the course some people would consider you selfish, and I would agree with them as the meaning of selfish to me is that you are doing something just for you, and putting other people second – forwarding your education and career is primarily about you, although there may be long term benefits for others in your life such as an increased salary. **But that doesn't automatically make it the wrong decision.** Maybe its time you did something just for you; maybe others expect too much from you and have started to take you for granted – it might even do them good to learn that you are not always there for them.

When it comes to making a decision to give up drinking and stay dry you will be faced with many decisions like this. People you have known for years and who you enjoy drinking with will expect you to still be there with them. You may get invited to a wedding, or a party; you may usually see your relatives at Christmas – all these situations will usually involve readily available alcohol. Are you going to place yourself in a situation surrounded by people who are drinking, and who may be trying to persuade you to have a drink? Or are you going to give your apologies and not turn up? I know what I would advise you to do – especially for the first few months following detox – I would definitely advise you to be 100% selfish about the matter. Politely give your apologies, and don't turn up. Think about you first.

Why am I so clear about this? **Because if you have become addicted to alcohol, the only way you stand a realistic chance of being selfless and giving and helping in the longer term, is to be totally single-minded and selfish about what you have to do (stay dry) in the short term. I call this 'healthy selfishness'.**

Giving up and staying dry (or drinking within controlled, healthy limits) is such a hard task, that if you are to achieve it then everything else must take second place for at least the first period of months after you have become dry. This doesn't mean that you always have to be thinking just about yourself, or that you can never do anything for anyone else. But when certain situations arise and you are faced with a difficult choice of either letting someone down or keeping yourself safe from a relapse, then you must put yourself first and avoid the high risk situation such as the party or wedding.

And don't expect them to understand either. Most people have no idea what a difficult task you are undertaking. You may lose some friends along the way; your relationships with family may actually get worse for a while rather than better. Are you prepared for that to happen? I think you need to be. And if you persevere, you will be stronger and have stronger relationships in the long run.

QUESTION NINE: ARE YOU PLANNING TO STOP DRINKING BECAUSE YOU WANT TO DO THIS FOR YOURSELF, AND NOT SOLELY FOR THE BENEFIT OF ANOTHER PERSON?

Sometimes people seek help for their drinking problem because someone else has told them to. If I see someone in my clinic and they tell me the reason they have come for help is because they have been sent by someone else, I know immediately that the odds are stacked high against this person giving up drinking successfully. There are two reasons for this; the first reason is related to Question Eight ('healthy selfishness') and the second reason is related to Question Four (Do the gains of giving up for you outweigh the losses of giving up drinking?).

Giving up drinking and staying dry is such a hard task, that however much you would like to do it for someone else's benefit, you probably won't achieve it. Maybe you think I'm cynical, but my observation of most people is that they are much more likely to achieve something if they are doing it for themselves, rather than for someone else. I mean, do you really go to work to make your boss richer? No, you go there so that you get paid. Would you rather go out for the evening to do something that you enjoy doing, or go out for the evening to do something your partner or friends enjoy doing?

Now I'm sure there are some exceptions to this, and if you are desperate to give up drinking just because your partner wants you to, then good on you. Having said this, even if you are truly motivated to give up drinking for someone else's benefit, there's a second problem here. Under Question Four I talked about weighing up the pros and cons of giving up drinking. If the only reason you want to give up drinking is that you would like to do it for someone else who has asked you to, then there's going to be a large imbalance in your list in favour of keeping drinking. This is a bad sign, and really means that when it comes down to it, beneath it all you have some doubts about whether you really do want to give up. If this is the case you stand a high chance of relapsing to heavy alcohol use in due course.

There will be many people who list one of their reasons for giving up drinking as improving their relationships, and that's great. The problem arises if this is your **only** reason for giving up. Equally, it's fine to take **advice** from others that you really should give up drinking; BUT, the actual **decision** to do something about it really should be yours and not someone else's.

QUESTION TEN: DO YOU TAKE FULL, PERSONAL RESPONSIBILITY FOR ALL THE PROBLEMS IN YOUR LIFE, WHETHER OR NOT YOU BELIEVE THEY ARE CAUSED BY DRINKING?

You accept that you have problems in your life otherwise you would not be reading this book. Some of those problems you will attribute to drinking. And if you are still reading by now, then you are probably prepared to take responsibility for those problems, rather than blame someone else for them. After all, it's your arm lifting the bottle. However, I suggest to you that you should put yourself in a state of mind, whereby you take full personal responsibility for all the problems in your life, whether or not you think they have been caused by drinking. When I say this, I do not mean that you should blame yourself for these problems, or that they are your fault. Everyone has problems, even though some might like to convince you otherwise. Problems are simply a part of life. And there is no need to blame yourself for them, or put yourself down about them. More importantly, there is no need to blame others for your problems, and to do so may actually be damaging for you and reduce your chances of staying off alcohol.

The reason for this is that if you blame others for problems in your life, this is really the same as saying "I can't do anything to change that problem; I can't sort it out because it's their fault – it's them that must do something about it, not me." This approach to things means that you will get stuck with some problems because you are always waiting for someone else to sort them out. And if you're thinking about changing that person's mind and getting them to behave a little more reasonably, you're probably best to forget it. It is very difficult to change other people – it is difficult to change yourself, but not nearly as difficult as changing someone else.

But why should you be taking responsibility for sorting out problems that may not be yours when they are not even caused by your drinking? You accept that heavy drinking has caused problems in your life. You are probably also aware that problems in your life have led you to drink more heavily, or to relapse to drinking in the past. If you fail to take personal responsibility for sorting out problems as best you can, then in time these problems will build up and place you at risk of a return to drinking as a means of escape. The only person you can really rely on to sort things out in the way that is in your best interests is you.

Why not **empower yourself** to change your life for the best?

CONCLUSION

You have now reached the end of this chapter and should be able to answer the question:

ARE YOU READY TO ACT NOW?

If you remain uncertain about this, I suggest that you take a few days to think about it, and then come back to read Chapter Three again. If you are convinced that you are ready to make a plan, then please continue to Part II of this book.

If you have any questions about how this chapter applies to you, or simply want professional advice on a one-to-one basis, then I advise you to contact the DryOutNow.com Immediate Response Service. All advice is free, totally confidential, and is provided by an expert in the field of alcoholism. Their telephone number is: 0800 160 1020.

Free home consultations are available in certain circumstances.

Alternatively, use the dryoutnow.com email advice service by email: freeadvice@dryoutnow.com

---

PART TWO

HOW TO PLAN YOUR ROUTE TO HEALTH

If at any time you require urgent access to treatment, or need an immediate response for any other reason, do not hesitate to telephone the DryOutNow.com Immediate Response Service (IRS) on:

0800 160 1020
(8am-9pm, seven days weekly)

INTRODUCTION

You have now completed Part I, and as you are still reading you will have hopefully come to a decision about the following three questions:

1. ARE YOU PHYSICALLY ADDICTED TO ALCOHOL?

2. DO YOU PLAN TO STOP DRINKING COMPLETELY (FOREVER) OR TO RETURN TO DRINKING WITHIN HEALTH LIMITS (CONTROLLED DRINKING)

3. ARE YOU READY TO DO SOMETHING ABOUT IT?

If you can answer questions 1 and 2, and are convinced that having read Chapter 3, you are ready to do something about it, then you should continue as follows:

EITHER:	OR:
IF YOU ARE PHYSICALLY ADDICTED to ALCOHOL, then START READING the INTRODUCTION to SECTION A.	IF YOU ARE NOT PHYSICALLY ADDICTED to ALCOHOL, then SKIP SECTION A completely, and START READING again at the INTRODUCTION to SECTION B on page 118.

PART TWO

SECTION A

If at any time you require urgent access to treatment, or need an immediate response for any other reason, do not hesitate to telephone the DryOutNow.com Immediate Response Service (IRS) on:

0800 160 1020
(8am-9pm, seven days weekly)

SECTION A : INTRODUCTION

**READ ON ONLY IF YOU ARE PHYSICALLY ADDICTED TO ALCOHOL –
IF YOU ARE NOT PHYSICALLY ADDICTED TO ALCOHOL, THEN GO
STRAIGHT TO THE INTRODUCTION TO SECTION B on page 118.**

If you have read Chapters One and Two of this book, then you will hopefully have reached a conclusion about the following two questions.

1. Are you physically addicted to alcohol?

2. Do you plan to cease drinking completely, or just to cut down drinking to healthy limits and control it there?

If you have read Chapter Three, then you will hopefully have come to a decision about whether you are ready to progress with making a plan to achieve your objective.

In this section, I will outline the best way forward for you, according to the research evidence. The research evidence applies to the majority of people but not to every single individual. Of course, the best way forward for you as an individual will depend on what your exact needs and problems are. In order to fine tune your plan, I suggest that you make use of free, one-to-one expert medical advice by email or telephone. If you have answered the questions in Chapters One and Two, and are physically addicted to alcohol, then one of the following two options will be suitable for you.

OPTION 1.
You are physically addicted to alcohol AND you plan to cease drinking completely.

OPTION 2.
You are physically addicted to alcohol AND you DO NOT plan to cease drinking completely.

Your route through treatment will vary depending on which one of the above options matches your needs.

The standard route for **Option 1** is discussed in Chapter 4.

The standard route for **Option 2** is discussed in Chapter 5.

Continue to read the relevant chapter for you.

CHAPTER FOUR

YOU ARE PHYSICALLY ADDICTED TO ALCOHOL AND YOU PLAN TO CEASE DRINKING COMPLETELY

If at any time you require urgent access to treatment, or need an immediate response for any other reason, do not hesitate to telephone the DryOutNow.com Immediate Response Service (IRS) on:

0800 160 1020
(8am-9pm, seven days weekly)

CHAPTER FOUR

YOU ARE PHYSICALLY ADDICTED TO ALCOHOL AND YOU PLAN TO CEASE DRINKING COMPLETELY

There are 3 stages through which you should progress, along your route to becoming abstinent from alcohol.

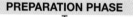

PREPARATION PHASE

DETOXIFICATION/REHAB PHASE

MAINTAINING ABSTINENCE/AFTERCARE PHASE

THE PREPARATION PHASE.

The preparation phase mainly involves planning/booking the help you will need to get dry and stay dry. Remember the rule of thumb: **"The detox is the easy bit, staying off is much harder…and again…"**. You should give very serious thought to committing to a period of residential rehabilitation (rehab) to continue straight on from detox. Many rehab centres provide both detox and on-going rehab, so that both can be received seamlessly in the same treatment centre. Rehab involves intensive counselling aimed at teaching you the skills to stay off alcohol on your return home. Typically people commit to at least one month in rehab, and this time can also be used to deal with some of the issues discussed below ('preparing yourself socially'), discussed as part of the preparation phase. The single most important fact to remember about rehab is that people who commit to a period of rehab have much better outcomes than those who only complete detox. Probably 75% of those completing a course of detox and rehab are dry at one year, whereas in the region of only 25% remain dry for this long if they commit only to detox.

Unless you are severely physically ill (e.g. in serious liver failure, suffering from regular seizures, becoming disorientated about what day it is and who people are, hallucinating etc.) then you should not rush to get admitted for treatment as soon as possible. **Yes, you should book a date for treatment,** so that you have something to aim for, but you should leave yourself enough time in between now and the detox starting to prepare adequately.

So what does preparing for staying dry involve?

There are three things to do:

1. Prepare yourself psychologically, and also seek out professional psychological support (various forms of counselling).

2. Prepare yourself socially, and seek out the available professional support.

3. Consider the possibility of medication to help you stay dry.

TO PREPARE YOURSELF PSYCHOLOGICALLY:

Make absolutely sure that you are fully committed to doing this, and that you are 100% realistic about how hard it's going to be. Re-read Chapter Three to help you to do this.

TO PREPARE YOURSELF SOCIALLY:

Firstly you should make a decision about whether you are going to stay in a **residential rehabilitation unit** for a period of time after detox, or whether you are **going to return home** immediately after detox.

Residential rehabilitation. Residential rehabilitation involves staying in a specialist psychological unit for a period of time (durations of stay range from two weeks to nine months) immediately following on from detox. The advantages of a period of residential rehabilitation include i) an alcohol-free environment so there is minimal risk of relapse ii) the person is living and learning from others with alcohol problems iii) as a generalisation, this is the best form of counselling as it is so intensive. The evidence clearly shows that those who go to a residential rehabilitation unit and complete the course without leaving early, are much more likely to remain dry from alcohol in the long term than those who do not go to residential rehabilitation. For more information on how residential rehabilitation works, go to

....

- **www.dryoutnow.com – find the online Professional Treatment Guidelines, and then download Section E of the Treatment Guidelines. Pages 73-74 are the relevant ones.**

....

Most residential rehabilitation units are not in the NHS. However, the NHS will sometimes pay for you to go to one if they think you need it. If you want to plan for a period of residential rehabilitation after detox, and wish the NHS to pay for it, then you will need to contact your local NHS Community Alcohol Team. They will arrange for you to be assessed, and if they think you meet their criteria for paying, will then arrange for your admission to follow immediately after detox. Waits may be long for assessment and admission (many months in some cases) and often

there is no funding available at all, but if you get treatment at the end of the day, it should be of the same quality as going privately.

....

• **For details of your local NHS Community Alcohol Team phone the DryOutNow.com Immediate Response Service on 0800 160 1020, or go to www.dryoutnow.com – and send the email from the Local Advice section to receive details of your local NHS Community Alcohol Team.**

....

If you decide to pay for residential rehabilitation yourself, then you will usually be able to access it within a matter of days.

• **For details of UK residential rehabilitation units phone the DryOutNow. com Immediate Response Service on 0800 160 1020 or go to www. dryoutnow.com – and look under the Alcohol Rehab Centres section.**

OTHER THINGS TO PREPARE FOR SOCIALLY:

1. ACCOMMODATION.

Is your accommodation situation stable and are you living with others who drink?

At the point of leaving detox you will wish for the amount of stress in your life to be as minimal as is possible; stress is a major reason for starting to drink heavily and it is also a major reason for relapse. If you do not have permanent accommodation, or you are at risk of losing permanent accommodation for whatever reason, do your best to sort this out in advance of detox. Lack of a stable environment in which to re-start your life will greatly increase your chances of relapse. If you are living with others who drink heavily, then you should very seriously consider either asking them to leave or leaving yourself. The odds of you managing to remain sober when there is someone living with you who drinks on a regular basis are very small indeed. Of course, if that person is also planning to seek help for an alcohol problem, then ideally this should be planned so that neither of you are living together at the time that one of you is still drinking. This will probably mean either planning for detox to take place at the same time as each other, or one immediately after the other, or at least one of you arranging for admission to a residential rehabilitation unit. If you live with other(s) who do drink, but do not drink heavily, you should see if they will agree to avoid drinking in the house. Ideally, the house should be completely empty of alcohol on your return from detox, and it should stay that way for the foreseeable future.

2. WORK.

Is your working situation stable? Are you unemployed? Are you facing some kind of disciplinary action? Are you on sick leave?

If you are in work and have no problems there, then this is usually the ideal situation. You will need to plan to take a period of leave during which time you will be in detox/rehab, or arrange a 'sick-note'. If you are on sick leave due to your alcohol problem, you should try to arrange to return to work, possibly on a part-time basis initially, as soon as detox/rehab is completed (unless you are seriously physically unwell). Of course, there is a fine balance here between too much stress at work, and too much time on your hands if you do not return to work. If work related stress is a problem for you, then your return to work should be a graded one. If you are facing some kind of disciplinary action at work as a direct or indirect result of your drinking, do your best to get this resolved before detox. Remember the aim is to limit the amount of stress you will have to deal with in those vital first few months when you may be battling to stay dry.

Of course, there's a bit of a Catch 22 about this; while you are drinking heavily you may not feel up to sorting these kind of things out. Overall, do your best to sort out what you can before detox/rehab; what you cannot do, you just cannot do. If you are unemployed at the moment, then make some initial plans for a return to work following detox/rehab. Ideally, arrange for a return to employment as soon as detox is completed. Of course this may well not be practical for you – if it is not, spend some time before detox thinking about what kinds of employment you may wish to get, and how you may go about searching for this on completion of detox. Build this into your weekly diary (see below).

3. RELATIONSHIPS

If you are in a relationship with a person who has a drinking problem, then the ideal is that you should both deal with this at the same time – it's highly unlikely to work for either of you if one person becomes abstinent while the other continues to drink. If you are unable to convince your partner of this, then if you are committed to aiming for an alcohol free life, you should seriously consider whether or not to continue with the relationship. If you are in a relationship with someone who does not drink heavily, then you may well be experiencing problems in your relationship.

You may find that your relationship improves dramatically when you cease drinking, but sometimes this will not be the case. Whatever, if you are having relationship problems at the moment, consider whether to book some relationship counselling with RELATE. This organization often has waiting lists of several months – if you book now, then the counselling will probably start when you have completed detox and are sober. Here is the central contact telephone number for RELATE: **0845 130 4016**

THE DETOXIFICATION/REHAB PHASE.

If you are physically addicted to alcohol, then on cessation of alcohol use you will experience alcohol withdrawal symptoms such as tremor, sweating, nausea, vomiting, raised blood pressure and raised pulse. In severe alcohol withdrawal you may experience epileptic seizures, hallucinations, delusions and disorientation in time and place. In some cases, severe alcohol withdrawal can be fatal, and if not fatal may lead to permanent brain damage. All the symptoms of alcohol withdrawal are caused by what doctors call 'hyper-excitability of the central nervous system' – in other words the brain becomes massively overactive. In order to control this over-activity of the brain, sedative medication is prescribed – detox. Quite large doses of sedative medication are prescribed at first, and then the dosage gradually reduced down to zero over a number of days. If the detox is performed professionally, the risk of epileptic seizures occurring is very small indeed, and no other complications of alcohol withdrawal are likely to occur. Equally, you should expect to feel quite comfortable during detox, and by the time it's completed, you will probably feel the best you have in years.

Don't get confused between sedative medication and sleeping tablets – although they are similar, you will not be sent to sleep for the detox. The medication you are prescribed (usually a medicine called chlordiazepoxide (Librium) or diazepam (Valium)) is not aimed at sending you to sleep, rather just to calm you and prevent the brain's over-activity that occurs during alcohol withdrawal. You will most likely be prescribed other medicines as well. These may include anti-nausea tablets such as 'metoclopramide', sleeping tablets (at night only) such as 'temazepam or zopiclone' and anti-epileptic tablets such as 'carbamazepine'. Most importantly you should be prescribed vitamin B tablets (vitamin B1 to be precise) or injections. Years of heavy drinking result in your levels of vitamin B being particularly low; the brain over-activity that occurs in alcohol withdrawal may burn up the final stores of this vital vitamin. If the stores drop below a critical level, you may suffer permanent brain damage which affects the memory in particular.

Detox can usually be accomplished safely within days, and some detox units will offer a 7-day programme. However, 10 days to two weeks is more typical. This allows for you to take it slowly and comfortably. Just as importantly the emotional side of things should be considered as well as the physical during detoxification. If you are admitted to a specialist detoxification unit, you will receive counselling and be encouraged to attend group therapy with other patients during the detox. It is important that this forms part of the detoxification plan - the easy bit is the detox, the difficult bit is staying off in the longer term - skills need to be learned to remain abstinent, and underlying emotional issues resolved to prevent a return to drinking.

If you would like to know more about the technical side of alcohol detox, go to:

- **www.dryoutnow.com – find the online 'Professional Treatment Guidelines', and then download Section C of the Treatment Guidelines.**

When you are planning detox there are several decisions that need to be made:

1. *Have you thought about the options of where detox may take place (home, psychiatric ward, hospital medical ward, specialist detoxification unit)?*

2. *Are you looking for a free detox or a self-pay service?*

3. *Have you decided whether or not you wish to continue to residential rehabilitation after detox?*

1. Where is the best place for the detox to take place?

a. Home. Detox at home may sound more appealing than having to be admitted to a hospital of some kind. However, it is a less safe and less effective means of undergoing detoxification on average. Approximately 50% of people who undergo detoxification at home will manage to complete the detox without starting to drink again during the detox, while over 90% will complete detoxification when admitted to a specialist detoxification unit. Equally, if anything does go wrong during detox, then being in hospital should mean that you get the right care immediately, whereas you may wait hours at home. In particular, home detox is generally agreed to be the wrong option if you have a history of epileptic fits when coming off alcohol, if you suffer from any serious medical condition, if you suffer from any serious psychiatric illness or feel suicidal, if you have a tendency to get disorientated, if you are unable to arrange for another adult to be with you at home for the detox, or if you live with others who drink.

b. Psychiatric ward. Sometimes alcohol detox arranged through the NHS occurs on a psychiatric ward. From a doctor's perspective, the main problem here is that staff on psychiatric wards often have less experience of dealing with alcohol detoxification, than do those in a specialist unit. The psychological aspect of detoxification (preparing you to deal with life without drinking when you leave) is less likely to be addressed, and you are probably less likely overall to complete the detoxification without returning to drinking. Equally, you may not feel comfortable with the idea of admission to a psychiatric ward in view of the fact that most other patients there will be suffering from serious psychiatric illnesses.

c. Hospital medical ward. If you are seriously physically ill as a result of your drinking (e.g. jaundiced, having fits, bleeding from the rectum or vomiting blood, having hallucinations or delusions) or have another serious illness such as poorly controlled diabetes or active pancreatitis, then a hospital medical ward is probably the best place to receive detoxification. The reason I say this, is that if you are this ill, the absolute priority must be to place you where you will be provided with immediate attention from a doctor who is used to dealing with emergencies if things go wrong. There is a fine judgment to be made here, because you are unlikely to get the best overall treatment as far as completing the detox and staying dry afterwards. Some specialist detox units are very capable of dealing with all the common emergencies very effectively, and they will also be able to offer the 'full package' aimed at your drinking problem. On a hospital medical ward, you will probably be treated as just another patient who has to be kept alive until they are discharged.

d. Specialist detox unit. Admission to a specialist unit for your detox is clearly the ideal in most cases. Such units have the most expertise in getting you through detox comfortably, and have the best chances of getting you through detox without relapsing to alcohol use before completion of the detox. Unless you are very ill indeed, they should also offer the safest option overall for detox. In addition to this, you will receive specialist counselling as part of the detox 'package'. This should improve your chances of staying dry after detox considerably, and unless you are seriously physically ill, that should be your main consideration. Remember that only around 25% of people who have detoxed from alcohol are still dry after one year. Any treatment you can get that will improve your chances of staying dry you should grab. Your main consideration must be to aim at that – 'The detox is the easy bit, staying dry is much harder.'

2. Are you looking for a free detox or a self-pay service?

2a. Free alcohol detoxification.

This may be accessible through the NHS. If you wish to proceed along this route, the starting place is usually your local 'Community Alcohol Team' (sometimes 'Community Drug and Alcohol Team').

....

- **For details of your local NHS Community Alcohol Team phone the DryOutNow.com Immediate Response Service on 0800 160 1020, or go to www.dryoutnow.com – click on 'Local Help' section, complete the required fields, and send the email to receive details of your local community alcohol team.**

....

Usually these days you can book in direct with your community alcohol team by telephone. However, in some cases they may require you to go to your GP first in

order to be referred to them by your GP. When you have either referred yourself or been referred by your GP, you will be given an appointment for an assessment with the alcohol team. They will formulate a plan with you, which should include a detoxification if you are assessed as needing one.

That's the theory and in some cases it will work exactly like this. In some cases you will get an excellent service from the NHS. In other cases you will not – it all depends on where you live. If you are lucky enough to live in an area where the treatment of alcoholism has been well funded over the last few years, then you are likely to experience few problems. However, the funding for alcohol treatment has been very poor in most areas for many years, and in some cases has got even worse over the last several years, as money has been diverted to treating illicit drug problems rather than alcohol problems. This is what is known as the 'postcode lottery'. There is no way of my predicting whether you will be lucky with the NHS or not. The problems you may experience are:

- Long waits to be seen in the first place (many months).

- Long waits to access detoxification after you have been assessed (months to years).

- No detoxification available in practice whatsoever.

- Detoxification only available at home, (see above – home detoxification).

- Detoxification only available in the local psychiatric ward.

Now, as I stated above, in some areas you will get a service by going the NHS route – the only way to find out if this applies to you, is to give it a try.

2b. Self-pay alcohol detox.

The large majority of self-pay detox units are dedicated, specialist units. In such units, you should receive good quality medical care and psychological support aimed at keeping you dry after completion of the detox. The main differences in price are accounted for by:

- The quality of the accommodation.

- The quality of the medical cover.

- How long you are prepared to wait.

As a generalisation, the more you pay the better hotel services you will receive, and the quicker you will be admitted. The degree of medical cover in self-pay units ranges from non-specialist GPs available for telephone advice and to attend in an emergency only, to specialist consultants seeing you on a daily basis with a ward doctor on-site to attend to you 24 hours/day. The more expensive units will tend to have invested more in their medical cover than the less expensive units.

Deciding on the best self-pay unit to use depends on how ill you are, how long you are prepared to wait, how entrenched your alcoholism is, and what your needs are in terms of accommodation. Probably you will want to minimise the cost that you pay whilst making sure you get the best possible treatment for you. If you choose to seek detoxification privately, then DryOutNow.com will arrange this for you.

DRYOUTNOW.COM WILL:

- *Find you the cheapest detox/rehab suitable to your needs.*

- *Find you the best detox/rehab (safest and highest rates of completion) suitable to your needs.*

- *For detox units that require a referral from a doctor, they can make that referral for you. (Some people will not wish to go via their GP).*

- **For details of detoxification units phone the DryOutNow.com Immediate Response Service on 0800 160 1020, or go to www.dryoutnow.com – and find the 'alcohol rehab centres' section.**

3. Have you decided whether or not you wish to continue to residential rehabilitation after detox?

Most specialist detoxification units will offer the option of staying on after completion of detoxification for a period of residential rehabilitation. If you have decided you would like to consider a period of residential rehabilitation to follow detox, then you should discuss this with an expert at the DryOutNow.com Immediate Response Service making use of their free telephone advice service. They have details of the full spectrum of UK residential rehabilitation units, and can help you plan in the most cost-effective way given your particular needs.

- **For details of residential rehabilitation units phone the DryOutNow. com Immediate Response Service on 0800 160 1020, or go to www. dryoutnow.com – and find the Alcohol Rehab Centres section.**

THE MAINTAINING ABSTINENCE/AFTERCARE PHASE.

You have arrived! You've stopped drinking successfully, and are ready to face a new world – a world without alcohol. Now this is where the serious work begins – the work of staying dry. If you've implemented most of the steps I outlined in the 'preparation phase' then you will have a head start over all the new challenges that are going to face you:

• **Craving for alcohol**

• **Sleeplessness**

• **Agitation**

• **Boredom**

• **NO IMMEDIATE SOLUTION TO ALL THESE THINGS**

On the other side of the coin, you are likely to be:

• **Feeling well for the first time in a long time**

• **Eating well**

• **Feeling in a better mood if you have been depressed**

• **Feeling more confident in yourself, especially if you suffered with paranoia and anxiety while you were drinking**

However, you must remember this – most of the advantages of giving up drinking are **long term advantages;** they will not be apparent to you immediately, and they will require a sustained period of abstinence from alcohol to occur:

• **Improved relationships with the important people in your life**

• **Building new relationships with the future important people in your life**

• **Improved performance at work**

• **Finding and holding down employment if you are unemployed**

• **Enjoyment of leisure activities you could never have enjoyed while you were drinking**

• **Improved financial situation**

• **A sense of pride in yourself that had been forgotten during years of heavy drinking**

Maintaining abstinence will bring you rewards whether these are delivered by living longer, feeling better in yourself and with yourself, or having better relationships with others. All of these things can disappear in a moment if you relapse, and most of the truly rewarding things take months and years to start to occur.

AFTERCARE:

Only 25-30% of people who have detoxed without rehab are still dry at the end of one year, and 75% who complete a period of rehab. How are you going to maximise your chances of being one of those who successfully remain abstinent in the longer term? For the first year (the highest risk time for relapse) you must implement your plan, and stick to it as much as is feasible for you. Your plan to maintain abstinence after detoxification and/or rehab is usually referred to as 'Aftercare'. The research evidence shows that people who persevere with an aftercare plan for a period of time following rehab or detox, significantly increase their chances of remaining abstinent in the longer term. So what should this plan involve?

1. Counselling with a specialist addictions counsellor.

Specialist 1-to-1 counselling can help in one of two ways: firstly by giving you the skills to avoid relapse to alcohol, and secondly by helping you to understand any underlying emotional issues which are leading you to drink heavily. For detailed information on how counselling works, go to:

....

- **www.dryoutnow.com – find the 'Professional Treatment Guidelines', and then download Section E of the Treatment Guidelines.**

....

Specialist counselling may be available from local NHS/charitable services for free. Or you can book with a private counsellor. In terms of the quality of service you will receive, there is probably little difference between NHS and private counsellors. However, in the NHS you may have to wait a long time (months or years in some cases) before you can access counselling. This varies between areas and depends on where you live. So, overall, I suggest contacting your local NHS/Charitable specialist alcohol counselling service first. If the waiting time seems unsatisfactory, or other things don't seem right, then try the self-pay route.

- **For details of your local NHS/charitable and private counselling services phone the DryOutNow.com Immediate Response Service on 0800 160 1020, or go to www.dryoutnow.com – find the 'local help' section and send the email to receive details of your local counselling services.**

Private counsellors who specialise in alcohol problems are not so many in number. There are probably in the region of 400 in the country. Many problems that lead to heavy drinking are general in nature (e.g. stress, relationship difficulties etc.). So, if your nearest specialist alcohol counsellor is too far away, a general counsellor may still be of help to you.

SPECIALIST TELEPHONE COUNSELLING

Alternatively, you can access specialist private alcohol counselling by telephone. You may wish to use this service if your nearest specialist counsellor is too far away, or if you would prefer the privacy and convenience of receiving counselling in your own home. This service is provided via DryOutNow.com. Call 0800 160 1020 to request details of the specialist telephone counselling service.

2. Alcoholics Anonymous meetings.

People are often nervous about attending these meetings, but those who attend have been shown to have better long term outcomes. There is no requirement to have stopped drinking in order to attend – just to be relatively sober at the time of attendance. There is no requirement to speak at a meeting – just to say 'pass' if asked to speak. The theme of the meetings is religious and requires a belief in a 'higher power', but there is no requirement to believe in God as such, or in any particular God. Some people think of the 'higher power' as the 'sober part' of themselves. There is no need to book in advance – just turn up to a meeting and sit alone just to observe at first. People will probably come to talk to you after the meeting – one of the main beliefs of Alcoholics Anonymous is that alcoholics need other alcoholics to help them to get sober – so people will be keen to help you. For more information on 'AA' meetings and how they work, go to:

....

- **www.dryoutnow.com – find the 'Professional Treatment Guidelines', and then download Section E.**

....

- **For details of your local Alcoholics Anonymous meetings phone the DryOutNow.com Immediate Response Service on 0800 160 1020, or go to www.dryoutnow.com – find the 'Local Help' section, and send the email to receive details of your local AA meetings.**

....

3. Medication to help prevent relapse to alcoholism.

There are two medications commonly used in the UK to help prevent a return to drinking.

i) Acamprosate, also known as Campral.

Acamprosate works to reduce the feeling of craving for alcohol. It is very effective for a few patients, quite effective for some, and simply doesn't work for others. As it is a relatively safe medicine to prescribe, in my NHS practice I prescribe it for most patients who have gone through detox. It is usually safe to continue to take it, even if you temporarily lapse to drinking again. There are several other medicines that are also used to create a similar effect, including naltrexone and nalmefene, but these have shown no advantages over acamprosate to date.

ii) Disulfiram, also known as Antabuse.

Disulfiram blocks the complete breakdown of alcohol by the liver. This causes you to feel absolutely terrible if you have a drink. Disulfiram can work well for people who are likely to relapse to drinking on the spur of the moment – you simply can't do this if you are taking it. However, its no magic cure, as you can decide to stop taking it, and within several days you are likely to be able to drink again without feeling ill. I prescribe disulfiram less often than acamprosate as it has the potential to cause some quite nasty side-effects in some people. In particular, it should generally be avoided in people who have a history of blood vessel problems (e.g. high blood pressure, history of stroke or heart attack), who have liver disease, or who have suffered serious psychiatric illness in the past.

For more information on both these medicines, go to:

....

- **www.dryoutnow.com – find the 'Professional Treatment Guidelines', and then download Section C.**

....

Of course, confidentiality may be an issue for you, and you will need to see a doctor to get these medicines prescribed. If you do not wish to see your GP about this, then the DryOutNow.com Immediate Response Service can give you details of your nearest private doctor who will be prepared to prescribe for you. Simply phone and ask for details of your nearest private doctor who specialises in addiction problems.

....

- **For details of your local private doctors who specialise in alcoholism phone the DryOutNow.com Immediate Response Service on 0800 160 1020.**

....

4. Self-help in the aftercare phase.

A: Prepare your weekly diary

Probably the single most important thing you can do without help from others is to **write out your weekly diary.** There are two aims of the weekly diary. Firstly it should enable you to fill your time completely from the day of discharge from detox/rehab, onwards. Your time should be full for the simple reason that this will leave you less time to think about alcohol. The nature of craving is such that if you give it a chance to build up, it will end up filling your head with repetitive thoughts: "Just one drink won't hurt – how could it? Just one drink won't hurt – how could it?" You must do your utmost to divert your attention from any such thoughts at all times. Being active and having to concentrate on a task of some kind is much more likely to result in the feeling of craving subsiding, than is sitting in a chair doing nothing. The vital element here is having to concentrate on something. This is very important if you are back in your usual routine, and not in specialist care.

Secondly it should provide you with the kind of activities that have a good chance of giving you some kind of sense of fulfillment or pleasure – that are rewarding. The aim here is to start to build up activities that will replace your need for alcohol in the longer term. As discussed in Chapter Three – don't expect anything to replace alcohol totally – there are very few activities that can result in your brain experiencing the reward that use of an addictive substance brings, and probably no healthy activities that produce that reward as easily and as immediately as does alcohol. You will need to re-think your objectives and search more for a sense of satisfaction and fulfillment in life than for the experience of immediate pleasure or immediate relief from unpleasant feelings which is delivered by alcohol.

You should think this through in great detail starting now. It must be ready to implement the very day you leave detox. You should try to think of activities that are purposeful, and have the potential to lead to some sense of satisfaction; this will depend very much on personal taste. Some examples might include: socialising with non-drinking friends, reading, gym, gardening, walking. You may well have found that your appetite has been terrible for as long as you can remember; during detox it is very likely that your appetite will start to improve, and by the time you have finished detox you will be enjoying food again. As such, one activity you plan may involve food, such as developing your culinary skills. Or more simply, what about planning to sit down to lunch and dinner every day – you probably haven't done that in a while. (Don't worry about weight gain – alcohol is much more fattening than many foods). If it's possible to devote yourself to some kind of work project with a long-term goal in mind this could be useful. In particular, if you are able to devote yourself to any kind of long-term project that involves dedication and a great deal of work, this might start to act to replace the psychological need for alcohol. (This kind of approach would be disagreed with by many professionals, especially those from a theoretical counselling background – they would argue that the addictive behaviour is merely being transferred from one object – drink – to another – work. However, if you are not considering residential rehabilitation, I think this is exactly what you should aim to do – replace the alcohol with healthy activity rather than destructive activity.)

In summary, you should create a diary ideally providing several options of activity for all times of every day of the week. This is not to say that you must or will complete every such activity – the important thing is that the diary is always there to turn to if you find yourself sitting and starting to dwell on the idea of having a drink. When that thought enters your head (and it will), you should immediately pick up the diary and implement one of the activities that are listed for that time of that day.

Following is an empty diary covering seven days of the week from 6 in the morning to 12 midnight. It also allows for you to enter two alternative activities for any two hour period. Now you may think that an 18 hour day is a long period of time to plan to fill, but bear the following in mind. The idea of the diary is not that you necessarily do every thing on it at the specified time, although you may choose to, and there will be no harm in this unless you get stressed thinking that you have to do everything on it. The idea of the diary IS that when you feel yourself starting to crave alcohol, you have something to occupy yourself with immediately, and which is already planned so that you can implement that activity immediately. If you wait until you start to crave before trying to think of something to occupy your mind, you may well not be able to do what you wish to immediately, and you may not even be able to concentrate effectively in order to think of something else to do. If you have your diary ready, you've got a great head-start over the craving.

Secondly, remember that your sleep may be disturbed for a period of months after detox. It is thus important to have planned activities from early in the morning to late at night – again you will not necessarily carry out all these activities, but if you are awake for long hours, you must make sure you have something to do. Poor sleep after detox is a major cause of relapse to drinking. Be prepared to have something to do if you cannot get to sleep – if you enjoyed reading in the past get some good books in. If you enjoyed film, get in a stack of videos or sign up for satellite channels (less expensive than your total alcohol costs). Poor sleep will improve as your brain gets used to a world free of alcohol – but you may have to be prepared to persevere for a good while.

If you are having difficulty thinking of the type of activities you should include in the diary the following questions may give you some ideas:

- What did you enjoy doing before alcohol started to replace other things in your life?

- What are the enjoyable things about drinking for you?

Can you replace these with activities that result in a similar reward? (E.g. you may drink after work to relax; can you arrange for a massage on some nights as an alternative form of relaxation?) If you completed the tables in Chapter 3 under Question 4, you may wish to use your answers to help you here.

- **What would you like to achieve from life? What would you need to do to achieve these things? Is there something you could dedicate yourself to achieving?**

....

- **How is your physical health? Could you improve it by eating well and healthily? Could you improve it by exercising regularly? What kinds of exercise would you enjoy?**

....

- **How is your social life? Do you have any non-drinking friends you could get in touch with? Can you think of a variety of social activities that don't involve drinking that you may enjoy?**

....

- **Do you need to search for work? What do you need to do to search for work?**

....

	MONDAY	TUESDAY	WEDNESDAY	THURSDAY	FRIDAY	SATURDAY	SUNDAY
Activity 1: 6-8							
Activity 2: 6-8							
Activity 1: 8-10							
Activity 2: 8-10							
Activity 1: 10-12							
Activity 2: 10-12							
Activity 1: 12-2							
Activity 2: 12-2							
Activity 1: 2-4							
Activity 2: 2-4							
Activity 1: 4-6							
Activity 2: 4-6							
Activity 1: 6-8							
Activity 2: 6-8							
Activity 1: 8-10							
Activity 2: 8-10							
Activity 1: 10-12							
Activity 2: 10-12							
NIGHT-TIME 1							
NIGHT-TIME 2							

B: ASSERTAIN YOUR NEEDS

Below is a 'formula' for ascertaining your needs and planning to make sure that they are met. Use this if you remain having difficulties in filling in your weekly diary.

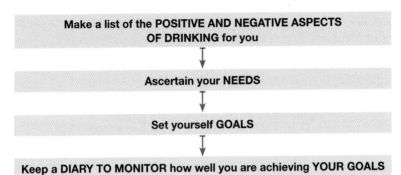

MAKE A LIST OF THE POSITIVE AND NEGATIVE ASPECTS OF DRINKING FOR YOU

Making a list of the things you find both helpful and unhelpful about drinking, is the starting point of this process. You will find that if you write this list, you will be able to see quite clearly what you need in your life, that at the present time you are trying to get from alcohol. If you made these lists when you read Chapter Three, then refer back to them now. Otherwise, continue right here. I've given some examples of the positive and negative reasons for drinking that people commonly write down. Cross these out if they don't apply to you, and then spend plenty of time thinking about the good and bad aspects of drinking for you – add to the list and make it your own. Let's start by considering the possible reasons that you find drinking an enjoyable or helpful activity. Tick off those things on this list that apply to you, and add items of your own as you think of them. If you wish to record this for the future, I have included an empty table for you in the appendix of this book.

POSITIVE THINGS ABOUT DRINKING FOR YOU:

		Tick here
	Physical Health Reasons	
1	I enjoy the feeling of drinking and getting drunk.	
2	Drinking stops me getting withdrawal symptoms.	
3	I have trouble getting to sleep – without a drink I cannot sleep well.	
	Psychological Reasons	
4	I tend to get depressed and drinking improves my mood.	
5	Drinking makes me less anxious.	
6	I tend to get a bit paranoid about going out. If I have a drink I can get out the house without worrying.	
7	I'm usually tense and stressed - drinking helps me to relax.	
	Social Reasons	
8	I have a much better time going out if I have a drink.	
9	I can't imagine going out without having a drink.	
10	I tend to be anxious in the company of other people; when I have a drink inside me I can talk more easily and get on with people better.	
11	I've become a bit of a loner over the years – the only time I ever get into a conversation is in the pub.	
	PUT YOUR OWN REASONS in the spaces below:	

NEGATIVE THINGS ABOUT DRINKING FOR YOU:

		Tick here
	Physical Health Reasons	
1	I'm feeling generally un-well most of the time.	
2	I never eat anything these days.	
3	I'm increasingly worried that I'm permanently damaging my physical health.	
4	I wake up early in the morning covered in sweat.	
	Psychological Reasons	
5	I feel horribly depressed when I wake up in the morning after drinking.	
6	My memory seems terrible these days.	
7	I seem so much more nervous than I used to be.	
8	I'm sick and tired of having this thing called alcohol in control of me. I want to get back in control of myself.	
	Social Reasons	
9	I want to be a better parent to my children.	
10	My relationship is a mess and I know it's because of my drinking.	
11	I've just been arrested for my second drink-drive offence – I might go to prison this time – I know I've got to do something about it.	
12	I'm finding it difficult to get into work on time – someone is going to say something soon.	
13	Of late my temper has got increasingly worse. I'm worried what I might do next time someone annoys me.	
	PUT YOUR OWN REASONS in the spaces below:	

When you have completed making the two lists above, you will be in a position to write down what your needs are. Use the table below to do this. By writing in a positive or negative reason for drinking, you should then be able to work out what you need to do to resolve that – write it down in the space below the reason for drinking. I've started by giving you a few examples. If you run out of space, I have included a blank table for you in the appendix.

Reason	I enjoy the feeling of drinking and getting drunk.
NEED	I need to have enjoyable feelings.
Reason	I have trouble getting to sleep – without a drink I cannot sleep well.
NEED	I need to sleep well.
Reason	I'm usually tense and stressed - drinking helps me to relax.
NEED	I need to relax.
Reason	I never eat anything these days
NEED	I need to eat well
Reason	I feel horribly depressed when I wake up in the morning after drinking.
NEED	I need to improve my mood
Reason	My relationship is a mess and I know it's because of my drinking.
NEED	I need to improve my relationship
Reason	
NEED	
Reason	
NEED	
Reason	
NEED	
Reason	
NEED	
Reason	
NEED	
Reason	
NEED	

C: SET YOURSELF GOALS

Your goals will involve meeting the needs you have made a list of above. If you manage to successfully achieve and maintain abstinence from alcohol, some of these things will automatically sort themselves out for themselves (e.g. morning sweats and withdrawal symptoms will not return). If you are lucky, other things like your relationship and your mood will also improve as a direct result of stopping drinking. However, many of the reasons you have used alcohol may have been there before you ever started drinking – these problems will not be resolved merely by a cessation of drinking (e.g. you may have started drinking heavily because of stress at work). Equally, some of the problems caused by drinking may have become so difficult that they will take more than just stopping drinking to sort them out. These will need to be addressed by other means. If you fail to address them, they will put you at risk of a return to heavy drinking in due course.

Let's consider an example.

Example 'need': 'I need to have enjoyable feelings'

When considering how to achieve this without getting drunk, you will need to get away from the idea (which may have become a dominant one for you), that the only way you can experience pleasure is by drinking. You will need to think of other means of experiencing pleasure without drinking. Having done this, you will need to write these things down in the form of 'goals'. Here are some common themes that come out of this exercise when I run it by people in my clinic: socialising, sex and eating. Many people who have developed an alcohol problem will have forgotten how to socialise without the use of alcohol, will have poor sex lives (when they may well have had excellent sex lives in the past) and currently eat very little and are not particularly bothered by food (despite the fact that they used to enjoy food). Focus on similar things for you, and turn them into goals:

Goal – I will arrange to socialise with non-drinking friends on one evening this week.

Goal – I will talk to my partner about our sex-life on one evening this week.

Goal – I will cook a lovely meal one night this week.

Before you set your goals, there are some other important things to take into account:

Goals must be **realistic;** e.g. do not plan to run The Marathon next month, or read The Lord of the Rings in one week.

Goals must be **specific** and measurable; e.g. I will see non-drinking friends once this week; I will cook a great meal on one night this week; I will go for a jog on two nights this week.

Goals must be **short-term** e.g. over the next week, or next day. While it is important to have a long-term objective in mind, this will not be reached overnight; if you are to achieve control over yourself, you must set short-term goals, and do your utmost to stick to them.

To achieve this, break your long-term goals down into **smaller steps;** e.g. if you plan to end up with a full social life away from the temptation of readily available alcohol, then arrange one activity per week at first. If your aim is to become physically fit, then arrange exercise on one night weekly first-of-all, and gradually increase. If you take things too quickly, you will probably experience a sense of failure when you fail to achieve your goals. Build up slowly, but surely.

Decide on the goals yourself – allow others to advise you, but make the decisions for yourself.

FINALLY: LEARN FROM YOUR FAILURES:

Doubtless, you will not achieve all your goals every day – that would not be human. The important thing is to question why you failed to achieve a particular goal, and then re-plan to make the goal more realistic. You should dwell on the positive more realistic plan and not berate yourself for failure. E.g.

- **You planned to go for a jog on two nights this week, but only managed this on one night.**

- **Why did this happen? Answer: I couldn't sleep the night before, and didn't have the energy.**

- **Possible solutions:**

- Reduce your expectations and set your plan for the next week back to one night of exercise OR

- Re-plan the time you will exercise for earlier in the day – for example at lunch-time if you work OR

- Change the type of exercise to a less strenuous form – e.g. go for a long walk rather than a jog, or – if you can afford it – play a round of golf (as with most activities that replace drinking, this will of course involve a degree of planning in advance).

Repeat this re-planning process, as often as you feel like it; but at least once weekly. Set your goals for the next week and keep a 'non-drinking goals diary' (see below). Fill this in every day before your memory fades, and then review it weekly. This will help you pick up patterns that you might otherwise miss, e.g. a tendency to 'miss' a goal if you had an argument that day; a tendency to achieve another goal if you went walking that day etc. etc.

NON-DRINKING GOALS DIARY

DAY OF WEEK

NON-DRINKING GOAL 1:

Did you achieve your goal?   Yes ☐   No ☐

If not, where did it go wrong?

How could you change it for the better?

What will you do the next time to make it work?

NON-DRINKING GOAL 2:

Did you achieve your goal?   Yes ☐   No ☐

If not, where did it go wrong?

How could you change it for the better?

What will you do the next time to make it work?

NON-DRINKING GOAL 3:

Did you achieve your goal?   Yes ☐   No ☐

If not, where did it go wrong?

How could you change it for the better?

What will you do the next time to make it work?

SUMMARY

So, let's re-cap:

1. Arrange a detox, preferable residentially, or if not, at home ('home detox').

2. If you have decided on a course of residential rehabilitation then you will learn more there about staying dry than anything I can tell you in this book. And remember this – the evidence shows that it is those that complete the course of rehabilitation that have the best chances of staying dry in the long term. Many people find residential rehabilitation hard going – it's not meant to be easy – it is meant to prepare you for a life without alcohol. As it is very hard work, many people leave before they have completed the course. If you commit yourself to a period of residential rehabilitation, then do your utmost to stay the course – if you don't, then you may have wasted your time.

3. After you have completed detox or/and rehab and you return home, have an 'aftercare plan' in place:

- Make sure you have some individual counselling in place to start immediately on your return home. You should aim to continue with counselling on a weekly basis for the first year of abstinence.

- If you are up for AA meetings, then attend them as often as you can – ideally daily.

- See if you can be prescribed Campral (acamprosate) and/or Antabuse (disulfiram) – continue these medications for up to one year after detox.

- Use your weekly diary to keep your time full with planned activity. Make slow but sure progress with long term plans and objectives. Assess why you failed to achieve particular goals, and do not berate yourself for failure. In particular, always get active and focus on an activity that involves concentration if you start to crave for alcohol.

- Whenever you experience craving, after it has calmed down, take some time to think how you have handled it without drinking, and how you will handle it more easily the next time it occurs. Think about the situation or feeling that triggered the craving – can you avoid this situation in the future? What did you do that enabled you to avoid drinking (e.g. walked away from the person that offered you a drink; started to do something you had planned in the diary)? Would there be a better way to deal with this same situation in the future that would make you even less likely to have a drink? If you can think of something, remember it and plan to behave in this way the next time you encounter a similar situation.

• Use free telephone advice from the **DryOutNow.com Immediate Response Service (0800 160 1020)** if you have any specific questions, or just need to speak to someone to help you on in the right direction. Alternatively, use the 'freeadvice' service on the www.dryoutnow.com website, to access individual advice by email.

CONCLUSION

You should now be in a position to implement the best possible plan for you, in order to achieve abstinence and to keep dry in the long term. Everything I have advised you to do in this book is based on the research which demonstrates the best way 'on average' for someone to stay dry. This fits the majority of people, but not everyone, and different elements of the overall plan will be better suited to some individuals than to others. To arrive at the best possible plan for you as an individual, and to limit those odds of relapsing to the minimum you will need individual advice about your particular situation. Use free telephone advice from the **DryOutNow.com Immediate Response Service (0800 160 1020)** if you have any specific questions, or just need to speak to someone to help you on in the right direction. Alternatively, use the 'freeadvice' service at dryoutnow.com, to access individual advice by email.

Now, at the point of reading this book you will most likely be in the 'planning phase' – getting ready for detox and the rest of your life without alcohol. So following is a check list of everything I advise you to have in place before you suddenly find yourself without a drink available to you. Continue straight to Part III of this book, when you are satisfied that you have made all your decisions.

PREPARATION PHASE CHECKLIST	Tick
1 Make absolutely sure you are ready to progress with planning for detox and abstinence. If you have any doubts re-read Chapter 3, telephone the DryOutNow.com Immediate Response Service on 0800 160 1020.	
2 Arrange for some individual counselling to start as soon as possible – ideally before detox and continuing afterwards. Get details of your local counsellors by telephoning the DryOutNow.com Immediate Response Service on 0800 160 1020.	
3 If you are up for it, attend some AA meetings – ideally before detox, and continuing afterwards. Get details of your local AA meetings by telephoning the DryOutNow.com Immediate Response Service on 0800 160 1020 or go to www.dryoutnow.com, and send your email message for 1:1 advice from a professional.	
4 Make a decision about whether or not you wish to carry on to residential rehabilitation after detox. If you wish to clarify this or get advice about the best residential rehabilitation units for you, telephone the DryOutNow.com Immediate Response Service on 0800 160 1020 or go to www.dryoutnow.com, and send your email message for 1:1 advice from a professional.	
5 Arrange a date for alcohol detoxification – either contact your local NHS community alcohol team (details available from the DryOutNow.com Immediate Response Service and www.dryoutnow.com) or if you are considering the self-pay option, telephone the DryOutNow.com Immediate Response Service (0800 160 1020) advice on the unit that will best suit your needs and budget.	
6 Start to think about your weekly diary. Make use of the tables in this chapter to assess your needs, and replace drinking with other activities that have the potential to lead to fulfillment.	
7 Speak to those you live with about drinking in the house after you return from detox.	

www.dryoutnow.com
IMMEDIATE RESPONSE SERVICE: CALL 0800 160 1020 NOW

PREPARATION PHASE CHECKLIST	Tick
8 If you have difficulties at work, then make a plan about how you are going to minimise these difficulties in advance of detox. If you would like confidential advice around these issues, then phone the DryOutNow.com Immediate Response Service on 0800 160 1020, or go to www.dryoutnow.com, and send your email message for 1:1 advice from a professional.	
9 If you have difficulties in your relationship with your partner, telephone Relate on 0845 130 4016, to book relationship counselling.	
10 Get expert medical advice about whether or not you can be prescribed medication to prevent relapse – either visit your GP, phone the DryOutNow.com Immediate Response Service (0800 160 1020) to get free telephone advice and/or details of your nearest private doctor who can advise on this, or go to www. dryoutnow.com, and send your email message for 1:1 advice from a professional.	

CHAPTER FIVE

YOU ARE PHYSICALLY ADDICTED TO ALCOHOL AND YOU PLAN TO CONTINUE DRINKING WITHIN HEALTHY LIMITS

If at any time you require urgent access to treatment, or need an immediate response for any other reason, do not hesitate to telephone the DryOutNow.com Immediate Response Service (IRS) on:

0800 160 1020
(8am-9pm, seven days weekly)

CHAPTER FIVE

YOU ARE PHYSICALLY ADDICTED TO ALCOHOL AND YOU PLAN TO CONTINUE DRINKING WITHIN HEALTHY LIMITS

There are 4 stages though which you should progress, along your route to achieving controlled drinking of alcohol.

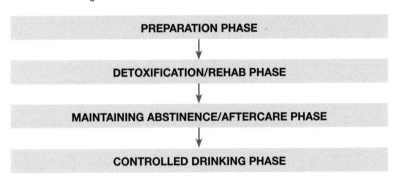

PREPARATION PHASE

DETOXIFICATION/REHAB PHASE

MAINTAINING ABSTINENCE/AFTERCARE PHASE

CONTROLLED DRINKING PHASE

It may be the case that you are looking for good advice about how to re-start drinking again immediately after detox. As far as I am aware, there is no such advice to give. If you have become physically addicted to alcohol, the odds of ever drinking again without relapsing to damaging levels of alcohol consumption are stacked against you. Of course some people will beat these odds, and if you are determined to give this a try, then the advice in this chapter is my best shot at helping you to do this successfully. I have only written this chapter because I know that it is you that has to make the decision about what you must do with your life, and not me; if you remain determined to try to drink again and keep it controlled within healthy limits then carry on reading. If you think you might be able to start to contemplate a future without any alcohol whatsoever, then I suggest you stop reading right now, and work a little more on that thought. The best advice is definitely to plan to never drink again. If, having thought about this for a while you resolve to aim for abstinence in the long term, then re-start reading this book at the beginning of Chapter Four.

Now, if you are still reading I assume that you plan to resume drinking again at some point. If you have made this decision it is vital that you resolve to have a period of at least six months completely abstinent from alcohol before you attempt to start controlled drinking. Why? In Chapter Three I explained how the brain takes a long time to readjust to a world without alcohol – drinking before significant readjustment has occurred will only trigger the brain into telling you to drink more and more …and more. It is also likely to take many months before you have started to replace the habit of drinking with alternative activities that fill the times when you used to drink. If you have not made progress on developing alternative activities by the time you start to drink again, you will probably find yourself drinking more and more…and more. For these reasons, I must advise you to aim to remain completely abstinent from alcohol for at least six months following detox. When this time is up, you may choose to attempt to start drinking again and control it within healthy limits. But don't be surprised if you quickly relapse to alcoholic levels of drinking within a matter of days or weeks.

THE PREPARATION PHASE.

The preparation phase mainly involves planning/booking the help you will need to get dry and stay dry. Remember the rule of thumb: "The detox is the easy bit, staying off is much harder…and again…". You should give very serious thought to committing to a period of residential rehabilitation (rehab) to continue straight on from detox. Many rehab centres provide both detox and on-going rehab, so that both can be received seamlessly in the same treatment centre. Rehab involves intensive counselling aimed at teaching you the skills to stay off alcohol on your return home. Typically people commit to at least one month in rehab, and this time can also be used to deal with some of the issues discussed below ('preparing yourself socially'), discussed as part of the preparation phase. The single most important fact to remember about rehab is that people who commit to a period of rehab have much better outcomes than those who only complete detox. Probably 75% of those completing a course of detox and rehab are dry at one year, whereas in the region of only 25% remain dry for this long if they commit only to detox.

Unless you are severely physically ill (e.g. in serious liver failure, suffering from regular seizures, becoming disorientated about what day it is and who people are, hallucinating etc.) then you should not rush to get admitted for treatment as soon as possible. Yes, you should book a date for treatment, so that you have something to aim for, but you should leave yourself enough time in between now and the detox starting to prepare adequately.

So what does preparing for staying dry involve?

There are three things to do:

1. *Prepare yourself psychologically, and also seek out professional psychological support (various forms of counselling).*

2. *Prepare yourself socially, and seek out the available professional support.*

3. *Consider the possibility of medication to help you stay dry.*

TO PREPARE YOURSELF PSYCHOLOGICALLY:

Make absolutely sure that you are fully committed to doing this, and that you are 100% realistic about how hard it's going to be. Re-read Chapter Three to help you to do this.

TO PREPARE YOURSELF SOCIALLY:

Firstly you should make a decision about whether you are going to stay in a residential rehabilitation unit for a period of time after detox, or whether you are going to return home immediately after detox.

Residential rehabilitation. Residential rehabilitation involves staying in a specialist psychological unit for a period of time (durations of stay range from two weeks to nine months) immediately following on from detox. The advantages of a period of residential rehabilitation include i) an alcohol-free environment so there is minimal risk of relapse ii) the person is living and learning from others with alcohol problems iii) as a generalisation, this is the best form of counselling as it is so intensive. The evidence clearly shows that those who go to a residential rehabilitation unit and complete the course without leaving early, are much more likely to remain dry from alcohol in the long term than those who do not go to residential rehabilitation. For more information on how residential rehabilitation works, go to

....

- **www.dryoutnow.com – find the online Professional Treatment Guidelines, and then download Section E of the Treatment Guidelines. Pages 73-74 are the relevant ones.**

....

Most residential rehabilitation units are not in the NHS. However, the NHS will sometimes pay for you to go to one if they think you need it. If you want to plan for a period of residential rehabilitation after detox, and wish the NHS to pay for it, then you will need to contact your local NHS Community Alcohol Team. They will arrange for you to be assessed, and if they think you meet their criteria for paying, will then arrange for your admission to follow immediately after detox. Waits may be long for assessment and admission (many months in some cases) and often there is no funding available at all, but if you get treatment at the end of the day, it should be of the same quality as going privately.

....

- **For details of your local NHS Community Alcohol Team phone the DryOutNow.com Immediate Response Service on 0800 160 1020, or go to www.dryoutnow.com – and send the email from the Local Advice section to receive details of your local NHS Community Alcohol Team.**

....

If you decide to pay for residential rehabilitation yourself, then you will usually be able to access it within a matter of days.

- **For details of UK residential rehabilitation units phone the DryOutNow. com Immediate Response Service on 0800 160 1020 or go to www. dryoutnow.com – and look under the Alcohol Rehab Centres section.**

OTHER THINGS TO PREPARE FOR SOCIALLY:

1. ACCOMMODATION.

Is your accommodation situation stable and are you living with others who drink?

At the point of leaving detox you will wish for the amount of stress in your life to be as minimal as is possible; stress is a major reason for starting to drink heavily and it is also a major reason for relapse. If you do not have permanent accommodation, or you are at risk of losing permanent accommodation for whatever reason, do your best to sort this out in advance of detox. Lack of a stable environment in which to re-start your life will greatly increase your chances of relapse. If you are living with others who drink heavily, then you should very seriously consider either asking them to leave or leaving yourself. The odds of you managing to remain sober when there is someone living with you who drinks on a regular basis are very small indeed. Of course, if that person is also planning to seek help for an alcohol problem, then ideally this should be planned so that neither of you are living together at the time that one of you is still drinking. This will probably mean either planning for detox to take place at the same time as each other, or one immediately after the other, or at least one of you arranging for admission to a residential rehabilitation unit. If you live with other(s) who do drink, but do not drink heavily, you should see if they will agree to avoid drinking in the house. Ideally, the house should be completely empty of alcohol on your return from detox, and it should stay that way for the foreseeable future.

2. WORK.

Is your working situation stable? Are you unemployed? Are you facing some kind of disciplinary action? Are you on sick leave?

If you are in work and have no problems there, then this is usually the ideal situation. You will need to plan to take a period of leave during which time you will be in detox/rehab, or arrange a 'sick-note'. If you are on sick leave due to your alcohol problem, you should try to arrange to return to work, possibly on a part-time basis initially, as soon as detox/rehab is completed (unless you are seriously physically unwell). Of course, there is a fine balance here between too much stress at work, and too much time on your hands if you do not return to work. If work related stress is a problem for you, then your return to work should be a graded one. If you are facing some kind of disciplinary action at work as a direct or indirect result of your drinking, do your best to get this resolved before detox. Remember the aim is to limit the amount of stress you will have to deal with in those vital first few months when you may be battling to stay dry.

Of course, there's a bit of a Catch 22 about this; while you are drinking heavily you may not feel up to sorting these kind of things out. Overall, do your best to sort out what you can before detox/rehab; what you cannot do, you just cannot do. If you are unemployed at the moment, then make some initial plans for a return to work following detox/rehab. Ideally, arrange for a return to employment as soon as detox is completed. Of course this may well not be practical for you – if it is not, spend some time before detox thinking about what kinds of employment you may wish to get, and how you may go about searching for this on completion of detox. Build this into your weekly diary (see below).

3. RELATIONSHIPS

If you are in a relationship with a person who has a drinking problem, then the ideal is that you should both deal with this at the same time – it's highly unlikely to work for either of you if one person becomes abstinent while the other continues to drink. If you are unable to convince your partner of this, then if you are committed to aiming for an alcohol free life, you should seriously consider whether or not to continue with the relationship. If you are in a relationship with someone who does not drink heavily, then you may well be experiencing problems in your relationship.

You may find that your relationship improves dramatically when you cease drinking, but sometimes this will not be the case. Whatever, if you are having relationship problems at the moment, consider whether to book some relationship counselling with RELATE. This organization often has waiting lists of several months – if you book now, then the counselling will probably start when you have completed detox and are sober. Here is the central contact telephone number for RELATE: **0845 130 4016**

THE DETOXIFICATION/REHAB PHASE

If you are physically addicted to alcohol, then on cessation of alcohol use you will experience alcohol withdrawal symptoms such as tremor, sweating, nausea, vomiting, raised blood pressure and raised pulse. In severe alcohol withdrawal you may experience epileptic seizures, hallucinations, delusions and disorientation in time and place. In some cases, severe alcohol withdrawal can be fatal, and if not fatal may lead to permanent brain damage. All the symptoms of alcohol withdrawal are caused by what doctors call 'hyper-excitability of the central nervous system' – in other words the brain becomes massively overactive. In order to control this over-activity of the brain, sedative medication is prescribed – detox. Quite large doses of sedative medication are prescribed at first, and then the dosage gradually reduced down to zero over a number of days. If the detox is performed professionally, the risk of epileptic seizures occurring is very small indeed, and no other complications of alcohol withdrawal are likely to occur. Equally, you should expect to feel quite comfortable during detox, and by the time it's completed, you will probably feel the best you have in years.

Don't get confused between sedative medication and sleeping tablets – although they are similar, you will not be sent to sleep for the detox. The medication you are prescribed (usually a medicine called chlordiazepoxide (Librium) or diazepam (Valium)) is not aimed at sending you to sleep, rather just to calm you and prevent the brain over-activity that occurs during alcohol withdrawal. You will most likely be prescribed other medicines as well. These may include anti-nausea tablets such as 'metoclopramide', sleeping tablets (at night only) such as 'temazepam or zopiclone' and anti-epileptic tablets such as 'carbamazepine'. Most importantly you should be prescribed vitamin B tablets (vitamin B1 to be precise) or injections. Years of heavy drinking result in your levels of vitamin B being particularly low; the brain over-activity that occurs in alcohol withdrawal may burn up the final stores of this vital vitamin. If the stores drop below a critical level, you may suffer permanent brain damage which affects the memory in particular.

Detox can usually be accomplished safely within days, and some detox units will offer a 7-day programme. However, 10 days to two weeks is more typical. This allows for you to take it slowly and comfortably. Just as importantly the emotional side of things should be considered as well as the physical during detoxification. If you are admitted to a specialist detoxification unit, you will receive counselling and be encouraged to attend group therapy with other patients during the detox. It is important that this forms part of the detoxification plan - the easy bit is the detox, the difficult bit is staying off in the longer term - skills need to be learned to remain abstinent, and underlying emotional issues resolved to prevent a return to drinking.

If you would like to know more about the technical side of alcohol detox, go to:

....

- **www.dryoutnow.com – find the online 'Professional Treatment Guidelines', and then download Section C of the Treatment Guidelines.**

....

When you are planning detox there are several decisions that need to be made:

1. *Have you thought about the options of where detox may take place (home, psychiatric ward, hospital medical ward, specialist detoxification unit)?*

2. *Are you looking for a free detox or a self-pay service?*

3. *Have you decided whether or not you wish to continue to residential rehabilitation after detox?*

1. Where is the best place for the detox to take place?

a. Home. Detox at home may sound more appealing than having to be admitted to a hospital of some kind. However, it is a less safe and less effective means of undergoing detoxification on average. Approximately 50% of people who undergo detoxification at home will manage to complete the detox without starting to drink again during the detox, while over 90% will complete detoxification when admitted to a specialist detoxification unit. Equally, if anything does go wrong during detox, then being in hospital should mean that you get the right care immediately, whereas you may wait hours at home. In particular, home detox is generally agreed to be the wrong option if you have a history of epileptic fits when coming off alcohol, if you suffer from any serious medical condition, if you suffer from any serious psychiatric illness or feel suicidal, if you have a tendency to get disorientated, if you are unable to arrange for another adult to be with you at home for the detox, or if you live with others who drink.

b. Psychiatric ward. Sometimes alcohol detox arranged through the NHS occurs on a psychiatric ward. From a doctor's perspective, the main problem here is that staff on psychiatric wards often have less experience of dealing with alcohol detoxification, than do those in a specialist unit. The psychological aspect of detoxification (preparing you to deal with life without drinking when you leave) is not likely to be addressed, and you are probably less likely overall to complete the detoxification without returning to drinking. Equally, you may not feel comfortable with the idea of admission to a psychiatric ward in view of the fact that most other patients there will be suffering from serious psychiatric illnesses.

c. Hospital medical ward. If you are seriously physically ill as a result of your drinking (e.g. jaundiced, having fits, bleeding from the rectum or vomiting blood, having hallucinations or delusions) or have another serious illness such as poorly controlled diabetes or active pancreatitis, then a hospital medical ward is probably the best place to receive detoxification. The reason I say this, is that if you are this ill, the absolute priority must be to place you where you will be provided with immediate attention from a doctor who is used to dealing with emergencies if things go wrong. There is a fine judgment to be made here, because you are unlikely to get the best overall treatment as far as completing the detox and staying dry afterwards. Some specialist detox units are very capable of dealing with all the common emergencies very effectively, and they will also be able to offer the 'full package' aimed at your drinking problem. On a hospital medical ward, you will probably be treated as just another patient who has to be kept alive until they are discharged.

d. Specialist detox unit. Admission to a specialist unit for your detox is clearly the ideal in most cases. Such units have the most expertise in getting you through detox comfortably, and have the best chances of getting you through detox without relapsing to alcohol use before completion of the detox. Unless you are very ill indeed, they should also offer the safest option overall for detox. In addition to this, you will receive specialist counselling as part of the detox 'package'. This should improve your chances of staying dry after detox considerably, and unless you are seriously physically ill, that should be your main consideration. Remember that only around 25% of people who have detoxed from alcohol are still dry after one year. Any treatment you can get that will improve your chances of staying dry you should grab. Your main consideration must be to aim at that – 'The detox is the easy bit, staying dry is much harder.'

2. Are you looking for a free detox or a self-pay service?

2a. Free alcohol detoxification.

This may be accessible through the NHS. If you wish to proceed along this route, the starting place is usually your local 'Community Alcohol Team' (sometimes 'Community Drug and Alcohol Team').

....

- **For details of your local NHS Community Alcohol Team phone the DryOutNow.com Immediate Response Service on 0800 160 1020, or go to www.dryoutnow.com – click on 'Local Help' section, complete the required fields, and send the email to receive details of your local community alcohol team.**

....

Usually these days you can book in direct with your community alcohol team by telephone. However, in some cases they may require you to go to your GP first in order to be referred to them by your GP. When you have either referred yourself or been referred by your GP, you will be given an appointment for an assessment with the alcohol team. They will formulate a plan with you, which should include a detoxification if you are assessed as needing one.

That's the theory and in some cases it will work exactly like this. In some cases you will get an excellent service from the NHS. In other cases you will not – it all depends on where you live. If you are lucky enough to live in an area where the treatment of alcoholism has been well funded over the last few years, then you are likely to experience few problems. However, the funding for alcohol treatment has been very poor in most areas for many years, and in some cases has got even worse over the last several years, as money has been diverted to treating illicit drug problems rather than alcohol problems. This is what is known as the 'postcode lottery'. There is no way of my predicting whether you will be lucky with the NHS or not. The problems you may experience are:

- **Long waits to be seen in the first place (many months).**

- **Long waits to access detoxification after you have been assessed (months to years).**

- **No detoxification available in practice whatsoever.**

- **Detoxification only available at home, (see above – home detoxification).**

- **Detoxification only available in the local psychiatric ward.**

Now, as I stated above, in some areas you will get a service by going the NHS route – the only way to find out if this applies to you, is to give it a try.

2b. Self-pay alcohol detox.

The large majority of self-pay detox units are dedicated, specialist units. In such units, you should receive good quality medical care and psychological support aimed at keeping you dry after completion of the detox. The main differences in price are accounted for by:

- The quality of the accommodation.

- The quality of the medical cover.

- How long you are prepared to wait.

As a generalisation, the more you pay the better hotel services you will receive, and the quicker you will be admitted. The degree of medical cover in self-pay units ranges from non-specialist GPs available for telephone advice and to attend in an emergency only, to specialist consultants seeing you on a daily basis with a ward doctor on-site to attend to you 24 hours/day. The more expensive units will tend to have invested more in their medical cover than the less expensive units.

Deciding on the best self-pay unit to use depends on how ill you are, how long you are prepared to wait, how entrenched your alcoholism is, and what your needs are in terms of accommodation. Probably you will want to minimise the cost that you pay whilst making sure you get the best possible treatment for you. If you choose to seek detoxification privately, then DryOutNow.com will arrange this for you.

DRYOUTNOW.COM WILL:

- Find you the **cheapest** detox/rehab suitable to your needs.

- Find you the **best** detox/rehab (safest and highest rates of completion) suitable to your needs.

- For detox units that **require a referral from a doctor,** they can make that referral for you. **(Some people will not wish to go via their GP).**

....

- **For details of detoxification units phone the DryOutNow.com Immediate Response Service on 0800 160 1020, or go to www.dryoutnow.com – and find the 'alcohol rehab centres' section.**

....

3. Have you decided whether or not you wish to continue to residential rehabilitation after detox?

Most specialist detoxification units will offer the option of staying on after completion of detoxification for a period of residential rehabilitation. If you have decided you would like to consider a period of residential rehabilitation to follow detox, then you should discuss this with an expert at the **DryOutNow.com Immediate Response Service** making use of their free telephone advice service. They have details of the full spectrum of UK residential rehabilitation units, and can help you plan in the most cost-effective way given your particular needs.

....

- **For details of residential rehabilitation units phone the DryOutNow. com Immediate Response Service on 0800 160 1020, or go to www. dryoutnow.com – and find the Alcohol Rehab Centres section.**

....

THE MAINTAINING ABSTINENCE/AFTERCARE PHASE.

You have arrived! You've stopped drinking successfully, and are ready to face a new world – a world without alcohol. Now this is where the serious work begins – the work of staying dry. If you've implemented most of the steps I outlined in the 'preparation phase' then you will have a head start over all the new challenges that are going to face you:

....

- **Craving for alcohol**

....

- **Sleeplessness**

....

- **Agitation**

....

- **Boredom**

....

- **NO IMMEDIATE SOLUTION TO ALL THESE THINGS**

....
....

On the other side of the coin, you are likely to be:

- **Feeling well for the first time in a long time**

- **Eating well**

- **Feeling in a better mood if you have been depressed**

- **Feeling more confident in yourself, especially if you suffered with paranoia and anxiety while you were drinking**

However, you must remember this – most of the advantages of giving up drinking are long term advantages; they will not be apparent to you immediately, and they will require a sustained period of abstinence from alcohol to occur:

- **Improved relationships with the important people in your life**

- **Building new relationships with the future important people in your life**

- **Improved performance at work**

- **Finding and holding down employment if you are unemployed**

- **Enjoyment of leisure activities you could never have enjoyed while you were drinking**

- **Improved financial situation**

- **A sense of pride in yourself that had been forgotten during years of heavy drinking**

Maintaining abstinence will bring you rewards whether these are delivered by living longer, feeling better in yourself and with yourself, or having better relationships with others. All of these things can disappear in a moment if you relapse, and most of the truly rewarding things take months and years to start to occur.

AFTERCARE:

Only 25-30% of people who have detoxed without rehab are still dry at the end of one year, and 75% who complete a period of rehab. How are you going to maximise your chances of being one of those who successfully remain abstinent in the longer term? For the first year (the highest risk time for relapse) you must implement your plan, and stick to it as much as is feasible for you. Your plan to maintain abstinence after detoxification and/or rehab is usually referred to as 'Aftercare'. The research evidence shows that people who persevere with an aftercare plan for a period of time following rehab or detox, significantly increase their chances of remaining abstinent in the longer term. So what should this plan involve?

1. Counselling with a specialist addictions counsellor.

Specialist 1-to-1 counselling can help in one of two ways: firstly by giving you the skills to avoid relapse to alcohol, and secondly by helping you to understand any underlying emotional issues which are leading you to drink heavily. For detailed information on how counselling works, go to:

....

- **www.dryoutnow.com – find the 'Professional Treatment Guidelines', and then download Section E of the Treatment Guidelines.**

....

Specialist counselling may be available from local NHS/charitable services for free. Or you can book with a private counsellor. In terms of the quality of service you will receive, there is probably little difference between NHS and private counsellors. However, in the NHS you may have to wait a long time (months or years in some cases) before you can access counselling. This varies between areas and depends on where you live. So, overall, I suggest contacting your local NHS/Charitable specialist alcohol counselling service first. If the waiting time seems unsatisfactory, or other things don't seem right, then try the self-pay route.

- **For details of your local NHS/charitable and private counselling services phone the DryOutNow.com Immediate Response Service on 0800 160 1020, or go to www.dryoutnow.com – find the 'local help' section and send the email to receive details of your local counselling services.**

Private counsellors who specialise in alcohol problems are not so many in number. There are probably in the region of 400 in the country. Many problems that lead to heavy drinking are general in nature (e.g. stress, relationship difficulties etc.). So, if your nearest specialist alcohol counsellor is too far away, a general counsellor may still be of help to you.

SPECIALIST TELEPHONE COUNSELLING

Alternatively, you can access specialist private alcohol counselling by telephone. You may wish to use this service if your nearest specialist counsellor is too far away, or if you would prefer the privacy and convenience of receiving counselling in your own home. This service is provided via DryOutNow.com. Call 0800 160 1020 to request details of the specialist telephone counselling service.

2. Alcoholics Anonymous meetings.

People are often nervous about attending these meetings, but those who attend have been shown to have better long term outcomes. There is no requirement to have stopped drinking in order to attend – just to be relatively sober at the time of attendance. There is no requirement to speak at a meeting – just to say 'pass' if asked to speak. The theme of the meetings is religious and requires a belief in a 'higher power', but there is no requirement to believe in God as such, or in any particular God. Some people think of the 'higher power' as the 'sober part' of themselves. There is no need to book in advance – just turn up to a meeting and sit alone just to observe at first. People will probably come to talk to you after the meeting – one of the main beliefs of Alcoholics Anonymous is that alcoholics need other alcoholics to help them to get sober – so people will be keen to help you. For more information on 'AA' meetings and how they work, go to:

....

* **www.dryoutnow.com – find the 'Professional Treatment Guidelines', and then download Section E.**

....

* **For details of your local Alcoholics Anonymous meetings phone the DryOutNow.com Immediate Response Service on 0800 160 1020, or go to www.dryoutnow.com – find the 'Local Help' section, and send the email to receive details of your local AA meetings.**

....

3. Medication to help prevent relapse to alcoholism.

There are two medications commonly used in the UK to help prevent a return to drinking.

i) Acamprosate, also known as Campral.

Acamprosate works to reduce the feeling of craving for alcohol. It is very effective for a few patients, quite effective for some, and simply doesn't work for others. As it is a relatively safe medicine to prescribe, in my NHS practice I prescribe it for most patients who have gone through detox. It is usually safe to continue to take it, even if you temporarily lapse to drinking again. There are several other medicines that are also used to create a similar effect, including naltrexone and nalmefene, but these have shown no advantages over acamprosate to date.

ii) Disulfiram, also known as Antabuse.

Disulfiram blocks the complete breakdown of alcohol by the liver. This causes you to feel absolutely terrible if you have a drink. Disulfiram can work well for people who are likely to relapse to drinking on the spur of the moment – you simply can't do this if you are taking it. However, its no magic cure, as you can decide to stop taking it, and within several days you are likely to be able to drink again without feeling ill. I prescribe disulfiram less often than acamprosate as it has the potential to cause some quite nasty side-effects in some people. In particular, it should generally be avoided in people who have a history of blood vessel problems (e.g. high blood pressure, history of stroke or heart attack), who have liver disease, or who have suffered serious psychiatric illness in the past.

For more information on both these medicines, go to:

....
- **www.dryoutnow.com – find the 'Professional Treatment Guidelines', and then download Section C.**
....

Of course, confidentiality may be an issue for you, and you will need to see a doctor to get these medicines prescribed. If you do not wish to see your GP about this, then the DryOutNow.com Immediate Response Service can give you details of your nearest private doctor who will be prepared to prescribe for you. Simply phone and ask for details of your nearest private doctor who specialises in addiction problems.

....
- **For details of your local private doctors who specialise in alcoholism phone the DryOutNow.com Immediate Response Service on 0800 160 1020.**
....

4. Self-help in the aftercare phase.

Probably the single most important thing you can do without help from others is to **write out your weekly diary.** There are two aims of the weekly diary. Firstly it should enable you fill your time completely from the day of discharge from detox/rehab, onwards. Your time should be full for the simple reason that this will leave you less time to think about alcohol. The nature of craving is such that if you give it a chance to build up, it will end up filling your head with repetitive thoughts: "Just one drink won't hurt – how could it? Just one drink won't hurt – how could it?" You must do your utmost to divert your attention from any such thoughts at all times. Being active and having to concentrate on a task of some kind is much more likely to result in the feeling of craving subsiding, than is sitting in a chair doing nothing. The vital element here is having to concentrate on something. This is very important if you are back in your usual routine, and not in specialist care.

Secondly it should provide you with the kind of activities that have a good chance of giving you some kind of sense of fulfillment or pleasure – that are rewarding. The aim here is to start to build up activities that will replace your need for alcohol in the longer term. As discussed in Chapter Three – don't expect anything to replace alcohol totally – there are very few activities that can result in your brain experiencing the reward that use of an addictive substance brings, and probably no healthy activities that produce that reward as easily and as immediately as does alcohol. You will need to re-think your objectives and search more for a sense of satisfaction and fulfillment in life than for the experience of immediate pleasure or immediate relief from unpleasant feelings which is delivered by alcohol.

You should think this through in great detail starting now. It must be ready to implement the very day you leave detox. You should try to think of activities that are purposeful, and have the potential to lead to some sense of satisfaction; this will depend very much on personal taste. Some examples might include: socialising with non-drinking friends, reading, gym, gardening, walking. You may well have found that your appetite has been terrible for as long as you can remember; during detox it is very likely that your appetite will start to improve, and by the time you have finished detox you will be enjoying food again. As such, one activity you plan may involve food, such as developing your culinary skills. Or more simply, what about planning to sit down to lunch and dinner every day – you probably haven't done that in a while. (Don't worry about weight gain – alcohol is much more fattening than many foods). If it's possible to devote yourself to some kind of work project with a long-term goal in mind this could be useful. In particular, if you are able to devote yourself to any kind of long-term project that involves dedication and a great deal of work, this might start to act to replace the psychological need for alcohol. (This kind of approach would be disagreed with by many professionals, especially those from a theoretical counselling background – they would argue that the addictive behaviour is merely being transferred from one object – drink – to another – work. However, if you are not considering residential rehabilitation, I think this is exactly what you should aim to do – replace the alcohol with healthy activity rather than destructive activity.)

In summary, you should create a diary ideally providing several options of activity for all times of every day of the week. This is not to say that you must or will complete every such activity – the important thing is that the diary is always there to turn to if you find yourself sitting and starting to dwell on the idea of having a drink. When that thought enters your head (and it will), you should immediately pick up the diary and implement one of the activities that are listed for that time of that day.

Following is an empty diary covering seven days of the week from 6 in the morning to 12 midnight. It also allows for you to enter two alternative activities for any two hour period. Now you may think that an 18 hour day is a long period of time to plan to fill, but bear the following in mind. The idea of the diary is not that you necessarily do every thing on it at the specified time, although you may chose to, and there will be no harm in this unless you get stressed thinking that you have to do everything on it. The idea of the diary IS that when you feel yourself starting to crave alcohol, you have something to occupy yourself with immediately, and which is already planned so that you can implement that activity immediately. If you wait until you start to crave before trying to think of something to occupy your mind, you may well not be able to do what you wish to immediately, and you may not even be

able to concentrate effectively in order to think of something else to do. If you have your diary ready, you've got a great head-start over the craving.

Secondly, remember that your sleep may be disturbed for a period of months after detox. It is thus important to have planned activities from early in the morning to late at night – again you will not necessarily carry out all these activities, but if you are awake for long hours, you must make sure you have something to do. Poor sleep after detox is a major cause of relapse to drinking. Be prepared to have something to do if you cannot get to sleep – if you enjoyed reading in the past get some good books in. If you enjoyed film, get in a stack of videos or sign up for satellite channels (less expensive that your total alcohol costs). Poor sleep will improve as your brain gets used to a world free of alcohol – but you may have to be prepared to persevere for a good while.

If you are having difficulty thinking of the type of activities you should include in the diary the following questions may give you some ideas:

- What did you enjoy doing before alcohol started to replace other things in your life?

- What are the enjoyable things about drinking for you? Can you replace these with activities that result in a similar reward? (E.g. you may drink after work to relax; can you arrange for a massage on some nights as an alternative form of relaxation?) If you completed the tables in Chapter 3 under Question 4, you may wish to use your answers to help you here.

- What would you like to achieve from life? What would you need to do to achieve these things? Is there something you could dedicate yourself to achieving?

- How is your physical health? Could you improve it by eating well and healthily? Could you improve it by exercising regularly? What kinds of exercise would you enjoy?

- How is your social life? Do you have any non-drinking friends you could get in touch with? Can you think of a variety of social activities that don't involve drinking that you may enjoy?

- Do you need to search for work? What do you need to do to search for work?

	MONDAY	TUESDAY	WEDNESDAY	THURSDAY	FRIDAY	SATURDAY	SUNDAY
Activity 1: 6-8							
Activity 2: 6-8							
Activity 1: 8-10							
Activity 2: 8-10							
Activity 1: 10-12							
Activity 2: 10-12							
Activity 1: 12-2							
Activity 2: 12-2							
Activity 1: 2-4							
Activity 2: 2-4							
Activity 1: 4-6							
Activity 2: 4-6							
Activity 1: 6-8							
Activity 2: 6-8							
Activity 1: 8-10							
Activity 2: 8-10							
Activity 1: 10-12							
Activity 2: 10-12							
NIGHT-TIME 1							
NIGHT-TIME 2							

THE CONTROLLED DRINKING PHASE

First of all, what is controlled drinking? Very simply, most doctors will consider it to be drinking within healthy limits as defined by the World Health Organization. These are as follows:

FOR MALES:

- A maximum of 21 units should be consumed in any one week.

- Within a period of one week there should be at least two drink-free days.

- No more than 4 units should be consumed in any one day.

Effectively this means the following:

- You should drink no more than 2 pints of 3-4% lager/beer (Carlsberg/Heinekin) or 1.5 pints of 5% lager/beer (like Stella/Kronenberg) or 1/3 bottle of wine or 1/9th bottle of spirits on any one night.

- You should have at least two days in the week when you drink no alcohol at all.

- You should drink no more than 9 pints of 3-4% lager/beer per week or no more than 7 pints of 5% lager/beer per week or no more than 2 bottles wine per week or no more than 2/3 bottle spirits per week.

FOR FEMALES:

- A maximum of 14 units should be consumed in any one week.

- Within a period of one week there should be at least two drink-free days.

- No more than 3 units should be consumed in any one day.

Effectively this means the following:

- You should drink no more than 1.5 pints of 3-4% lager/beer (Carlsberg/Heinekin) **or** 1 pint of 5% lager/beer (like Stella/Kronenberg) **or** 1/4 bottle of wine **or** 1/10th bottle of spirits on any one night.

- You should have at least two days in the week when you drink no alcohol at all.

- You should drink no more than 6 pints of 3-4% lager/beer per week **or** no more than 4.5 pints of 5% lager/beer per week **or** no more than 1.5 bottles wine per week **or** no more than 1/2 bottle of spirits per week.

So your aim (if you choose to start drinking again) should be to control your drinking to within these limits. If you do relapse to heavy drinking when trying to keep drinking at safe amounts (controlled drinking), you will then know that complete abstinence is the only way forward for you in the long term. People will often need to demonstrate this to themselves before coming to a decision to aim for complete abstinence from alcohol. And that's not necessarily a bad thing. In order to have a good chance of staying off alcohol for ever, your mind will have to be completely made-up that this is the way you have to do it. If you have any doubt about this, then you are likely to relapse in time anyway. To prepare to control your drinking, and keep it within healthy limits there are four stages to go through:

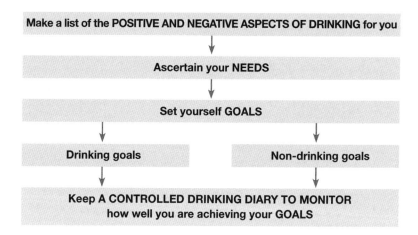

Make a list of the **POSITIVE AND NEGATIVE ASPECTS OF DRINKING** for you

↓

Ascertain your NEEDS

↓

Set yourself GOALS

↓   ↓

Drinking goals   **Non-drinking goals**

↓   ↓

Keep **A CONTROLLED DRINKING DIARY TO MONITOR**
how well you are achieving your **GOALS**

1. MAKE A LIST OF THE POSITIVE AND NEGATIVE ASPECTS OF DRINKING FOR YOU

Making a list of the things you find both helpful and unhelpful about drinking, is the starting point of this process. You will find that if you write this list, you will be able to see quite clearly what you need in your life, that at the present time you are trying to get from alcohol. If you made these lists when you read Chapter Three, then refer back to them now. Otherwise, continue right here. I've given some examples of the positive and negative reasons for drinking that people commonly write down. Cross these out if they don't apply to you, and then spend plenty of time thinking about the good and bad aspects of drinking for you – add to the list and make it your own. Let's start by considering the possible reasons that you find drinking an enjoyable or helpful activity. Tick off those things on this list that apply to you, and add items of your own as you think of them. If you wish to record this for the future, I have included an empty table for you in the appendix of this book.

POSITIVE THINGS ABOUT DRINKING FOR YOU:

		Tick here
	Physical Health Reasons	
1	I enjoy the feeling of drinking and getting drunk.	
2	Drinking stops me getting withdrawal symptoms.	
3	I have trouble getting to sleep – without a drink I cannot sleep well.	
	Psychological Reasons	
4	I tend to get depressed and drinking improves my mood.	
5	Drinking makes me less anxious.	
6	I tend to get a bit paranoid about going out. If I have a drink I can get out the house without worrying.	
7	I'm usually tense and stressed - drinking helps me to relax.	
	Social Reasons	
8	I have a much better time going out if I have a drink.	
9	I can't imagine going out without having a drink.	
10	I tend to be anxious in the company of other people; when I have a drink inside me I can talk more easily and get on with people better.	
11	I've become a bit of a loner over the years - the only time I ever get into a conversation is at the pub.	
	PUT YOUR OWN REASONS in the spaces below:	

NEGATIVE THINGS ABOUT DRINKING FOR YOU:

		Tick here
	Physical Health Reasons	
1	I'm feeling generally un-well most of the time.	
2	I never eat anything these days.	
3	I'm increasingly worried that I'm permanently damaging my physical health.	
4	I wake up early in the morning covered in sweat.	
	Psychological Reasons	
5	I feel horribly depressed when I wake up in the morning after drinking.	
6	My memory seems terrible these days.	
7	I seem so much more nervous than I used to be.	
8	I'm sick and tired of having this thing called alcohol in control of me. I want to get back in control of myself.	
	Social Reasons	
9	I want to be a better parent to my children.	
10	My relationship is a mess and I know it's because of my drinking.	
11	I've just been arrested for my second drink-drive offence – I might go to prison this time – I know I've got to do something about it.	
12	I'm finding it difficult to get into work on time – someone is going to say something soon.	
13	Of late my temper has got increasingly worse. I'm worried what I might do next time someone annoys me.	
	PUT YOUR OWN REASONS in the spaces below:	

2. ASCERTAIN YOUR NEEDS

When you have completed making the two lists above, you will be in a position to write down what your needs are. Use the table below to do this. By writing in a positive or negative reason for drinking, you should then be able to work out what you need to do to resolve that – write it down in the space below the reason for drinking. I've started by giving you a few examples. If you run out of space, I have included a blank table for you in the appendix.

Reason	I enjoy the feeling of drinking and getting drunk.
NEED	I need to have enjoyable feelings.
Reason	I have trouble getting to sleep – without a drink I cannot sleep well.
NEED	I need to sleep well.
Reason	I'm usually tense and stressed - drinking helps me to relax.
NEED	I need to relax.
Reason	I never eat anything these days
NEED	I need to eat well
Reason	I feel horribly depressed when I wake up in the morning after drinking.
NEED	I need to improve my mood
Reason	My relationship is a mess and I know it's because of my drinking.
NEED	I need to improve my relationship
Reason	
NEED	
Reason	
NEED	
Reason	
NEED	
Reason	
NEED	
Reason	
NEED	
Reason	
NEED	

3. SET YOURSELF GOALS

You should set yourself two types of goals – 'drinking goals' and 'non-drinking goals'. 'Non-drinking goals' do not necessarily mean that you do not drink when you are trying to achieve these goals; it's just that they are not directly about drinking. E.g., a 'drinking goal' might be to drink 2 units and no more on a particular evening. A 'non-drinking goal' might be to cook a meal. Your drinking goals will be what you plan to drink (how many units) on a particular day of the week. If you are to attempt to return to controlled drinking, then I advise you to take it slowly at first – do not plan to return immediately to drinking 21 units weekly, or as much as 3 units in one night. Gradually get to these levels over a period of months, or settle for drinking less than this in the long term. Your 'non-drinking' goals will involve meeting the needs you have made a list of above. Now if you manage to successfully control your drinking, some of these things will automatically sort themselves out for themselves (e.g. morning sweats and withdrawal symptoms will not return). If you are lucky, other things like your relationship and your mood will also improve as a direct result of reduced drinking.

However, many of the reasons you have used alcohol, may have been there before you ever started drinking – these problems will not be resolved merely by a cessation of drinking (e.g. you may have started drinking heavily because of stress at work). Equally, some of the problems caused by drinking may have become so difficult that they will take more than just stopping drinking to sort them out. These will need to be addressed by other means. If you fail to address them, they will put you at risk of a return to heavy drinking in due course.

And when you set your non-drinking goals in order to resolve these problems, you will also need to take into account your drinking goals.

Let's consider an example.

Example 'need': 'I need to have enjoyable feelings'

When considering how to achieve this without getting drunk, you will need to get away from the idea (which may have become a dominant one for you), that the only way you can experience pleasure is by drinking. You will need to think of other means of experiencing pleasure without drinking. Having done this, you will need to write these things down in the form of 'goals'. Here are some common themes that come out of this exercise when I run it by people in my clinic: socialising, sex and eating. Many people who have developed an alcohol problem will have forgotten how to socialise without the use of alcohol, will have poor sex lives (when they may well have had excellent sex lives in the past) and currently eat very little and are not particularly bothered by food (despite the fact that they used to enjoy food). Focus on similar things for you, and turn them into goals:

- **Goal – I will arrange to socialise with non-drinking friends on one evening this week.**

....

- **Goal – I will talk to my partner about our sex-life on one evening this week.**

....

- **Goal – I will cook a lovely meal one night this week.**

....

Of vital importance is to link these goals up with your 'drinking goals'. Say this is your first week back drinking after a period of abstinence, and you have decided to drink on two nights of the week, and have one unit on one night, and two units on the other night. How will you tie this up with your 'non-drinking goals'. Here's an example of how you might do that:

Firstly, on the evening that you go out with non-drinking friends, there will be no need to drink alcohol.

Secondly, on the night you decide to talk to your partner about your sex life, you may decide to make it a touch more relaxing and even romantic by opening a half-bottle of wine – why not have the two units on that night? (Be prepared to re-cork the bottle if your partner does not drink).

Thirdly, why not have a single glass of wine on the night you cook the meal?

By doing things in such a manner, you may manage to slightly enhance the activities you have planned by the healthy, controlled use of alcohol. And, of course, that must be your aim if you are planning to return to controlled drinking. Your drinking should never again be about getting drunk, or forgetting unpleasant feelings. It must only be about **slightly enhancing** the pleasures you get from non-drinking activities. If you ever allow the idea of the main plan for the evening being about having a drink, then you will surely relapse to heavy, uncontrolled drinking again in good time. As someone who has had a drink problem in the past, this is going to be difficult to get your head around. Really, the safest option is to aim for abstinence in the long term – for life. If you cannot imagine yourself having only a small amount to drink, with the aim of just slightly enhancing the pleasure you take from another activity, then you should think twice before starting to drink again. If you see no point in drinking like this, then you are probably best not drinking at all.

Before you set your goals, there are some other important things to take into account:

Goals must be **realistic**; e.g. do not plan to drink 21 units on Saturday and nothing for the rest of the week. Spread your planned drinking out over the week, allowing for at least 2 days without drinking at all. When you start to drink again, aim at first to keep it well below the total units 'allowed in a week'.

Goals must be **specific** and measurable; e.g. I will drink 2 units of alcohol on two days this week; I will go to the pub only once this week; I will see non-drinking friends once this week.

Goals must be **short-term** e.g. over the next week, or next day. While it is important to have a long-term objective in mind, this will not be reached overnight; if you are to achieve control over yourself, you must set short-term goals, and do your utmost to stick to them.

To achieve this, break your long-term goals down into **smaller steps;** e.g. if you plan to end up drinking 21 units per week, then plan to start by drinking 2 units on one day weekly, then every other day, then on five days weekly. Once you have achieved this, think about increasing by another unit on one day weekly etc.etc..

Decide on the goals **yourself** – allow others to advise you, but make the decisions for yourself.

FINALLY: LEARN FROM YOUR FAILURES:

Doubtless, you will not achieve all your goals every day – that would not be human. The important thing is to question why you failed to achieve a particular goal, and then re-plan to make the goal more realistic.

You should dwell on the positive more realistic plan and not berate yourself for failure. e.g.

· ·

- **You planned to drink 2 glasses of wine with your friends at a pub on Wednesday evening but ended up drinking 6 glasses:**

· ·

- **Why did this happen? Answer: you were offered another drink after the 2 glasses and did not find it in yourself to refuse.**

· ·

- **Possible solutions:**

· ·

  - **at the beginning of the next evening out, ask your friends not to offer you another drink after you have drunk two; OR**

· ·

  - **get up and leave half-way through the second drink, so that your friends are not given an opportunity to offer you another; OR**

· ·

  - **drink non-alcoholic drinks for the first half of the evening, and only start to drink alcohol one hour before closing time.**

· ·

Repeat this re-planning process, as often as you feel like it; but at least once weekly. Set your goals for the next week and keep a 'drinking diary' (see below). Fill this in every day before your memory fades, and then review it weekly. This will help you pick up patterns that you might otherwise miss, e.g. a tendency to drink more if you had an argument that day; a tendency to drink less if you went walking that day etc. etc.

So here are some examples of a mixture of drinking and other goals:

Examples of goals include:

· **I will see my drinking friends only once weekly at first.**

· **I will see my non-drinking friends at least once this week.**

· **I will spend two evenings reading this week, and drink nothing.**

· **I will drink a maximum of 2 units on Monday this week.**

· **I will spend all Tuesday looking at jobs advertised in the paper.**

· **On Thursday evening I will go to Relate with my partner.**

· **I will phone a dating agency on Wednesday.**

· **I will drink a maximum of 1 unit on Friday evening.**

CONTROLLED DRINKING DIARY

DAY OF WEEK

BEFORE
....
DRINKING GOAL 1:
....
Do you plan to drink?   Yes ☐   No ☐
....
How much do you plan to drink?
....
AFTER
....
Did you keep to your drinking plan?   Yes ☐   No ☐
....
If not, where did it go wrong?
....
How could you change it for the better?
....
What will you do the next time to make it work?

BEFORE
....
DRINKING GOAL 2:
....
Do you plan to drink?   Yes ☐   No ☐
....
How much do you plan to drink?
....
AFTER
....
Did you keep to your drinking plan?   Yes ☐   No ☐
....
If not, where did it go wrong?
....
How could you change it for the better?
....
What will you do the next time to make it work?

BEFORE
....
DRINKING GOAL 3:
....
Do you plan to drink?   Yes ☐   No ☐
....
How much do you plan to drink?
....
AFTER
....
Did you keep to your drinking plan?   Yes ☐   No ☐
....
If not, where did it go wrong?
....
How could you change it for the better?
....
What will you do the next time to make it work?

SUMMARY

So, let's re-cap:

1. Arrange a detox, preferable residentially, or if not, at home ('home detox').

2. If you have decided on a course of residential rehabilitation then you will learn more there about staying dry than anything I can tell you in this book. And remember this – the evidence shows that it is those that complete the course of rehabilitation that have the best chances of staying dry in the long term. Many people find residential rehabilitation hard going – it's not meant to be easy – it is meant to prepare you for a life without alcohol. As it is very hard work, many people leave before they have completed the course. If you commit yourself to a period of residential rehabilitation, then do your utmost to stay the course – if you don't, then you may have wasted your time.

3. After you have completed detox or/and rehab and you return home, have an 'aftercare plan' in place:

- Make sure you have some individual counselling in place to start immediately on your return home. You should aim to continue with counselling on a weekly basis for the first year of abstinence.

- If you are up for AA meetings, then attend them as often as you can – ideally daily.

- See if you can be prescribed Campral (acamprosate) and/or Antabuse (disulfiram) – continue these medications for up to one year after detox.

- Use your weekly diary to keep your time full with planned activity. Make slow but sure progress with long term plans and objectives. Assess why you failed to achieve particular goals, and do not berate yourself for failure. In particular, always get active and focus on an activity that involves concentration if you start to crave for alcohol.

- Whenever you experience craving, after it has calmed down, take some time to think how you have handled it without drinking, and how you will handle it more easily the next time it occurs. Think about the situation or feeling that triggered the craving – can you avoid this situation in the future? What did you do that enabled you to avoid drinking (e.g. walked away from the person that offered you a drink; started to do something you had planned in the diary)? Would there be a better way to deal with this same situation in the future that would make you even less likely to have a drink? If you can think of something, remember it and plan to behave in this way the next time you encounter a similar situation.

- Use free telephone advice from the DryOutNow.com Immediate Response Service (0800 160 1020) if you have any specific questions, or just need to speak to someone to help you on in the right direction. Alternatively, use the 'freeadvice' service on the www.dryoutnow.com website, to access individual advice by email.

CONCLUSION

You should now be in a position to implement the best possible plan for you, in order to achieve abstinence and to keep dry in the long term. Everything I have advised you to do in this book is based on the research which demonstrates the best way 'on average' for someone to stay dry. This fits the majority of people, but not everyone, and different elements of the overall plan will be better suited to some individuals than to others. To arrive at the best possible plan for you as an individual, and to limit those odds of relapsing to the minimum you will need individual advice about your particular situation. Use free telephone advice from the DryOutNow.com Immediate Response Service (0800 160 1020) if you have any specific questions, or just need to speak to someone to help you on in the right direction. Alternatively, use the 'freeadvice' service at dryoutnow.com, to access individual advice by email.

Now, at the point of reading this book you will most likely be in the 'planning phase' – getting ready for detox and the rest of your life without alcohol. So following is a check list of everything I advise you to have in place before you suddenly find yourself without a drink available to you. Continue straight to Part III of this book, when you are satisfied that you have made all your decisions.

PREPARATION PHASE CHECKLIST	Tick
1 Make absolutely sure you are ready to progress with planning for detox and abstinence. If you have any doubts re-read Chapter 3, telephone the DryOutNow.com Immediate Response Service on 0800 160 1020.	
2 Arrange for some individual counselling to start as soon as possible – ideally before detox and continuing afterwards. Get details of your local counsellors by telephoning the DryOutNow. com Immediate Response Service on 0800 160 1020.	
3 If you are up for it, attend some AA meetings – ideally before detox, and continuing afterwards. Get details of your local AA meetings by telephoning the DryOutNow.com Immediate Response Service on 0800 160 1020 or go to www.dryoutnow. com, and send your email message for 1:1 advice from a professional.	
4 Make a decision about whether or not you wish to carry on to residential rehabilitation after detox. If you wish to clarify this or get advice about the best residential rehabilitation units for you, telephone the DryOutNow.com Immediate Response Service on 0800 160 1020 or go to www.dryoutnow.com, and send your email message for 1:1 advice from a professional.	
5 Arrange a date for alcohol detoxification – either contact your local NHS community alcohol team (details available from the DryOutNow.com Immediate Response Service and www. dryoutnow.com) or if you are considering the self-pay option, telephone the DryOutNow.com Immediate Response Service (0800 160 1020) advice on the unit that will best suit your needs and budget.	
6 Start to think about your weekly diary. Make use of the tables in this chapter to assess your needs, and replace drinking with other activities that have the potential to lead to fulfillment.	
7 Speak to those you live with about drinking in the house after you return from detox.	

PREPARATION PHASE CHECKLIST	Tick
8 If you have difficulties at work, then make a plan about how you are going to minimise these difficulties in advance of detox. If you would like confidential advice around these issues, then phone the DryOutNow.com Immediate Response Service on 0800 160 1020, or go to www.dryoutnow.com, and send your email message for 1:1 advice from a professional.	
9 If you have difficulties in your relationship with your partner, telephone Relate on 0845 130 4016, to book relationship counselling.	
10 Get expert medical advice about whether or not you can be prescribed medication to prevent relapse – either visit your GP, phone the DryOutNow.com Immediate Response Service (0800 160 1020) to get free telephone advice and/or details of your nearest private doctor who can advise on this, or go to www. dryoutnow.com, and send your email message for 1:1 advice from a professional.	

PART TWO

SECTION B

If at any time you require urgent access to treatment, or need an immediate response for any other reason, do not hesitate to telephone the DryOutNow.com Immediate Response Service (IRS) on:

0800 160 1020
(8am-9pm, seven days weekly)

SECTION B

READ ON ONLY IF YOU ARE NOT PHYSICALLY ADDICTED TO ALCOHOL – IF YOU ARE PHYSICALLY ADDICTED TO ALCOHOL, THEN GO STRAIGHT BACK TO THE INTRODUCTION TO SECTION A

Before you can plan further, you will need to decide whether you are binge drinking or are drinking heavily on a regular basis. Chapters 6 and 7 are aimed at helping you if you are binge drinking and Chapters 8 and 9 are aimed at helping you if you are drinking heavily on a regular basis. Chapter 10 is for you if you have a mixed pattern of heavy binges with regular heavy drinking in between binges. This introduction to Section B should help you to decide whether you are a 'regular heavy drinker' or a 'binge drinker', or are drinking in a 'mixed pattern'. You may have a very clear idea already whether you drink only in heavy binges, or whether you drink heavily on a regular basis. If so, then skip straight to the relevant chapter for you. If you need to clarify this, then read on.

FIRST OF ALL, LET'S RE-CAP ON UNITS OF ALCOHOL:

You can work out your daily units of alcohol consumption by using the following calculation:

....

- **Litres of drink consumed in a day TIMES '% abv' of the particular drink EQUALS units of alcohol.**

....

The % abv is the alcohol content of the particular drink you are consuming – it is always recorded on the label of the can or bottle of the drink- have a look, 'abv' stands for 'Alcohol-by-Volume'. To work out how many units of alcohol you are drinking you may need to convert pints to litres, and you will also need to know the '% abv' of the different types of alcohol you are drinking. As a rough approximation, 2 pints = just over 1 litre (1.13litres to be precise).

- **Beer varies from 3% abv to 16% abv.**

- **Wine is typically 12% abv.**

- **All spirits are typically 40% abv.**

- **Licquers are usually in the region of 20 - 30% abv but may be as high as 80% abv.**

EXAMPLE 1:

*So for example, if you are drinking **4 pints of Stella Artois daily**, and nothing else, then your total units will be:*

*4 pints = 2 litres (plus a little extra). %abv of Stella = 5% (infact 5.2% to be precise). Thus total daily units = 2 TIMES 5 EQUALS 10. **Thus total weekly units = 70 units.** As such you are unlikely to be physically addicted if you are male, although you will doubtless cause yourself damage if you continue to drink at these levels for a period of time.*

EXAMPLE 2:

*Another example: if you are drinking **1 bottle of spirits daily**, and nothing else then your total units will be:*

1 bottle EQUALS 3/4 litre. (Sometimes 1 litre).

% abv of spirits usually equals 40%.

*Thus, 3/4 TIMES 40 = 30 units daily. **Thus total weekly units will be 210 units** – you are highly likely to be physically addicted drinking at these levels.*

There are two important points to take away when calculating units:

1. As far as your physical health is concerned, there is no known difference between drinking spirits and drinking wine or beer. It is nothing to do with the type of drink you use. It is everything to do with the total amount of actual alcohol that you consume – this is calculated by units. Don't fall into the trap of telling yourself that you "only drink beer/wine" and thus are not alcoholic – what kind of drink you use has absolutely nothing to do with it.

2. Don't fall into the trap of underestimating your units by using the old fashioned estimates. The old estimates of units – "one unit = half a pint of beer or one glass of wine" are completely out-of-date. The reasons for this are due to the 'drinks industry'. There has been a slow but sure increase in the amount of alcohol in commonly drunk beer and wine (% abv), and a slow but sure increase in the size of wine glasses in pubs and wine bars/restaurants. Whereas in times gone by a typical pint of bitter was 3% abv, it is now the case that commonly consumed lagers (Stella and Kronenberg) are in the region of 5% abv. Equally wine has increased from 8 or 9% abv to 12 or 13% abv. In the meantime, wine glasses have increased in size. If you go out these days and order a large glass of wine, you are probably drinking approximately 3 units per glass (a large difference from the old 1 unit per glass).

1. BINGE DRINKING

Binge drinking is defined by the World Health Organization as drinking **more than 10 units on an occasion if you are male, and more than 7 units on an occasion if you are female.** To 'qualify' as a 'true binge drinker' (rather than someone who just has the occasional heavy night out) I suggest that you should be drinking like this more than once every month on average. So if you drink the equivalent of more than 4 pints of Stella/Kronenburg in a night more than once every month on average, but drink much less than this on most nights, then you are binge drinking.

2. REGULAR HEAVY DRINKING

Regular drinking that is potentially damaging to your health in the long term is defined by the World Health Organization as drinking more than the following:

FOR MALES:

- A maximum of 21 units should be consumed in any one week.

- Within a period of one week there should be at least two drink-free days.

- No more than 4 units should be consumed in any one day.

Effectively this means the following:

- You should drink no more than 2 pints of 3-4% lager/beer (Carlsberg/Heinekin) **or** 1.5 pints of 5% lager/beer (like Stella/Kronenberg) **or** 1/3 bottle of wine **or** 1/9th bottle of spirits on any one night.

- You should have at least two days in the week when you drink no alcohol at all.

- You should drink no more than 9 pints of 3-4% lager/beer per week **or** no more than 7 pints of 5% lager/beer per week **or** no more than 2 bottles wine per week **or** no more than 2/3 bottle spirits per week.

FOR FEMALES:

- A maximum of 14 units should be consumed in any one week.

- Within a period of one week there should be at least two drink-free days.

- No more than 3 units should be consumed in any one day.

Effectively this means the following:

- You should drink no more than 1.5 pints of 3-4% lager/beer (Carlsberg/Heinekin) **or** 1 pint of 5% lager/beer (like Stella/Kronenberg) **or** 1/4 bottle of wine **or** 1/10th bottle of spirits on any one night.

- You should have at least two days in the week when you drink no alcohol at all.

- You should drink no more than 6 pints of 3-4% lager/beer per week **or** no more than 4.5 pints of 5% lager/beer per week **or** no more than 1.5 bottles wine per week **or** no ,more than 1/2 bottle of spirits per week.

If you are drinking more than these limits on a regular basis then you are most likely drinking at levels that will damage your health in due course. In short, you are drinking too heavily on a regular basis.

3. ARE YOU STILL NOT SURE WHETHER YOU ARE BINGE DRINKING OR DRINKING HEAVILY ON A REGULAR BASIS? DO YOU DRINK IN A MIXED BINGE/REGULAR HEAVY PATTERN?

Many people who have heavy binges on some occasions, also drink heavily (but less so) between these binges. For example, you may drink well over 10 units per day for a period of time (bingeing), and then go through a phase of drinking more than 4 units per day, on a regular basis (regular heavy drinking) in between the binges.

If you drink much more on some occasions, or for periods of days (binges) than on other days, but still drink heavily on the days in between binges then you have a mixed pattern of bingeing and regular heavy drinking.

If you drink in this **mixed pattern,** then you will be unlikely to achieve abstinence from alcohol or controlled drinking by choosing the 'cut down slowly but surely' route.

You should now be able to decide whether you are binge drinking or drinking too heavily on a regular basis.

- **If you are binge drinking, and plan to cease alcohol use completely, then continue to read Chapter 6.**

- **If you are binge drinking, and plan to continue to drink within healthy limits, then continue to read Chapter 7.**

- **If you are drinking too heavily on a regular basis and plan to cease alcohol use completely, then continue to read Chapter 8.**

- **If you are drinking too heavily on a regular basis and plan to continue to drink within healthy limits, then continue to read Chapter 9.**

- **If you are drinking in a mixed regular heavy/binge pattern, then continue to read Chapter 10.**

If you remain unclear about this, or any other point, and want individual advice about your particular situation, you can get this for free and in complete confidence by phoning the DryOutNow.com Immediate Response Service on: **0800 160 1020.** Alternatively, use the 'freeadvice' service at **dryoutnow.com**, to access individual advice by email.

BINGE DRINKING & STOP COMPLETELY	**CHAPTER 6**
BINGE DINKING & CONTINUE to DRINK HEALTHILY	**CHAPTER 7**
REGULAR HEAVY & STOP COMPLETELY	**CHAPTER 8**
REGULAR HEAVY & CONTINUE to DRINK HEALTHILY	**CHAPTER 9**
MIXED REGULAR HEAVY/BINGE DRINKING	**CHAPTER 10**

CHAPTER SIX

YOU ARE NOT PHYSICALLY ADDICTED
TO ALCOHOL AND YOU PLAN TO CEASE
DRINKING COMPLETELY AND YOUR
DRINKING IS IN A BINGE PATTERN

If at any time you require urgent access to treatment, or need an
immediate response for any other reason, do not hesitate to telephone
the DryOutNow.com Immediate Response Service (IRS) on:

0800 160 1020
(8am-9pm, seven days weekly)

CHAPTER SIX

YOU ARE NOT PHYSICALLY ADDICTED TO ALCOHOL AND YOU PLAN TO CEASE DRINKING COMPLETELY AND YOUR DRINKING IS IN A BINGE PATTERN

There are 3 stages though which you will need to progress, along your route to achieving and maintaining abstinence from alcohol.

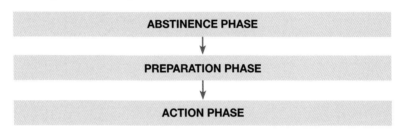

In the case of someone who is binge drinking, there will usually be periods of drinking nothing (or at least very little), and as such the only realistic option is to prepare to cease drinking suddenly during one of these periods. Of course, there are binge drinkers who drink heavily on most days, and then especially heavily on other days. If your pattern of drinking is like this, then you should really be considering yourself as having a **mixed binge/regular heavy pattern. See Chapter 10 if this is the case.**

THE PREPARATION PHASE

The preparation phase mainly involves planning/booking the help you will need and getting ready to stay dry in the long term. So what does preparing for staying dry involve? There are three things to do:

1. *Prepare yourself psychologically, and also seek out professional psychological support (various forms of counselling).*

2. *Prepare yourself socially, and seek out the available professional support.*

3. *Consider the possibility of medication to help you stay dry.*

TO PREPARE YOURSELF PSYCHOLOGICALLY:

a. Make absolutely sure that you are fully committed to doing this, and that you are 100% realistic about how hard it's going to be. Re-read Chapter Three to help you to do this.

b. Book some specialist individual (1-to-1) alcohol counselling as soon as possible to start BEFORE you stop drinking.

c. Consider attending some Alcoholics Anonymous (AA) meetings BEFORE you stop drinking.

Specialist 1-to-1 counselling can help in one of two ways: firstly by giving you the skills to avoid relapse to alcohol, and secondly by helping you to understand any underlying emotional issues which are leading you to drink heavily. For detailed information on how counselling works, go to:

....

- **www.dryoutnow.com – and download Section E of the Professional Treatment Guidelines.**

....

Specialist counselling is available from the NHS/charitable services for free. Or you can book with a private counsellor. In terms of the quality of service you will receive, there is probably little difference between NHS and private counsellors. However, in the NHS you may have to wait a long time (months or years in some cases) before you can access counselling. This varies between areas and depends on where you live. So, overall, I suggest contacting your local NHS/charitable specialist alcohol counselling service first. If the waiting time seems unsatisfactory, or other things don't seem right, then try the self-pay route.

....

- **For details of your local NHS/charitable and private counselling services, phone the DryOutNow.com Immediate Response Service on: 0800 160 1020.**

....

Private counsellors who specialise in alcohol problems are not so many in number. There are probably in the region of 400 in the country. Many problems that lead to heavy drinking are general in nature (e.g. stress, relationship difficulties etc.). So, if your nearest specialist alcohol counsellor is too far away, a general counsellor may still be of help to you:

SPECIALIST TELEPHONE COUNSELLING

Alternatively, you can access specialist private alcohol counselling by telephone. You may wish to use this service if your nearest specialist counsellor is too far away, or if you would prefer the privacy and convenience of receiving

counselling in your own home. This service is provided via **DryOutNow.com.**
*Call 0800 160 1020 to request details of the specialist telephone counselling
service.*

Alcoholics Anonymous meetings: People are often nervous about attending
these meetings, but those who attend have been shown to have **better long term
outcomes.** There is no requirement to have stopped drinking in order to attend
– just to be relatively sober at the time of attendance. There is no requirement
to speak at a meeting – just to say 'pass' if asked to speak. The theme of the
meetings is religious and requires a belief in a 'higher power', but there is no
requirement to believe in God as such, or in any particular God. Some people think
of the 'higher power' as the 'sober part' of themselves. There is no need to book
in advance – just turn up to a meeting and sit alone just to observe at first. People
will probably come to talk to you after the meeting – one of the main beliefs of
Alcoholics Anonymous is that alcoholics need other alcoholics to help them to get
sober – so people will be keen to help you. For more information on 'AA' meetings
and how they work, go to:

....

- **www.dryoutnow.com – and download Section E of the Professional
  Treatment Guidelines.**

....

- For details of your nearest Alcoholics Anonymous meetings phone the
  DryOutNow.com Immediate Response Service on: 0800 160 1020 or go to
  www.dryoutnow.com – click on 'Local Help' and send the email to receive
  details of your local AA meetings.

TO PREPARE YOURSELF SOCIALLY:

Firstly you should make a decision about whether you are going to stay in a
residential rehabilitation unit for a period of time, or whether you plan to deal
with this at home.

Residential rehabilitation. This is a very intense form of treatment, and many
people will not wish to go through it, or just cannot for practical reasons. Residential
rehabilitation involves staying in a specialist psychological unit for a period of time
(durations of stay range from 4 weeks to 9 months). The advantages of a period of
residential rehabilitation include i) an alcohol-free environment so there is minimal
risk of relapse ii) the person is living and learning from others with alcohol problems
iii) as a generalisation, this is the best form of counselling available, as it is so
intense, and because people are confronted every time they try to deny they have
a problem. Most people will decide this is not for them, especially if it is your first
attempt at staying dry. However – bear this in mind – the evidence clearly shows
that those who go to a residential rehabilitation unit and complete the course
without leaving early, are more likely to remain dry from alcohol in the long term

than those who do not go to residential rehabilitation. For more information on how residential rehabilitation works, go to:

⋯⋯⋯⋯⋯⋯⋯⋯⋯⋯⋯⋯⋯⋯⋯⋯⋯⋯⋯⋯⋯⋯⋯⋯⋯⋯⋯⋯⋯⋯⋯⋯⋯⋯⋯⋯⋯⋯

- **www.dryoutnow.com – and download Section E of the Professional Treatment Guidelines.**

⋯⋯⋯⋯⋯⋯⋯⋯⋯⋯⋯⋯⋯⋯⋯⋯⋯⋯⋯⋯⋯⋯⋯⋯⋯⋯⋯⋯⋯⋯⋯⋯⋯⋯⋯⋯⋯⋯

Most residential rehabilitation units are not in the NHS. However, the NHS will sometimes pay for you to go to one if they think you need it. If you want to plan for a period of residential rehabilitation, and wish the NHS to pay for it, then you will need to contact your local NHS Community Alcohol Team. They will arrange for you to be assessed, and if they think you meet their criteria for paying, will then arrange for your admission. Waits may be long for assessment and admission (many months in some cases), but the treatment you get at the end of the day will be of the same quality as going privately to one of the cheaper units.

⋯⋯⋯⋯⋯⋯⋯⋯⋯⋯⋯⋯⋯⋯⋯⋯⋯⋯⋯⋯⋯⋯⋯⋯⋯⋯⋯⋯⋯⋯⋯⋯⋯⋯⋯⋯⋯⋯

- **For contact details of your local NHS Community Alcohol Team phone the DryOutNow.com Immediate Response Service on: 0800 160 1020.**

⋯⋯⋯⋯⋯⋯⋯⋯⋯⋯⋯⋯⋯⋯⋯⋯⋯⋯⋯⋯⋯⋯⋯⋯⋯⋯⋯⋯⋯⋯⋯⋯⋯⋯⋯⋯⋯⋯

If you decide to pay for residential rehabilitation yourself, then you will usually be able to access it within a matter of several days at most. Costs vary from £400 per week to £5000 per week, and remember the duration of stay is anything from four weeks to nine months. In other words this is not cheap but it may make the difference between abstinence and relapse. If you would like details about admission to residential rehabilitation units I suggest you contact: **phone the DryOutNow.com Immediate Response Service on: 0800 160 1020.**

ACHIEVING AND MAINTAINING ABSTINENCE AT HOME:

If you plan to stay at home, probably the single most important part of planning for this is to **write out your weekly diary.** There are two aims of the weekly diary. Firstly it should enable you fill your time completely from the day you cease drinking, onwards. Your time should be full for the simple reason that this will leave you less time to think about alcohol. The nature of craving is such that if you give it a chance to build up, it will end up filling your head with repetitive thoughts: "Just one drink won't hurt – how could it? Just one drink won't hurt – how could it?" You must do your utmost to divert your attention from any such thoughts at all times. Being active and having to concentrate on a task of some kind is much more likely to result in the feeling of craving subsiding, than is sitting in a chair doing nothing. The vital element here is having to concentrate on something. This is very important if you are back in your usual routine, and not in specialist care.

Secondly it should provide you with the kind of activities that have a good chance of giving you some kind of sense of fulfillment or pleasure – that are rewarding.

The aim here is to start to build up activities that will replace your need for alcohol in the longer term. As discussed in Chapter Three – don't expect anything to replace alcohol totally – there are very few activities that can result in you brain experiencing the reward that use of an addictive substance brings, and probably no healthy activities that produce that reward as easily and as immediately as does alcohol. You will need to re-think your objectives and search more for a sense of satisfaction and fulfillment in life than for the experience of immediate pleasure or immediate relief from unpleasant feelings which is delivered by alcohol.

You should think this through in great detail starting now. It must be ready to implement the very day you stop drinking. You should try to think of activities that are purposeful, and have the potential to lead to some sense of satisfaction; this will depend very much on personal taste. Some examples might include: socialising with non-drinking friends, reading, gym, gardening, walking. In particular, if you are able to devote yourself to any kind of long-term project that involves dedication and a great deal of work, this might start to act to replace the psychological need for alcohol. (This kind of approach would be disagreed with by many professionals, especially those from a theoretical counselling background – they would argue that the addictive behaviour is merely being transferred from one object – drink – to another – work. However, if you are not considering residential rehabilitation, I think this is exactly what you should aim to do – replace the alcohol with healthy activity rather than destructive activity.) In summary, you should create a diary ideally providing several options of activity for all times of every day of the week. This is not to say that you must or will complete every such activity – the important thing is that the diary is always there to turn to if you find yourself sitting and starting to dwell on the idea of having a drink. When that thought enters your head (and it will), you should immediately pick up the diary and implement one of the activities that are listed for that time of that day. Following is an empty diary covering seven days of the week from 6 in the morning to 12 midnight. It also allows for you to enter two alternative activities for any two hour period. Now you may think that an 18 hour day is a long period of time to plan to fill, but bear the following in mind. The idea of the diary is not that you necessarily do every thing on it at the specified time, although you may chose to, and there will be no harm in this unless you get stressed thinking that you have to do everything on it. The idea of the diary IS that when you feel yourself starting to crave alcohol, you have something to occupy yourself with immediately, and which is already planned so that you can implement that activity immediately. If you wait until you start to crave before trying to think of something to occupy your mind, you may well not be able to do what you wish to immediately, and you may not even be able to concentrate effectively in order to think of something else to do. If you have your diary ready, you've got a great head-start over the craving. Secondly, remember that your sleep may be disturbed for a period after cessation of drinking. It is thus important to have planned activities from early in the morning to late at night – again you will not necessarily carry out all these activities, but if you are awake for long hours, you must make sure you have something to do. Poor sleep is a major cause of relapse to drinking. Be prepared to have something to do if you cannot get to sleep – if you enjoyed reading in the past get some good books in. If you enjoyed film, get in a stack of videos or sign up for satellite channels (probably less expensive that your total alcohol costs). Poor sleep will improve as your brain gets used to a world free of alcohol – but you may have to be prepared to persevere for a good while.

Finally, if you are having difficulty thinking of the type of activities you should include in the diary the following questions may give you some ideas:

- What did you enjoy doing before alcohol started to replace other things in your life?

- What are the enjoyable things about drinking for you? Can you replace these with activities that result in a similar reward? (E.g. you may drink after work to relax; can you arrange for a massage on some nights as an alternative form of relaxation?) If you completed the tables in Chapter 3 under Question 4, you may wish to use your answers to help you here.

- What would you like to achieve from life? What would you need to do to achieve these things? Is there something you could dedicate yourself to achieving?

- How is your physical health? Could you improve it by eating well and healthily? Could you improve it by exercising regularly? What kinds of exercise would you enjoy?

- How is your social life? Do you have any non-drinking friends you could get in touch with? Can you think of a variety of social activities that don't involve drinking that you may enjoy?

- Do you need to search for work? What do you need to do to search for work?

	MONDAY	TUESDAY	WEDNESDAY	THURSDAY	FRIDAY	SATURDAY	SUNDAY
Activity 1: 6-8							
Activity 2: 6-8							
Activity 1: 8-10							
Activity 2: 8-10							
Activity 1: 10-12							
Activity 2: 10-12							
Activity 1: 12-2							
Activity 2: 12-2							
Activity 1: 2-4							
Activity 2: 2-4							
Activity 1: 4-6							
Activity 2: 4-6							
Activity 1: 6-8							
Activity 2: 6-8							
Activity 1: 8-10							
Activity 2: 8-10							
Activity 1: 10-12							
Activity 2: 10-12							
NIGHT-TIME 1							
NIGHT-TIME 2							

As this is such an important element of the planning process, you may wish to examine this in some more detail. Below is a 'formula' for ascertaining your needs and planning to make sure that they are met. Use this if you remain having difficulties in filling in your weekly diary.

> ### Make a list of the POSITIVE AND NEGATIVE ASPECTS OF DRINKING for you

> ### Ascertain your NEEDS

> ### Set yourself GOALS

> ### Keep a DIARY TO MONITOR how well you are achieving YOUR GOALS

1. MAKE A LIST OF THE POSITIVE AND NEGATIVE ASPECTS OF DRINKING FOR YOU

Making a list of the things you find both helpful and unhelpful about drinking, is the starting point of this process. You will find that if you write this list, you will be able to see quite clearly what you need in your life, that at the present time you are trying to get from alcohol. If you made these lists when you read Chapter Three, then refer back to them now. Otherwise, continue right here. I've given some examples of the positive and negative reasons for drinking that people commonly write down. Cross these out if they don't apply to you, and then spend plenty of time thinking about the good and bad aspects of drinking for you – add to the list and make it your own.

Let's start by considering the possible reasons that you find drinking an enjoyable or helpful activity. Tick off those things on this list that apply to you, and add items of your own as you think of them. If you wish to record this for the future, I have included an empty table for you in the appendix of this book.

POSITIVE THINGS ABOUT DRINKING FOR YOU:

		Tick here
	Physical Health Reasons	
1	I enjoy the feeling of drinking and getting drunk.	
2	Drinking stops me getting withdrawal symptoms.	
3	I have trouble getting to sleep – without a drink I cannot sleep well.	
	Psychological Reasons	
4	I tend to get depressed and drinking improves my mood.	
5	Drinking makes me less anxious.	
6	I tend to get a bit paranoid about going out. If I have a drink I can get out the house without worrying.	
7	I'm usually tense and stressed - drinking helps me to relax.	
	Social Reasons	
8	I have a much better time going out if I have a drink.	
9	I can't imagine going out without having a drink.	
10	I tend to be anxious in the company of other people; when I have a drink inside me I can talk more easily and get on with people better.	
11	I've become a bit of a loner over the years – the only time I ever get into a conversation is in the pub.	
	PUT YOUR OWN REASONS in the spaces below:	

NEGATIVE THINGS ABOUT DRINKING FOR YOU:

		Tick here
	Physical Health Reasons	
1	I'm feeling generally un-well most of the time.	
2	I never eat anything these days.	
3	I'm increasingly worried that I'm permanently damaging my physical health.	
4	I wake up early in the morning covered in sweat.	
	Psychological Reasons	
5	I feel horribly depressed when I wake up in the morning after drinking.	
6	My memory seems terrible these days.	
7	I seem so much more nervous than I used to be.	
8	I'm sick and tired of having this thing called alcohol in control of me. I want to get back in control of myself.	
	Social Reasons	
9	I want to be a better parent to my children.	
10	My relationship is a mess and I know it's because of my drinking.	
11	I've just been arrested for my second drink-drive offence – I might go to prison this time – I know I've got to do something about it.	
12	I'm finding it difficult to get into work on time – someone is going to say something soon.	
13	Of late my temper has got increasingly worse. I'm worried what I might do next time someone annoys me.	
	PUT YOUR OWN REASONS in the spaces below:	

2. ASCERTAIN YOUR NEEDS

When you have completed making the two lists above, you will be in a position to write down what your needs are. Use the table below to do this. By writing in a positive or negative reason for drinking, you should then be able to work out what you need to do to resolve that – write it down in the space below the reason for drinking. I've started by giving you a few examples. If you run out of space, I have included a blank table for you in the appendix.

Reason	I enjoy the feeling of drinking and getting drunk.
NEED	I need to have enjoyable feelings.
Reason	I have trouble getting to sleep – without a drink I cannot sleep well.
NEED	I need to sleep well.
Reason	I'm usually tense and stressed - drinking helps me to relax.
NEED	I need to relax.
Reason	I never eat anything these days
NEED	I need to eat well
Reason	I feel horribly depressed when I wake up in the morning after drinking.
NEED	I need to improve my mood
Reason	My relationship is a mess and I know it's because of my drinking.
NEED	I need to improve my relationship
Reason	
NEED	
Reason	
NEED	
Reason	
NEED	
Reason	
NEED	
Reason	
NEED	
Reason	
NEED	

3. SET YOURSELF GOALS

Your goals will involve meeting the needs you have made a list of above. If you manage to successfully achieve and maintain abstinence from alcohol, some of these things will automatically sort themselves out for themselves (e.g. morning sweats and withdrawal symptoms will not return). If you are lucky, other things like your relationship and your mood will also improve as a direct result of stopping drinking. However, many of the reasons you have used alcohol may have been there before you ever started drinking – these problems will not be resolved merely by a cessation of drinking (e.g. you may have started drinking heavily because of stress at work). Equally, some of the problems caused by drinking may have become so difficult that they will take more than just stopping drinking to sort them out. These will need to be addressed by other means. If you fail to address them, they will put you at risk of a return to heavy drinking in due course.

Let's consider an example.

Example 'need': 'I need to have enjoyable feelings'

Considering how to achieve this without getting drunk, you will need to get away from the idea (which may have become a dominant one for you), that the only way you can experience pleasure is by drinking. You will need to think of other means of experiencing pleasure without drinking. Having done this, you will need to write these things down in the form of 'goals'. Here are some common themes that come out of this exercise when I run it by people in my clinic: socialising, sex and eating. Many people who have developed an alcohol problem will have forgotten how to socialise without the use of alcohol, will have poor sex lives (when they may well have had excellent sex lives in the past) and currently eat very little and are not particularly bothered by food (despite the fact that they used to enjoy food). Focus on similar things for you, and turn them into goals:

Goal – I will arrange to socialise with nondrinking friends on one evening this week.

Goal – I will talk to my partner about our sex-life on one evening this week.

Goal – I will cook a lovely meal one night this week.

Before you set your goals, there are some other important things to take into account:

Goals must be **realistic;** e.g. do not plan to run The Marathon next month, or read The Lord of the Rings in one week.

Goals must be **specific** and measurable; e.g. I will see non-drinking friends once this week; I will cook a great meal on one night this week; I will go for a jog on two nights this week.

Goals must be **short-term** e.g. over the next week, or next day. While it is important to have a long-term objective in mind, this will not be reached overnight; if you are to achieve control over yourself, you must set short-term goals, and do your utmost to stick to them.

To achieve this, break your long-term goals down into **smaller steps;** e.g. if you plan to end up with a full social life away from the temptation of readily available alcohol, then arrange one activity per week at first. If your aim is to become physically fit, then arrange exercise on one night weekly first-of-all, and gradually increase. If you take things too quickly, you will probably experience a sense of failure when you fail to achieve your goals. Build up slowly, but surely. Decide on the goals **yourself** – allow others to advise you, but make the decisions for **yourself.**

FINALLY: LEARN FROM YOUR FAILURES:

Doubtless, you will not achieve all your goals every day – that would not be human. The important thing is to question why you failed to achieve a particular goal, and then re-plan to make the goal more realistic. You should dwell on the positive more realistic plan and not berate yourself for failure. E.g.

- **You planned to go for a jog on two nights this week, but only managed this on one night.**

- **Why did this happen? Answer: I couldn't sleep the night before, and didn't have the energy.**

- **Possible solutions:**

- Reduce your expectations and set your plan for the next week back to one night of exercise OR

- Re-plan the time you will exercise for earlier in the day – for example at lunch-time if you work OR

- Change the type of exercise to a less strenuous form – e.g. go for a long walk rather than a jog, or – if you can afford it – play a round of golf (as with most activities that replace drinking, this will of course involve a degree of planning in advance).

Repeat this re-planning process, as often as you feel like it; but at least once weekly. Set your goals for the next week and keep a **'non-drinking goals diary'** (see below). Fill this in every day before your memory fades, and then **review it weekly.** This will help you pick up patterns that you might otherwise miss, e.g. a tendency to 'miss' a goal if you had an argument that day; a tendency to achieve another goal if you went walking that day etc. etc.

NON-DRINKING GOALS DIARY

DAY OF WEEK

NON-DRINKING GOAL 1:
....
Did you achieve your goal?   Yes ☐   No ☐
....
If not, where did it go wrong?
....
How could you change it for the better?
....
What will you do the next time to make it work?

NON-DRINKING GOAL 2:
....
Did you achieve your goal?   Yes ☐   No ☐
....
If not, where did it go wrong?
....
How could you change it for the better?
....
What will you do the next time to make it work?

NON-DRINKING GOAL 3:
....
Did you achieve your goal?   Yes ☐   No ☐
....
If not, where did it go wrong?
....
How could you change it for the better?
....
What will you do the next time to make it work?

OTHER THINGS TO PREPARE FOR SOCIALLY:

1. ACCOMMODATION.

Is your accommodation situation stable and are you living with others who drink?

At the point of stopping drinking you will wish for the amount of stress in your life to be as minimal as is possible; stress is a major reason for starting to drink heavily and it is also a major reason for relapse. If you do not have permanent accommodation, or you are at risk of losing permanent accommodation for whatever reason, do your best to sort this out in advance of stopping drinking. Lack of a stable environment in which to re-start your life will greatly increase your chances of relapse. If you are living with others who drink heavily, then you should very seriously consider either asking them to leave or leaving yourself. The odds of you managing to remain sober when there is someone living with you who drinks on a regular basis are very small indeed. Of course, if that person is also planning to seek help for an alcohol problem, then ideally this should be planned so that neither of you are living together at the time that one of you is still drinking. This will probably mean either planning to cease drinking at the same time as each other, or at least one of you arranging for admission to a residential rehabilitation unit. If you live with other(s) who do drink, but do not drink heavily, you should see if they will agree to avoid drinking in the house. Ideally, the house should be completely empty of alcohol at the point you stop drinking, and it should stay that way for the foreseeable future.

2. WORK.

Is your working situation stable? Are you unemployed? Are you facing some kind of disciplinary action? Are you on sick leave?

If you are in work and have no problems there, then this is usually the ideal situation. If you are on sick leave due to your alcohol problem, again you should try to arrange to return to work, possibly on a part-time basis initially. Of course, there is a fine balance here between too much stress at work, and too much time on your hands if you do not return to work. If work-related stress is a problem for you, then your return to work should be a graded one. If you are facing some kind of disciplinary action at work as a direct or indirect result of your drinking, do your best to get this resolved before stopping drinking. Remember the aim is to limit the amount of stress you will have to deal with in those vital first few months when you may be battling to stay dry. Of course, there's a bit of a catch 22 about this; while you are drinking heavily you may not feel up to sorting these kind of things out. Overall, do your best to sort out what you can before stopping drinking; what you cannot do, you just cannot do. If you are unemployed at the moment, then make some initial

plans for a return to work following cessation of alcohol use. Ideally, arrange for a return to employment as soon as you have stopped drinking. Of course this may well not be practical for you – if it is not, spend some time before you stop drinking thinking about what kinds of employment you may wish to get, and how you may go about searching for this. Build this into your weekly diary (see above).

3. RELATIONSHIPS

If you are in a relationship with a person who has a drinking problem, then the ideal is that you should both deal with this at the same time – it's highly unlikely to work for either of you if one person becomes abstinent while the other continues to drink. If you are unable to convince your partner of this, then if you are committed to aiming for an alcohol free life, you should seriously consider whether or not to continue with the relationship. If you are in a relationship with someone who does not drink heavily, then you may well be experiencing problems in your relationship. You may find that your relationship improves dramatically when you cease drinking, but sometimes this will not be the case. Whatever, if you are having relationship problems at the moment, consider whether to book some relationship counselling with RELATE. This organization often has waiting lists of several months – if you book now, then the counselling will probably have started by the time you cease to drink.

Here is the central contact telephone number for RELATE: **0845 130 4016**

MEDICATION THAT CAN HELP PREVENT RELAPSE TO DRINKING.

There are two medications commonly use in the UK to help prevent a return to drinking.

1. Acamprosate, also known as Campral.

Acamprosate works to reduce the feeling of craving for alcohol. It is very effective for a few patients, quite effective for some, and simply doesn't work for others. As it is a relatively safe medicine to prescribe, in my NHS practice I prescribe it for most patients who decide to cease drinking. It is usually safe to continue to take it, even if you temporarily lapse to drinking again.

2. Disulfiram, also known as Antabuse.

Disulfiram blocks the complete breakdown of alcohol by the liver. This causes you to feel absolutely terrible if you have a drink. Disulfiram can work well for people who are likely to relapse to drinking on the spur of the moment – you simply can't do this if you are taking disulfiram. However, it's no magic cure, as you can decide to stop taking it, and within several days you are likely to be able to drink again without feeling ill. I prescribe disulfiram less often than acamprosate as it has the potential to cause some quite nasty side-effects in some people. In particular, it should generally be avoided in people who have a history of blood vessel problems (e.g. high blood pressure, history of stroke or heart attack), who have liver disease, or who have suffered serious psychiatric illness in the past.

For more information on both these medicines, go to:

....

• **www.dryoutnow.com – and download Section C of the Professional Treatment Guidelines.**

....

Of course, confidentiality may be an issue for you, and you will need to see a doctor to get these medicines prescribed. If you do not wish to see your GP about this, then the DryOutNow.com Immediate Response Service can give you details of your nearest private doctor who will be prepared to prescribe for you. Simply telephone 0800 160 1020 and ask for details of your nearest private doctor who specialises in addiction problem.

THE ACTION PHASE

The action phase is the time when you go for it, and stop drinking! You should implement this when:

....

• **You have prepared thoroughly as described above in 'the preparation phase'**

....

• **At a time of minimal stress**

....

BUT BEWARE – there is not likely to be any time in your life when there is no stress whatsoever. In planning the right time to stop drinking, you should have minimised the possibility of stress to lead to an immediate relapse to uncontrolled drinking; but you will never get rid of it completely. Assuming you are not physically addicted to alcohol, then this should not lead to any permanent damage if you cease drinking suddenly – overnight. Having said this, some people who binge drink, drink heavily enough to drink to induce physical addiction to alcohol for periods of time. If you think this might apply to you, then read Chapter One of this book to establish this. If you find that it does apply to you, then you should not be reading this chapter – rather, you should follow the advice in Chapter Four or Chapter Five.

If you have any doubts about this, then get individual advice by telephoning the: **DryOutNow.com Immediate Response Service on 0800 160 1020.**

THE ABSTINENCE PHASE

You have arrived! You've stopped drinking successfully, and are ready to face a new world – a world without alcohol. Now this is where the serious work begins – the work of staying dry. If you've implemented most of the steps I outlined in the 'preparation phase' then you will have a head start over all the new challenges that are going to face you:

- **Craving for alcohol**

- **Sleeplessness**

- **Agitation**

- **Boredom**

- **NO IMMEDIATE SOLUTION TO ALL THESE THINGS**

On the other side of the coin, you are likely to be:

- **Feeling well**

- **Eating well**

- **Feeling in a better mood if you have been depressed**

- **Feeling more confident in yourself, especially if you suffered with paranoia and anxiety while you were drinking**

However, you must remember this – most of the advantages of giving up drinking are **long term advantages;** they will not be apparent to you immediately, and they will require a sustained period of abstinence from alcohol to occur:

- **Improved relationships with the important people in your life**

- **Building new relationships with the future important people in your life**

- **Improved performance at work**

- **Finding and holding down employment if you are unemployed**

- **Enjoyment of leisure activities you could never have enjoyed while you were drinking**

- **Improved financial situation**

- **A sense of pride in yourself that had been forgotten during years of heavy drinking**

Maintaining abstinence will bring you rewards whether these are delivered by living longer, feeling better in yourself and with yourself, or having better relationships with others. All of these things can disappear in a moment if you relapse, and most of the truly rewarding things take months and years to start to occur. Probably only 25% of people who decide to stop drinking are still dry at the end of one year. How are you going to maximise your chances of being one of these 25%? For the first year (the highest risk time for relapse) you must implement your plan, and stick to it as much as is feasible for you. Let's re-cap:

1. If you have decided on a course of residential rehabilitation then you will learn more there about staying dry than anything I can tell you in this book. But remember this – the evidence shows that it is those that complete the course of rehabilitation that have the best chances of staying dry in the long term. Many people find residential rehabilitation hard going – it's not meant to be easy – it is meant to prepare you for a life without alcohol. As it is very hard work, many people leave before they have completed the course. If you commit yourself to a period of residential rehabilitation, then do your utmost to stay the course – if you don't, then you have probably wasted your time.

2. If you are staying at home having stopped drinking:

- Make sure you have some individual counselling in place to start before you stop drinking, and to continue afterwards. You should aim to continue with counselling on a weekly basis for the first year of abstinence.

- If you are up for AA meetings, then attend them as often as you can – ideally daily.

- See if you can be prescribed Campral (acamprosate) and/or Antabuse (disulfiram) – continue these medications for between six months and one year after you stop drinking. You have to stop taking Antabuse if you decide to start drinking again, but you can continue to take Campral – this may work to limit your chances of starting to drink again at harmful levels.

- Use your weekly diary to keep your time full with planned activity. Make slow but sure progress with long term plans and objectives. In particular, always get active and focus on an activity that involves concentration if you start to crave for alcohol.

- Use the table ('ascertain you needs') from earlier in this chapter to ascertain your needs and plan activities which are likely to fulfil those needs as much as possible.

- Use your non-drinking goals diary to assess your progress and gradually achieve your life goals.

- Whenever you experience craving, after it has calmed down, take some time to think how you have handled it without drinking, and how you will handle it more easily the next time it occurs. Think about the situation or feeling that triggered the craving – can you avoid this situation in the future? What did you do that enabled you to avoid drinking (e.g. walked away from the person that offered you a drink; started to do something you had planned in the diary)? Would there be a better way to deal with this same situation in the future that would make you even less likely to have a drink? If you can think of something, remember it and plan to behave in this way the next time you encounter a similar situation.

- Use telephone advice from the DryOutNow.com Immediate Response Service (0800 160 1020) if you have any specific questions, or just need to speak to someone to help you on in the right direction.

CONCLUSION

You should now be in a position to implement the best possible plan for you, in order to achieve abstinence. Everything I have advised you to do in this book is based on the research which demonstrates the best way 'on average' for someone to stay dry or to achieve controlled drinking. This fits the majority of people, but not everyone, and different elements of the overall plan will be better suited to some individuals than to others. To arrive at the best possible plan for you as an individual, and to limit those odds of relapsing to the minimum you will need individual advice about your particular situation. You can get this for free by telephoning the **DryOutNow.com Immediate Response Service on 0800 160 1020.**

Following is a check list of everything I advise you to have in place before you suddenly find yourself without a drink available to you. Continue straight to Part III, when you are satisfied that you have made all your decisions.

PREPARATION PHASE CHECKLIST	Tick
1 Make absolutely sure you are ready to progress with planning for abstinence. If you have any doubts re-read Chapter 3, telephone the DryOutNow.com Immediate Response Service on 0800 160 1020.	
2 Arrange for some individual counselling to start as soon as possible – ideally before detox and continuing afterwards. Get details of your local counsellors by telephoning the DryOutNow. com Immediate Response Service on 0800 160 1020.	
3 If you are up for it, attend some AA meetings – ideally before detox, and continuing afterwards. Get details of your local AA meetings by telephoning the DryOutNow.com Immediate Response Service on 0800 160 1020 or go to www.dryoutnow.com – click on 'Local Help' and send the email to get details of your local AA meetings.	
4 Make a decision about whether or not you wish to go to residential rehabilitation. If you wish to clarify this or get advice about the best residential rehabilitation units for you, telephone the DryOutNow.com Immediate Response Service on 0800 160 1020.	
5 Start to write your weekly diary. Make use of the various tables in this chapter to assess your needs and replace drinking with other activities that have the potential to lead to fulfilment.	
6 Speak to those you live with about drinking in the house after you have become abstinent.	
7 If you have difficulties at work, then make a plan about how you are going to minimize these difficulties in advance of cessation of drinking. If you would like confidential advice around these issues, then phone the DryOutNow.com Immediate Response Service on 0800 160 1020.	
8 If you have difficulties in your relationship with your partner, telephone Relate on 0845 130 4016, to book relationship counselling.	
9 Get expert medical advice about whether or not you can be prescribed medication to prevent relapse – either visit your GP or phone the DryOutNow.com Immediate Response Service (0800 160 1020) to get free telephone advice and/or details of your nearest private doctor who can advise on this.	

CHAPTER SEVEN

YOU ARE NOT PHYSICALLY ADDICTED TO ALCOHOL AND YOU PLAN TO CONTINUE DRINKING WITHIN HEALTHY LIMITS. YOUR DRINKING IS IN A BINGE PATTERN

If at any time you require urgent access to treatment, or need an immediate response for any other reason, do not hesitate to telephone the DryOutNow.com Immediate Response Service (IRS) on:

0800 160 1020
(8am-9pm, seven days weekly)

CHAPTER SEVEN

YOU ARE NOT PHYSICALLY ADDICTED TO ALCOHOL AND YOU PLAN TO CONTINUE DRINKING WITHIN HEALTHY LIMITS. YOUR DRINKING IS IN A BINGE PATTERN

It may be the case that you are looking for good advice about how to re-start drinking again immediately after ceasing binge drinking. As far as I am aware, there is no such advice to give. If you are binge drinking, you will need to give yourself a good period without any drinking whatsoever, if you are to restart drinking within healthy limits and keep it there.

Why is this? In Chapter Three I explained how the brain takes a long time to readjust to a world without alcohol – drinking before significant readjustment has occurred will only trigger the brain into telling you to drink more and more …and more. It is also likely to take many months before you have started to replace the habit of drinking with alternative activities that fill the times when you used to drink. If you have not made progress on developing alternative activities by the time you start to drink again, you will probably find yourself drinking more and more…and more. It is also likely to take you many months before you have started to come to terms with the reasons for, and sorted out the problems that led to your binges. For these reasons, I must advise you to aim to remain completely abstinent from alcohol for at least six months following cessation of alcohol use. Of course, you may prove me wrong, and I congratulate you if you do – you will be one of the few people to have beaten the odds and recommenced drinking quickly in a way that enhances your life rather than diminishes it. However, if you would prefer to minimise your chances of returning quickly to the old pattern of heavy binge drinking rather than take the risk of a quick relapse, then read on.

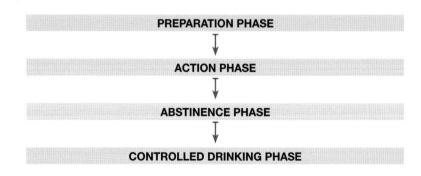

PREPARATION PHASE

↓

ACTION PHASE

↓

ABSTINENCE PHASE

↓

CONTROLLED DRINKING PHASE

In the case of someone who is binge drinking, they will usually have periods of drinking nothing (or at least very little), and as such the only realistic option is to prepare to cease drinking suddenly during one of these periods. Of course, there are binge drinkers who drink heavily on most days, and then especially heavily on other days. If your pattern of drinking is like this, then you should really be considering yourself as having a mixed binge/regular heavy pattern of drinking – read Chapter 10 if this is the case. There are 4 stages through which you will need to progress, along your route to achieving and maintaining abstinence from alcohol.

THE PREPARATION PHASE.

The preparation phase mainly involves planning/booking the help you will need and getting ready to stay dry in the medium term. So what does preparing for staying dry involve? There are three things to do:

1. Prepare yourself psychologically, and also seek out professional psychological support (various forms of counselling).

2. Prepare yourself socially, and seek out the available professional support.

3. Consider the possibility of medication to help you stay dry.

TO PREPARE YOURSELF PSYCHOLOGICALLY:

a. Make absolutely sure that you are fully committed to doing this, and that you are 100% realistic about how hard it's going to be. Re-read Chapter Three to help you to do this.

b. Book some specialist individual (1-to-1) alcohol counselling as soon as possible to start BEFORE you stop drinking.

c. Consider attending some Alcoholics Anonymous (AA) meetings BEFORE you stop drinking.

Specialist 1-to-1 counselling can help in one of two ways: firstly by giving you the skills to control your drinking, and secondly by helping you to understand any underlying emotional issues which are leading you to drink heavily. For detailedinformation on how counselling works, go to:

....

- **www.dryoutnow.com – download Section E of the Professional treatment Guidelines.**

....

Specialist counselling is available from the NHS/charitable services for free. Or you can book with a private counsellor. In terms of the quality of service you will receive, there is probably little difference between NHS and private counsellors. However, in the NHS you may have to wait a long time (months or years in some cases) before you can access counselling. This varies between areas and depends on where you live. So, overall, I suggest contacting your local NHS/charitable specialist alcohol counselling service first. If the waiting time seems unsatisfactory, or other things don't seem right, then try the self-pay route.

- For details of your local NHS/charitable and private counselling services phone the DryOutNow.com Immediate Response Service on 0800 160 1020

SPECIALIST TELEPHONE COUNSELLING

Alternatively, you can access specialist private alcohol counselling by telephone. You may wish to use this service if your nearest specialist counsellor is too far away, or if you would prefer the privacy and convenience of receiving counselling in your own home. This service is provided via DryOutNow.com.

Call 0800 160 1020 to request details of the specialist counselling service.

Alcoholics Anonymous meetings: People are often nervous about attending these meetings, but those who attend have been shown to have **better long term outcomes.** There is no requirement to have stopped drinking in order to attend – just to be relatively sober at the time of attendance. There is no requirement to speak at a meeting – just to say 'pass' if asked to speak. The theme of the meetings is religious and requires a belief in a 'higher power', but there is no requirement to believe in God as such, or in any particular God. Some people think of the 'higher power' as the 'sober part' of themselves. There is no need to book in advance – just turn up to a meeting and sit alone just to observe at first. People will probably come to talk to you after the meeting – one of the main beliefs of Alcoholics Anonymous is that alcoholics need other alcoholics to help them to get sober – so people will be keen to help you. For more information on 'AA' meetings and how they work, go to:

....

- **www.dryoutnow.com – download Section E of the Treatment Guidelines.**

....

- **For details of your nearest Alcoholics Anonymous meetings phone the DryOutNow.com Immediate Response Service on 0800 160 1020**

....

TO PREPARE YOURSELF SOCIALLY:

Firstly you should make a decision about whether you are going to stay in a residential rehabilitation unit for a period of time, or whether you plan to deal with this at home.

ACHIEVING AND MAINTAINING ABSTINENCE AT HOME:

If you plan to stay at home, probably the single most important part of planning for this is to **write out your weekly diary.** There are two aims of the weekly diary. Firstly it should enable you to fill your time completely from the day you cease drinking, onwards. Your time should be full for the simple reason that this will leave you less time to think about alcohol. The nature of craving is such that if you give it a chance to build up, it will end up filling your head with repetitive thoughts: "Just one drink won't hurt – how could it? Just one drink won't hurt – how could it?" You must do your utmost to divert your attention from any such thoughts at all times. Being active and having to concentrate on a task of some kind is much more likely to result in the feeling of craving subsiding, than is sitting in a chair doing nothing. The vital element here is having to concentrate on something. This is very important if you are back in your usual routine, and not in specialist care. Secondly it should provide you with the kind of activities that have a good chance of giving you some kind of sense of fulfillment or pleasure – that are rewarding. The aim here is to start to build up activities that will replace your need for alcohol in the longer term. As discussed in Chapter Three – don't expect anything to replace alcohol totally – there are very few activities that can result in your brain experiencing the reward that use of an addictive substance brings, and probably no healthy activities that produce that reward as easily and as immediately as does alcohol. You will need to re-think your objectives and search more for a sense of satisfaction and fulfillment in life than for the experience of immediate pleasure or immediate relief from unpleasant feelings which is delivered by alcohol. You should think this through in great detail starting now. It must be ready to implement the very day you stop drinking. You should try to think of activities that are purposeful, and have the potential to lead to some sense of satisfaction; this will depend very much on personal taste. Some examples might include: socialising with non-drinking friends, reading, gym, gardening, walking. In particular, if you are able to devote yourself to any kind of long-term project that involves dedication and a great deal of work, this might start to act to replace the psychological need for alcohol. (This kind of approach would be disagreed with by many professionals, especially those from a theoretical counselling background – they would argue that the addictive behaviour is merely being transferred from one object – drink – to another – work. However, if you are not considering residential rehabilitation, I think this is exactly what you should aim to do – replace the alcohol with healthy activity rather than destructive activity.

In summary, you should create a diary ideally providing several options of activity for all times of every day of the week. This is not to say that you must or will complete every such activity – the important thing is that the diary is always there to turn to if you find yourself sitting and starting to dwell on the idea of having a drink. When that thought enters your head (and it will), you should immediately pick up the diary and implement one of the activities that are listed for that time of that day.

Following is an empty diary covering seven days of the week from 6 in the morning to 12 midnight. It also allows for you to enter two alternative activities for any two hour period. Now you may think that an 18 hour day is a long period of time to plan to fill, but bear the following in mind. The idea of the diary is not that you necessarily do every thing on it at the specified time, although you may choose to, and there will be no harm in this unless you get stressed thinking that you have to do everything on it. The idea of the diary IS that when you feel yourself starting to crave alcohol, you have something to occupy yourself with immediately, and which is already planned so that you can implement that activity immediately. If you wait until you start to crave before trying to think of something to occupy your mind, you may well not be able to do what you wish to immediately, and you may not even be able to concentrate effectively in order to think of something else to do. If you have your diary ready, you've got a great head-start over the craving. Secondly, remember that your sleep may be disturbed for a period after cessation of drinking. It is thus important to have planned activities from early in the morning to late at night – again you will not necessarily carry out all these activities, but if you are awake for long hours, you must make sure you have something to do. Poor sleep is a major cause of relapse to drinking. Be prepared to have something to do if you cannot get to sleep – if you enjoyed reading in the past get some good books in. If you enjoyed film, get in a stack of videos or sign up for satellite channels (probably less expensive than your total alcohol costs). Poor sleep will improve as your brain gets used to a world free of alcohol – but you may have to be prepared to persevere for a good while.

Finally, if you are having difficulty thinking of the type of activities you should include in the diary the following questions may give you some ideas:

- What did you used to enjoy doing before alcohol started to replace other things in your life?

- What are the enjoyable things about drinking for you? Can you replace these with activities that result in a similar reward? (E.g. you may drink after work to relax; can you arrange for a massage on some nights as an alternative form of relaxation?) If you completed the tables in Chapter 3 under Question 4, you may wish to use your answers to help you here.

- What would you like to achieve from life? What would you need to do to achieve these things? Is there something you could dedicate yourself to achieving?

- How is your physical health? Could you improve it by eating well and healthily? Could you improve it by exercising regularly? What kinds of exercise would you enjoy?

- How is your social life? Do you have any nondrinking friends you could get in touch with? Can you think of a variety of social activities that don't involve drinking that you may enjoy?

- Do you need to search for work? What do you need to do to search for work?

	MONDAY	TUESDAY	WEDNESDAY	THURSDAY	FRIDAY	SATURDAY	SUNDAY
Activity 1: 6-8							
Activity 2: 6-8							
Activity 1: 8-10							
Activity 2: 8-10							
Activity 1: 10-12							
Activity 2: 10-12							
Activity 1: 12-2							
Activity 2: 12-2							
Activity 1: 2-4							
Activity 2: 2-4							
Activity 1: 4-6							
Activity 2: 4-6							
Activity 1: 6-8							
Activity 2: 6-8							
Activity 1: 8-10							
Activity 2: 8-10							
Activity 1: 10-12							
Activity 2: 10-12							
NIGHT-TIME 1							
NIGHT-TIME 2							

OTHER THINGS TO PREPARE FOR SOCIALLY:

1. ACCOMMODATION.

Is your accommodation situation stable and are you living with others who drink?

At the point of stopping drinking you will wish for the amount of stress in your life to be as minimal as is possible; stress is a major reason for starting to drink heavily and it is also a major reason for relapse. If you do not have permanent accommodation, or you are at risk of losing permanent accommodation for whatever reason, do your best to sort this out in advance of stopping drinking. Lack of a stable environment in which to re-start your life will greatly increase your chances of relapse. If you are living with others who drink heavily, then you should very seriously consider either asking them to leave or leaving yourself. The odds of you managing to remain sober when there is someone living with you who drinks on a regular basis are very small indeed. Of course, if that person is also planning to seek help for an alcohol problem, then ideally this should be planned so that neither of you are living together at the time that one of you is still drinking. This will probably mean either planning to cease drinking at the same time as each other, or at least one of you arranging for admission to a residential rehabilitation unit. If you live with other(s) who do drink, but do not drink heavily, you should see if they will agree to avoid drinking in the house. Ideally, the house should be completely empty of alcohol at the point you stop drinking, and it should stay that way for the foreseeable future.

2. WORK

Is your working situation stable? Are you unemployed? Are you facing some kind of disciplinary action? Are you on sick leave?

If you are in work and have no problems there, then this is usually the ideal situation. If you are on sick leave due to your alcohol problem, again you should try to arrange to return to work, possibly on a part-time basis initially. Of course, there is a fine balance here between too much stress at work, and too much time on your hands if you do not return to work. If work-related stress is a problem for you, then your return to work should be a graded one. If you are facing some kind of disciplinary action at work as a direct or indirect result of your drinking, do your best to get this resolved before stopping drinking. Remember the aim is to limit the amount of stress you will have to deal with in those vital first few months when you may be battling to stay dry. Of course, there's a bit of a Catch 22 about this; while you are drinking heavily you may not feel up to sorting these kind of things out. Overall, do your best to sort out what you can before you stop drinking; what you cannot do, you just cannot do. If you are unemployed at the moment, then make some initial plans for a return to work following cessation of drinking. Ideally, arrange for a return to employment as soon as you have stopped drinking. Of course this may well not be practical for you – if it is not, spend some time before you stop drinking thinking about what kinds of employment you may wish to get, and how you may go about searching for this. Build this into your weekly diary (see above).

3. RELATIONSHIPS

If you are in a relationship with a person who has a drinking problem, then the ideal is that you should both deal with this at the same time – it's highly unlikely to work for either of you if one person stops drinking while the other continues to drink. If you are unable to convince your partner of this, then if you are committed to aiming for a period of abstinence from alcohol, you should seriously consider whether or not to continue with the relationship. If you are in a relationship with someone who does not drink heavily, then you may well be experiencing problems in your relationship. You may find that your relationship improves dramatically when you cease drinking, but sometimes this will not be the case. Whatever, if you are having relationship problems at the moment, consider whether to book some relationship counselling with RELATE. This organization often has waiting lists of several months – if you book now, then the counselling will probably have started by the time you have ceased to drink. Here is the central contact telephone number for RELATE: **0845 130 4016**

MEDICATION THAT CAN HELP PREVENT RELAPSE TO DRINKING.

There are two medications commonly use in the UK to help prevent a return to drinking.

1. Acamprosate, also known as Campral.

Acamprosate works to reduce the feeling of craving for alcohol. It is very effective for a few patients, quite effective for some, and simply doesn't work for others. As it is a relatively safe medicine to prescribe, in my NHS practice I prescribe it for most patients who decide to cease drinking. It is usually safe to continue to take it, even if you temporarily lapse to drinking again.

2. Disulfiram, also known as Antabuse.

Disulfiram blocks the complete breakdown of alcohol by the liver. This causes you to feel absolutely terrible if you have a drink. Disulfiram can work well for people who are likely to relapse to drinking on the spur of the moment – you simply can't do this if you are taking disulfiram. However, it's no magic cure, as you can decide to stop taking it, and within several days you are likely to be able to drink again without feeling ill. I prescribe disulfiram less often than acamprosate as it has the potential to cause some quite nasty side-effects in some people. In particular, it should generally be avoided in people who have a history of blood vessel problems (e.g. high blood pressure, history of stroke or heart attack), who have liver disease, or who have suffered serious psychiatric illness in the past. Clearly, before you start drinking again, you will have to stop taking disulfiram for a period of days before your first drink. For more information on both these medicines, go to:

....

* **www.dryoutnow.com – download Section C of the Professional Treatment Guidelines.**

....

Of course, confidentiality may be an issue for you, and you will need to see a doctor to get these medicines prescribed. If you do not wish to see your GP about this, then the DryOutNow.com Immediate Response Service can give you details of your nearest private doctor who will be prepared to prescribe for you. Phone the DryOutNow.com Immediate Response Service on 0800 160 1020.

THE ACTION PHASE.

The action phase is the time when you go for it, and stop drinking! You should implement this when:

* **You have prepared thoroughly as described above in 'the preparation phase'**

* **At a time of minimal stress**

BUT BEWARE – there is not likely to be any time in your life when there is no stress whatsoever. In planning the right time to stop drinking, you should have minimised the possibility of stress to lead to an immediate relapse to uncontrolled drinking; but you will never get rid of it completely. Assuming you are not physically addicted to alcohol, then this should not lead to any permanent damage if you cease drinking suddenly – overnight. Having said this, some people who binge drink, drink heavily enough to drink to induce physical addiction to alcohol for periods of time. If you think this might apply to you, then read Chapter One of this book to establish this. If you find that it does apply to you, then you should not be reading this chapter – rather, you should follow the advice in Chapter Four or Chapter Five. If you have any doubts about this, then get individual advice by telephoning: the DryOutNow.com Immediate Response Service on 0800 160 1020.

THE ABSTINENCE PHASE.

You have arrived! You've stopped drinking successfully, and are ready to face a new world – a world without alcohol in control of you. Now this is where the serious work begins – the work of staying dry, before a return to controlled drinking within healthy limits. If you've implemented most of the steps I outlined in the 'preparation phase' then you will have a head start over all the new challenges that are going to face you:

- **Craving for alcohol**

- **Sleeplessness**

- **Agitation**

- **Boredom**

- **NO IMMEDIATE SOLUTION TO ALL THESE THINGS**

On the other side of the coin, you are likely to be:

- **Feeling well**

- **Eating well**

- **Feeling in a better mood if you have been depressed**

- **Feeling more confident in yourself, especially if you suffered with paranoia and anxiety while you were drinking**

However, you must remember this – most of the advantages of giving up uncontrolled drinking are long term advantages; they will not be apparent to you immediately, and they will require a sustained period of abstinence from alcohol to occur:

- **Improved relationships with the important people in your life**

- **Building new relationships with the future important people in your life**

- **Improved performance at work**

- **Finding and holding down employment if you are unemployed**

- **Enjoyment of leisure activities you could never have enjoyed while you were drinking**

- **Improved financial situation**

- **A sense of pride in yourself that had been forgotten during years of heavy drinking.**

Controlling your drinking will bring you rewards whether these are delivered by living longer, feeling better in yourself and with yourself, or having better relationships with others. All of these things can disappear in a moment if you relapse, and most of the truly rewarding things take months and years to start to occur.

Probably only 25% of people who decide to stop drinking in a damaging way are actually achieving this at the end of one year. How are you going to maximise your chances of being one of these 25%? For the first year (the highest risk time for relapse) you must implement your plan, and stick to it as much as is feasible for you. Let's re-cap:

1. If you have decided on a course of residential rehabilitation then you will learn more there about staying dry than anything I can tell you in this book. But remember this – the evidence shows that it is those that complete the course of rehabilitation that have the best chances of staying dry in the long term. Many people find residential rehabilitation hard going – it's not meant to be easy – it is meant to prepare you for a life without alcohol. As it is very hard work, many people leave before they have completed the course. If you commit yourself to a period of residential rehabilitation, then do your utmost to stay the course – if you don't, then you have probably wasted your time.

2. If you are staying at home having stopped drinking:

- Make sure you have some individual counselling in place to start before you stop drinking, and to continue afterwards. You should aim to continue with counselling on a weekly basis for the first year of abstinence.

- If you are up for AA meetings, then attend them as often as you can – ideally daily.

- See if you can be prescribed Campral (acamprosate) and/or Antabuse (disulfiram) – continue these medications for between six months and one year after you stop drinking. You have to stop taking Antabuse if you decide to start drinking again, but you can continue to take Campral – this may work to limit your chances of starting to drink again at harmful levels.

- Use your weekly diary to keep your time full with planned activity. Make slow but sure progress with long term plans and objectives. In particular, always get active and focus on an activity that involves concentration if you start to crave for alcohol.

- Whenever you experience craving, after it has calmed down, take some time to think how you have handled it without drinking, and how you will handle it more easily the next time it occurs. Think about the situation or feeling that triggered the craving – can you avoid this situation in the future? What did you do that enabled you to avoid drinking (e.g. walked away from the person that offered you a drink; started to do something you had planned in the diary)? Would there be a better way to deal with this same situation in the future that would make you even less likely to have a drink? If you can think of something, remember it and plan to behave in this way the next time you encounter a similar situation.

- Use telephone advice from the DryOutNow.com Immediate Response Service (0800 160 1020) if you have any specific questions, or just need to speak to someone to help you on in the right direction.

THE CONTROLLED DRINKING PHASE.

First of all, what is controlled drinking? Very simply, most doctors will consider it to be drinking within healthy limits as defined by the World Health Organization. These are as follows:

FOR MALES:

- A maximum of 21 units should be consumed in any one week.

- Within a period of one week there should be at least two drink-free days.

- No more than 4 units should be consumed in any one day.

Effectively this means the following:

- You should drink no more than 2 pints of 3-4% lager/beer (Carlsberg/Heineken) or 1.5 pints of 5% lager/beer (like Stella/ Kronenberg) or 1/3 bottle of wine or 1/9th bottle of spirits on any one night.

- You should have at least two days in the week when you drink no alcohol at all.

- You should drink no more than 9 pints of 3-4% lager/beer per week or no more than 7 pints of 5% lager/beer per week or no more than 2 bottles wine per week or no more than 2/3 bottle spirits per week.

FOR FEMALES:

- A maximum of 14 units should be consumed in any one week.

- Within a period of one week there should be at least two drink-free days.

- No more than 3 units should be consumed in any one day.

Effectively this means the following:

- You should drink no more than 1.5 pints of 3-4% lager/beer (Carlsberg/ Heinekin) or 1 pint of 5% lager/beer (like Stella/ Kronenberg) or 1/4 bottle of wine or 1/10th bottle of spirits on any one night.

- You should have at least two days in the week when you drink no alcohol at all.

- You should drink no more than 6 pints of 3-4% lager/beer per week or no more than 4.5 pints of 5% lager/beer per week or no more than 1.5 bottles wine per week or no more than 1/2 bottle of spirits per week. So if your aim is to start drinking again and control your drinking, then you should keep your drinking within these limits. If you do relapse to heavy drinking when trying to keep drinking at safe amounts (controlled drinking), you will then know that complete abstinence is the only way forward for you in the long term. People will often need to demonstrate this to themselves before coming to a decision to aim for complete abstinence from alcohol. And that's not necessarily a bad thing. In order to have a good chance of staying off alcohol for ever, your mind will have to be completely made-up that this is the way you have to do it. If you have any doubt about this, then you are likely to relapse in time anyway.

To prepare to control your drinking, and keep it within healthy limits there are four stages to go through

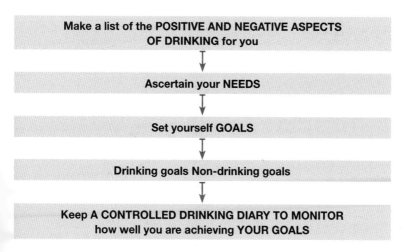

Make a list of the **POSITIVE AND NEGATIVE ASPECTS OF DRINKING** for you

↓

Ascertain your NEEDS

↓

Set yourself GOALS

↓

Drinking goals Non-drinking goals

↓

Keep **A CONTROLLED DRINKING DIARY TO MONITOR** how well you are achieving **YOUR GOALS**

1. MAKE A LIST OF THE POSITIVE AND NEGATIVE ASPECTS OF DRINKING FOR YOU

Making a list of the things you find both helpful and unhelpful about drinking, is the starting point of this process. You will find that if you write this list, you will be able to see quite clearly what you need in your life, that at the present time you are trying to get from alcohol. If you made these lists when you read Chapter Three, then refer back to them now. Otherwise, continue right here. I've given some examples of the positive and negative reasons for drinking that people commonly write down. Cross these out if they don't apply to you, and then spend plenty of time thinking about the good and bad aspects of drinking for you – add to the list and make it your own.

Let's start by considering the possible reasons that you find drinking an enjoyable or helpful activity. Tick off those things on this list that apply to you, and add items of your own as you think of them. If you wish to record this for the future, I have included an empty table for you in the appendix of this book.

POSITIVE THINGS ABOUT DRINKING FOR YOU:

		Tick here
	Physical Health Reasons	
1	I enjoy the feeling of drinking and getting drunk.	
2	Drinking stops me getting withdrawal symptoms.	
3	I have trouble getting to sleep – without a drink I cannot sleep well.	
	Psychological Reasons	
4	I tend to get depressed and drinking improves my mood.	
5	Drinking makes me less anxious.	
6	I tend to get a bit paranoid about going out. If I have a drink I can get out the house without worrying.	
7	I'm usually tense and stressed - drinking helps me to relax.	
	Social Reasons	
8	I have a much better time going out if I have a drink.	
9	I can't imagine going out without having a drink.	
10	I tend to be anxious in the company of other people; when I have a drink inside me I can talk more easily and get on with people better.	
11	I've become a bit of a loner over the years - the only time I ever get into a conversation is at the pub.	
	PUT YOUR OWN REASONS in the spaces below:	

NEGATIVE THINGS ABOUT DRINKING FOR YOU:

		Tick here
	Physical Health Reasons	
1	I'm feeling generally un-well most of the time.	
2	I never eat anything these days.	
3	I'm increasingly worried that I'm permanently damaging my physical health.	
4	I wake up early in the morning covered in sweat.	
	Psychological Reasons	
5	I feel horribly depressed when I wake up in the morning after drinking.	
6	My memory seems terrible these days.	
7	I seem so much more nervous than I used to be.	
8	I'm sick and tired of having this thing called alcohol in control of me. I want to get back in control of myself.	
	Social Reasons	
9	I want to be a better parent to my children.	
10	My relationship is a mess and I know it's because of my drinking.	
11	I've just been arrested for my second drink-drive offence – I might go to prison this time – I know I've got to do something about it.	
12	I'm finding it difficult to get into work on time – someone is going to say something soon.	
13	Of late my temper has got increasingly worse. I'm worried what I might do next time someone annoys me.	
	PUT YOUR OWN REASONS in the spaces below:	

2. ASCERTAIN YOUR NEEDS

When you have completed making the two lists above, you will be in a position to write down what your needs are – and in particular those needs that you will need to meet if you are to successfully control your drinking.

Use the table below to do this. By writing in a positive or negative reason for drinking, you should then be able to work out what you need to do to resolve that – write it down in the space below the reason for drinking. I've started by giving you a few examples. If you run out of space, I have included a blank table for you in the appendix.

Reason	I enjoy the feeling of drinking and getting drunk.
NEED	I need to have enjoyable feelings.
Reason	I have trouble getting to sleep – without a drink I cannot sleep well.
NEED	I need to sleep well.
Reason	I'm usually tense and stressed - drinking helps me to relax.
NEED	I need to relax.
Reason	I never eat anything these days
NEED	I need to eat well
Reason	I feel horribly depressed when I wake up in the morning after drinking.
NEED	I need to improve my mood
Reason	My relationship is a mess and I know it's because of my drinking.
NEED	I need to improve my relationship
Reason	
NEED	
Reason	
NEED	
Reason	
NEED	
Reason	
NEED	
Reason	
NEED	
Reason	
NEED	

3. SET YOURSELF GOALS

You should set yourself two types of goals – 'drinking goals' and 'non-drinking goals'. 'Non-drinking goals' do not necessarily mean that you do not drink when you are trying to achieve these goals; it's just that they are not directly about drinking. E.g., a 'drinking goal' might be to drink 2 units and no more on a particular evening. A 'non-drinking goal' might be to cook a meal.

Your drinking goals will be what you plan to drink (how many units) on a particular day of the week. If you are to attempt to return to controlled drinking, then I advise you to take it slowly at first – do not plan to return immediately to drinking 21 units weekly, or as much as 3 units in one night. Gradually get to these levels over a period of months, or settle for drinking less than this in the long term. Your 'non-drinking' goals will involve meeting the needs you have made a list of above. Now if you manage to successfully control your drinking, some of these things will automatically sort themselves out for themselves (e.g. morning sweats and withdrawal symptoms will not return). If you are lucky, other things like your relationship and your mood will also improve as a direct result of reduced drinking. However, many of the reasons you have used alcohol, may have been there before you ever started drinking – these problems will not be resolved merely by a cessation of drinking (e.g. you may have started drinking heavily because of stress at work). Equally, some of the problems caused by drinking may have become so difficult that they will take more than just stopping drinking to sort them out. These will need to be addressed by other means. If you fail to address them, they will put you at risk of a return to heavy drinking in due course.

And when you set your non-drinking goals in order to resolve these problems, you will also need to take into account your drinking goals.

Let's consider an example.

Example 'need': 'I need to have enjoyable feelings'

When considering how to achieve this without getting drunk, you will need to get away from the idea (which may have become a dominant one for you), that the only way you can experience pleasure is by drinking. You will need to think of other means of experiencing pleasure without drinking. Having done this, you will need to write these things down in the form of 'goals'. Here are some common themes that come out of this exercise when I run it by people in my clinic: socialising, sex and eating. Many people who have developed an alcohol problem will have forgotten how to socialise without the use of alcohol, will have poor sex lives (when they may well have had excellent sex lives in the past) and currently eat very little and are not particularly bothered by food (despite the fact that they used to enjoy food). Focus on similar things for you, and turn them into goals:

- **Goal** – I will arrange to socialise with nondrinking friends on one evening this week.

....

- **Goal** – I will talk to my partner about our sex-life on one evening this week.

....

- **Goal** – I will cook a lovely meal one night this week.

....

Of vital importance is to link these goals up with your 'drinking goals'. Say this is your first week back drinking after a period of abstinence, and you have decided to drink on two nights of the week, and have one unit on one night, and two units on the other night. How will you tie this up with your 'nondrinking goals'. Here's an example of how you might do that:

Firstly, on the evening that you go out with non-drinking friends, there will be no need to drink alcohol.

Secondly, on the night you decide to talk to your partner about your sex life, you may decide to make it a touch more relaxing and even romantic by opening a half-bottle of wine – why not have the two units on that night? (Be prepared to re-cork the bottle if your partner does not drink).

Thirdly, why not have a single glass of wine on the night you cook the meal?

By doing things in such a manner, you may manage to slightly enhance the activities you have planned by the healthy, controlled use of alcohol. And, of course, that must be your aim if you are planning to return to controlled drinking. **Your drinking should never again be about getting drunk, or forgetting unpleasant feelings. It must only be about slightly enhancing the pleasures you get from nondrinking activities.** If you ever allow the idea of the main plan for the evening being about having a drink, then you will surely relapse to heavy, uncontrolled drinking again in good time. As someone who has had a drink problem in the past, this is going to be difficult to get your head around. Really, the safest option is to aim for abstinence in the long term – for life. **If you cannot imagine yourself having only a small amount to drink, with the aim of just slightly enhancing the pleasure you take from another activity, then you should probably think twice before starting to drink again.** If you see no point in drinking like this, then you are probably best not drinking at all.

Before you set your goals, there are some other important things to take into account:

Goals must be **realistic;** e.g. do not plan to drink 21 units on Saturday and nothing for the rest of the week. Spread your planned drinking out over the week, allowing for at least 2 days without drinking at all. When you start to drink again, aim at first to keep it well below the total units 'allowed in a week'.

Goals must be **specific** and measurable; e.g. I will drink 2 units of alcohol on two days this week; I will go to the pub only once this week; I will see nondrinking friends once this week.

Goals must be **short-term** e.g. over the next week, or next day. While it is important to have a long-term objective in mind, this will not be reached overnight; if you are to achieve control over yourself, you must set short-term goals, and do your utmost to stick to them.

To achieve this, break your long-term goals down into **smaller steps;** e.g. if you plan to end up drinking 21 units per week, then plan to start by drinking 2 units on one day weekly, then every other day, then on five days weekly. Once you have achieved this, think about increasing by another unit on one day weekly etc.etc..

Decide on the goals yourself – allow others to advise you, but make the decisions for yourself.

FINALLY: LEARN FROM YOUR FAILURES:

Doubtless, you will not achieve all your goals every day – that would not be human. The important thing is to question why you failed to achieve a particular goal, and then re-plan to make the goal more realistic. You should dwell on the positive more realistic plan and **not berate yourself for failure. E.g.**

- **You planned to drink 2 glasses of wine with your friends at a pub on Wednesday evening but ended up drinking 6 glasses:**

- **Why did this happen? Answer: you were offered another drink after the 2 glasses and did not find it in yourself to refuse.**

- **Possible solutions:**

  - at the beginning of the next evening out, ask your friends not to offer you another drink after you have drunk two; OR

  - get up and leave half-way through the second drink, so that your friends are not given an opportunity to offer you another; OR

  - drink non-alcoholic drinks for the first half of the evening, and only start to drink alcohol one hour before closing time.

Repeat this re-planning process, as often as you feel like it; but at least once weekly. Set your goals for the next week and keep a **'drinking diary'** (see below). Fill this in every day before your memory fades, and then **review it weekly.** This will help you pick up patterns that you might otherwise miss, e.g. a tendency to

drink more if you had an argument that day; a tendency to drink less if you went walking that day etc. etc.

So here are some examples of a mixture of drinking and other goals:

Examples of goals include:

- **I will see my drinking friends only once weekly at first.**

- **I will see my non-drinking friends at least once this week.**

- **I will spend two evenings reading this week, and drink nothing.**

- **I will drink a maximum of 2 units on Monday this week.**

- **I will spend all Tuesday looking at jobs advertised in the paper.**

- **On Thursday evening I will go to Relate with my partner.**

- **I will phone a dating agency on Wednesday.**

- **I will drink a maximum of 1 unit on Friday evening.**

CONTROLLED DRINKING DIARY

DAY OF WEEK

BEFORE
DRINKING GOAL 1:
Do you plan to drink?   Yes ☐   No ☐
How much do you plan to drink?
AFTER
Did you keep to your drinking plan?   Yes ☐   No ☐
If not, where did it go wrong?
How could you change it for the better?
What will you do the next time to make it work?

BEFORE

DRINKING GOAL 2:

Do you plan to drink?   Yes ☐   No ☐

How much do you plan to drink?

AFTER

Did you keep to your drinking plan?   Yes ☐   No ☐

If not, where did it go wrong?

How could you change it for the better?

What will you do the next time to make it work?

BEFORE

DRINKING GOAL 3:

Do you plan to drink?   Yes ☐   No ☐

How much do you plan to drink?

AFTER

Did you keep to your drinking plan?   Yes ☐   No ☐

If not, where did it go wrong?

How could you change it for the better?

What will you do the next time to make it work?

SO, IN SUMMARY:

- Identify the positive and negative aspects of drinking for you – I suggest you take at least a week over this during the time you are abstinent – write them down, and add to the list over the week.

- Identify your needs, using the list of the positive and negative aspects of drinking – take another week over this.

- Set goals – take another week to plan your goals.

- Try to put into practice the goals you have set yourself, and start to keep the drinking diary.

- Continue, by learning from failures and reviewing your drinking diary on a weekly basis. Praise yourself for your successes, and plan how you will turn this week's failures into next week's successes.

- If in time you find yourself starting to drink more and more heavily above healthy limits, but have not yet become physically addicted, then stop all drinking immediately if you can. Leave it a couple of months, and then try again to restart drinking, minimally at first, and increasing only as far as the World Health Organization guidelines.

- If after one year, you have not achieved your longterm goal of controlled drinking within healthy limits, re-consider whether this is a realistic alternative for you, or whether complete abstinence is the only way forward.

CONCLUSION

You should now be in a position to implement the best possible plan for you, in order to achieve abstinence and then control your drinking in the long term. Everything I have advised you to do in this book is based on the research which demonstrates the best way 'on average' for someone to stay dry. This fits the majority of people, but not everyone, and different elements of the overall plan will be better suited to some individuals than to others. To arrive at the best possible plan for you as an individual, and to limit those odds of relapsing to the minimum you will need individual advice about your particular situation. You can get this for free by telephoning the DryOutNow. com Immediate Response Service on **0800 160 1020.**

Now, at the point of reading this book you will most likely be in the 'planning phase' – getting ready for abstinence and the rest of your life without alcohol or with controlled drinking. Following is a check list of everything I advise you to have in place before you suddenly find yourself without a drink available to you. Continue straight to Part III, when you are satisfied that you have made all your decisions.

PREPARATION PHASE CHECKLIST	Tick
1 Make absolutely sure you are ready to progress with planning for abstinence. If you have any doubts re-read Chapter 3, telephone the **DryOutNow.com Immediate Response Service on 0800160 1020.**	
2 Arrange for some individual counselling to start as soon as possible – ideally before stopping drinking and continuing afterwards. Get details of your local counsellors by telephoning the **DryOutNow.com Immediate Response Service on 0800 160 1020**	
3 If you are up for it, attend some AA meetings – ideally before stopping drinking, and continuing afterwards. Get details of your AA meetings by telephoning the **DryOutNow.com Immediate Response Service on 0800 160 1020.**	
4 Make a decision about whether or not you wish to go to residential rehabilitation. If you wish to clarify this or get advice about the best residential rehabilitation units for you, telephone the **DryOutNow.com Immediate Response Service on 0800 160 1020.**	
5 Start to write your weekly diary. Make use of the various tables in this chapter to assess your needs and replace drinking with other activities that have the potential to lead to fulfilment.	
6 Speak to those you live with about drinking in the house after you have achieved abstinence.	
7 If you have difficulties at work, then make a plan about how you are going to minimise these difficulties. If you would like confidential advice around these issues, then phone the **DryOutNow.com Immediate Response Service on 0800 160 1020**.	
8 If you have difficulties in your relationship with your partner, telephone Relate on **0845 130 4016**, to book relationship counselling.	
9 Get expert medical advice about whether or not you can be prescribed medication to prevent relapse – either visit your GP or phone the **DryOutNow.com Immediate Response Service (0800 160 1020)** to get free telephone advice and/or details of your nearest private doctor who can advise on this.	

CHAPTER EIGHT

YOU ARE NOT PHYSICALLY ADDICTED
TO ALCOHOL AND YOU PLAN TO CEASE
DRINKING COMPLETELY. YOU DRINK
HEAVILY ON A REGULAR BASIS

If at any time you require urgent access to treatment, or need an
immediate response for any other reason, do not hesitate to telephone
the DryOutNow.com Immediate Response Service (IRS) on:

0800 160 1020
(8am-9pm, seven days weekly)

CHAPTER EIGHT

YOU ARE NOT PHYSICALLY ADDICTED TO ALCOHOL AND YOU PLAN TO CEASE DRINKING COMPLETELY. YOU DRINK HEAVILY ON A REGULAR BASIS

There are 3 stages though which you will need to progress, along your route to achieving and maintaining abstinence from alcohol.

PREPARATION PHASE

ACTION PHASE (sudden stop OR slow cut down OR detox)

ABSTINENCE PHASE

The 'action phase' involves actually stopping drinking, and in your case there are three possible routes of achieving this. You can either:

Stop drinking suddenly

OR

Cut your drinking down slowly but surely to zero

OR

Arrange for a medicated detoxification

In the case of someone who is physically addicted to alcohol, the only practical and safe means of ceasing alcohol use is to arrange for a medicated detoxification. As you are not physically addicted to alcohol, this is not necessary from a medical perspective. However, if you fail to achieve abstinence from alcohol by cutting down slowly, or stopping suddenly, then detox may still be the most practical route for you to achieve abstinence in the first place.

In the case of someone who is binge drinking, they will usually have periods of drinking nothing (or at least very little), and as such the only meaningful option is to prepare to cease drinking completely and keep it that way during one of these periods. Of course, there are binge drinkers who drink heavily on most days, and then especially heavily on other days (mixed pattern – see Chapter 10). People who drink in a pattern like this will have to aim for either a sudden cessation of alcohol use (assuming they are not physically addicted) or a detox. As a regular heavy drinker who is not physically addicted to alcohol, you also have a third

www.dryoutnow.com
IMMEDIATE RESPONSE SERVICE: CALL 0800 160 1020 NOW

option, that should be safe from a medical perspective, and also has at least a reasonable chance of success. This option is to cut down slowly, but surely.

The option of cutting down slowly but surely may seem to be the easiest and most comfortable of the possible alternatives; and this may well be the case. Even if you have tried this in the past without success, it may be possible to achieve if you follow the advice in this chapter, and work hard at it. If you have failed to reduce your drinking after several months of trying the 'slow but sure cut down' method, then you may wish to reconsider. Your options then would be to plan to stop suddenly, or to arrange detox. Both of these options may work where 'cut down' has failed, in particular because of the availability of medication (disulfiram (Antabuse)) which will protect you from relapsing to alcohol use, but can only be started when you have not had a drink for a period of several days.

So in summary, if you are undecided about which one of these three ways of stopping to drink you would prefer, then I suggest the following way forward:

1. Attempt to cut down slowly, but surely, using the advice in the first section of the 'Action Phase' below.

2. If you have made no progress after a period of several months, then read the preparation phase section of this chapter again, and plan to stop drinking suddenly.

3. If this fails after a couple of attempts, then you should probably consider a medicated detoxification, in order to successfully manage the transition from drinking to not drinking, and also so that you can receive extra advice and counselling during the period of detoxification.

More on all of this later…

First things first though – before implementing any of these options, you must prepare thoroughly.

THE PREPARATION PHASE.

The preparation phase mainly involves planning/booking the help you will need and getting ready to stay dry in the long term.

So what does preparing for staying dry involve? There are three things to do:

1. Prepare yourself psychologically, and also seek out professional psychological support (various forms of counselling).

2. Prepare yourself socially, and seek out the available professional support.

3. Consider the possibility of medication to help you stay dry.

TO PREPARE YOURSELF PSYCHOLOGICALLY:

a. Make absolutely sure that you are fully committed to doing this, and that you are 100% realistic about how hard it's going to be. Re-read Chapter Three to help you to do this.

b. Book some specialist individual (1-to-1) alcohol counselling as soon as possible to start BEFORE detox.

c. Consider attending some Alcoholics Anonymous (AA) meetings BEFORE detox.

Specialist 1-to-1 counselling can help in one of two ways: firstly by giving you the skills to avoid relapse to alcohol, and secondly by helping you to understand any underlying emotional issues which are leading you to drink heavily. For detailed information on how counselling works, go to:

....

• **www.dryoutnow.com – and download Section E of the professional treatment guidelines**

....

Specialist counselling is available from the NHS/charitable services for free. Or you can book with a private counsellor. In terms of the quality of service you will receive, there is probably little difference between NHS and private counsellors. However, in the NHS you may have to wait a long time (months or years in some cases) before you can access counselling. This varies between areas and depends on where you live. So, overall, I suggest contacting your local NHS/charitable specialist alcohol counselling service first. If the waiting time seems unsatisfactory, or other things don't seem right, then try the self-pay route.

....

• **For details of your local counselling services phone DryOutNow.com Immediate Response Service on 0800 160 1020.**

....

Private counsellors who specialise in alcohol problems are not so many in number. There are probably in the region of 400 in the country. Many problems that lead to heavy drinking are general in nature (e.g. stress, relationship difficulties etc.). So, if your nearest specialist alcohol counsellor is too far away, a general counsellor may still be of help to you:

SPECIALIST TELEPHONE Counselling

Alternatively, you can access specialist private alcohol counselling by telephone. You may wish to use this service if your nearest specialist counsellor is too far away, or if you would prefer the privacy and convenience of receiving counselling in your own home. This service is provided via DryOutNow.com. Call 0800 160 1020 to request details of the specialist counselling service.

Alcoholics Anonymous meetings: People are often nervous about attending these meetings, but those who attend have been shown to have better long term outcomes. There is no requirement to have stopped drinking in order to attend – just to be relatively sober at the time of attendance. There is no requirement to speak at a meeting – just to say 'pass' if asked to speak. The theme of the meetings is religious and requires a belief in a 'higher power', but there is no requirement to believe in God as such, or in any particular God. Some people think of the 'higher power' as the 'sober part' of themselves. There is no need to book in advance – just turn up to a meeting and sit alone just to observe at first. People will probably come to talk to you after the meeting – one of the main beliefs of Alcoholics Anonymous is that alcoholics need other alcoholics to help them to get sober – so people will be keen to help you. For more information on 'AA' meetings and how they work, go to:

- **www.DryOutNow.com and download section E of the professional treatment guidelines**

- **For details of your nearest Alcoholics Anonymous meetings phone the DryOutNow.com Immediate Response Service on 0800 160 1020.**

TO PREPARE YOURSELF SOCIALLY:

Firstly you should make a decision about whether you are going to stay in a residential rehabilitation unit for a period of time, or whether you plan to deal with this at home.

Residential rehabilitation. This is a very intense form of treatment, and many people will not wish to go through it, or just cannot for practical reasons. Residential rehabilitation involves staying in a specialist psychological unit for a period of time (durations of stay range from 4 weeks to 9 months). The advantages of a period of residential rehabilitation include i) an alcohol-free environment so there is minimal risk of relapse ii) the person is living and learning from others with alcohol problems iii) as a generalisation, this is the best form of counselling available, as it is so intense, and because people are confronted every time they try to deny they have a problem. Most people will decide this is not for them, especially if it is your first attempt at staying dry. However – bear this in mind – the evidence clearly shows that those who go to a residential rehabilitation unit and complete the course without leaving early, are more likely to remain dry from alcohol in the long term than those who do not go to residential rehabilitation. For more information on how residential rehabilitation works, open your browser and type in the following address:

- **www.dryoutnow.com – and download section E of the professional treatment guidelines**

Most residential rehabilitation units are not in the NHS. However, the NHS will sometimes pay for you to go to one if they think you need it. If you want to plan for a period of residential rehabilitation, and wish the NHS to pay for it, then **you will need to contact your local NHS Community Alcohol Team.** They will arrange for you to be assessed, and if they think you meet their criteria for paying, will then arrange for your admission. Waits may be long for assessment and admission (many months in some cases), but the treatment you get at the end of the day will be of the same quality as going privately to one of the cheaper units.

....

- **For details of your local NHS Community Alcohol Team phone the DryOutNow.com Immediate Response Service on 0800 160 1020**

....

- **If you would like details and free advice about admission to residential rehabilitation units, phone DryOutNow.com Immediate Response Service on 0800 160 1020.**

....

ACHIEVING AND MAINTAINING ABSTINENCE AT HOME:

If you plan to stay at home, probably the single most important part of planning for this is to write out **your weekly diary.**

There are two aims of the weekly diary. Firstly it should enable you to fill your time completely from the day you cease drinking, onwards. Your time should be full for the simple reason that this will leave you less time to think about alcohol. The nature of craving is such that if you give it a chance to build up, it will end up filling your head with repetitive thoughts: "Just one drink won't hurt – how could it? Just one drink won't hurt – how could it?" You must do your utmost to divert your attention from any such thoughts at all times. Being active and having to concentrate on a task of some kind is much more likely to result in the feeling of craving subsiding, than is sitting in a chair doing nothing. The vital element here is having to concentrate on something. This is very important if you are back in your usual routine, and not in specialist care.

Secondly it should provide you with the kind of activities that have a good chance of giving you some kind of sense of fulfillment or pleasure – that are rewarding. The aim here is to start to build up activities that will replace your need for alcohol in the longer term. As discussed in Chapter Three – don't expect anything to replace alcohol totally – there are very few activities that can result in your brain experiencing the reward that use of an addictive substance brings, and probably no healthy activities that produce that reward as easily and as immediately as does alcohol. You will need to re-think your objectives and search more for a sense of satisfaction and fulfillment in life than for the experience of immediate pleasure or immediate relief from unpleasant feelings which is delivered by alcohol.

You should think this through in great detail starting now. It must be ready to implement the very day you stop drinking. You should try to think of activities that are purposeful, and have the potential to lead to some sense of satisfaction; this will depend very much on personal taste. Some examples might include: socialising with non-drinking friends, reading, gym, gardening, walking. You may well have found that your appetite has been terrible for as long as you can remember; during detox it is very likely that your appetite will start to improve, and by the time you have finished detox you will be enjoying food again. As such, one activity you plan may involve food, such as developing your culinary skills. Or more simply, what about planning to sit down to lunch and dinner every day – you probably haven't done that in a while. (Don't worry about weight gain – alcohol is much more fattening than many foods). If it's possible to devote yourself to some kind of work project with a long-term goal in mind this could be useful.

In particular, if you are able to devote yourself to any kind of long-term project that involves dedication and a great deal of work, this might start to act to replace the psychological need for alcohol. (This kind of approach would be disagreed with by many professionals, especially those from a theoretical counselling background – they would argue that the addictive behaviour is merely being transferred from one object – drink – to another – work. However, if you are not considering residential rehabilitation, I think this is exactly what you should aim to do – replace the alcohol with healthy activity rather than destructive activity.)

In summary, you should create a diary ideally providing several options of activity for all times of every day of the week. This is not to say that you must or will complete every such activity – the important thing is that the diary is always there to turn to if you find yourself sitting and starting to dwell on the idea of having a drink. When that thought enters your head (and it will), you should immediately pick up the diary and implement one of the activities that are listed for that time of that day.

Following is an empty diary covering seven days of the week from 6 in the morning to 12 midnight. It also allows for you to enter two alternative activities for any two hour period. Now you may think that an 18 hour day is a long period of time to plan to fill, but bear the following in mind. The idea of the diary is not that you necessarily do every thing on it at the specified time, although you may choose to, and there will be no harm in this unless you get stressed thinking that you have to do everything on it. The idea of the diary IS that when you feel yourself starting to crave alcohol, you have something to occupy yourself with immediately, and which is already planned so that you can implement that activity immediately. If you wait until you start to crave before trying to think of something to occupy your mind, you may well not be able to do what you wish to immediately, and you may not even be able to concentrate effectively in order to think of something else to do. If you have your diary ready, you've got a great head-start over the craving.

Secondly, remember that your sleep may be disturbed for a period after cessation of drinking. It is thus important to have planned activities from early in the morning to late at night – again you will not necessarily carry out all these activities, but if you are awake for long hours, you must make sure you have something to do. Poor sleep is a major cause of relapse to drinking. Be prepared to have something to do if you cannot get to sleep – if you enjoyed reading in the past get some good books in. If you enjoyed film, get in a stack of videos or sign up for satellite channels (probably less expensive that your total alcohol costs). Poor sleep will improve as your brain gets used to a world free of alcohol – but you may have to be prepared to persevere for a good while.

Finally, if you are having difficulty thinking of the type of activities you should include in the diary the following questions may give you some ideas:

- What did you used to enjoy doing before alcohol started to replace other things in your life?

- What are the enjoyable things about drinking for you? Can you replace these with activities that result in a similar reward? (E.g. you may drink after work to relax; can you arrange for a massage on some nights as an alternative form of relaxation?) If you have completed the table in Chapter 3, Question 4, then this may help you at this point.

- What would you like to achieve from life? What would you need to do to achieve these things? Is there something you could dedicate yourself to achieving?

- How is your physical health? Could you improve it by eating well and healthily? Could you improve it by exercising regularly? What kinds of exercise would you enjoy?

- How is your social life? Do you have any non-drinking friends you could get in touch with? Can you think of a variety of social activities that don't involve drinking that you may enjoy?

- Do you need to search for work? What do you need to do to search for work?

	MONDAY	TUESDAY	WEDNESDAY	THURSDAY	FRIDAY	SATURDAY	SUNDAY
Activity 1: 6-8							
Activity 2: 6-8							
Activity 1: 8-10							
Activity 2: 8-10							
Activity 1: 10-12							
Activity 2: 10-12							
Activity 1: 12-2							
Activity 2: 12-2							
Activity 1: 2-4							
Activity 2: 2-4							
Activity 1: 4-6							
Activity 2: 4-6							
Activity 1: 6-8							
Activity 2: 6-8							
Activity 1: 8-10							
Activity 2: 8-10							
Activity 1: 10-12							
Activity 2: 10-12							
NIGHT-TIME 1							
NIGHT-TIME 2							

OTHER THINGS TO PREPARE FOR SOCIALLY:

1. ACCOMMODATION.

Is your accommodation situation stable and are you living with others who drink?

At the point of stopping drinking you will wish for the amount of stress in your life to be as minimal as is possible; stress is a major reason for starting to drink heavily and it is also a major reason for relapse. If you do not have permanent accommodation, or you are at risk of losing permanent accommodation for whatever reason, do your best to sort this out in advance of stopping drinking. Lack of a stable environment in which to re-start your life will greatly increase your chances of relapse.

If you are living with others who drink heavily, then you should very seriously consider either asking them to leave or leaving yourself. The odds of you managing to remain sober when there is someone living with you who drinks on a regular basis are very small indeed. Of course, if that person is also planning to seek help for an alcohol problem, then ideally this should be planned so that neither of you are living together at the time that one of you is still drinking.

This will probably mean either planning to cease drinking at the same time as each other, or at least one of you arranging for admission to a residential rehabilitation unit. If you live with other(s) who do drink, but do not drink heavily, you should see if they will agree to avoid drinking in the house. Ideally, the house should be completely empty of alcohol at the point you stop drinking, and it should stay that way for the foreseeable future.

2. WORK

Is your working situation stable? Are you unemployed? Are you facing some kind of disciplinary action? Are you on sick leave?

If you are in work and have no problems there, then this is usually the ideal situation. If you are on sick leave due to your alcohol problem, again you should try to arrange to return to work, possibly on a part-time basis initially. Of course, there is a fine balance here between too much stress at work, and too much time on your hands if you do not return to work. If work-related stress is a problem for you, then your return to work should be a graded one.

If you are facing some kind of disciplinary action at work as a direct or indirect result of your drinking, do your best to get this resolved before stopping drinking. Remember the aim is to limit the amount of stress you will have to deal with in those vital first few months when you may be battling to stay dry. Of course, there's a bit of a catch 22 about this; while you are drinking heavily you may not feel up

to sorting these kind of things out. Overall, do your best to sort out what you can before you stop drinking; what you cannot do, you just cannot do.

If you are unemployed at the moment, then make some initial plans for a return to work following cessation of drinking. Ideally, arrange for a return to employment as soon as you have stopped drinking. Of course this may well not be practical for you – if it is not, spend some time before you stop drinking thinking about what kinds of employment you may wish to get, and how you may go about searching for this. Build this into your weekly diary (see above).

3. RELATIONSHIPS

If you are in a relationship with a person who has a drinking problem, then the ideal is that you should both deal with this at the same time – it's highly unlikely to work for either of you if one person stops drinking while the other continues to drink. If you are unable to convince your partner of this, then if you are committed to aiming for a period of abstinence from alcohol, you should seriously consider whether or not to continue with the relationship. If you are in a relationship with someone who does not drink heavily, then you may well be experiencing problems in your relationship. You may find that your relationship improves dramatically when you cease drinking, but sometimes this will not be the case. Whatever, if you are having relationship problems at the moment, consider whether to book some relationship counselling with RELATE. This organization often has waiting lists of several months – if you book now, then the counselling will probably have started by the time you have ceased to drink. Here is the central contact telephone number for RELATE:**0845 130 4016**

MEDICATION THAT CAN HELP PREVENT RELAPSE TO DRINKING

There are two medications commonly use in the UK to help prevent a return to drinking.

1. Acamprosate, also known as Campral.

Acamprosate works to reduce the feeling of craving for alcohol. It is very effective for a few patients, quite effective for some, and simply doesn't work for others. As it is a relatively safe medicine to prescribe, in my NHS practice I prescribe it for most patients who decide to cease drinking. It is usually safe to continue to take it, even if you temporarily lapse to drinking again.

2. Disulfiram, also known as Antabuse.

Disulfiram blocks the complete breakdown of alcohol by the liver. This causes you to feel absolutely terrible if you have a drink. Disulfiram can work well for people who are likely to relapse to drinking on the spur of the moment – you simply can't

do this if you are taking disulfiram. However, it's no magic cure, asyou can decide to stop taking it, and within several days you are likely to be able to drink again without feeling ill. I prescribe disulfiram less often than acamprosate as it has the potential to cause some quite nasty side-effects in some people. In particular, it should generally be avoided in people who have a history of blood vessel problems (e.g. high blood pressure, history of stroke or heart attack), who have liver disease, or who have suffered serious psychiatric illness in the past. Also, disulfiram cannot be started until you have had several days without drinking – it cannot be used during the 'cut-down' phase, if this is the way that you choose to stop drinking.

For more information on both these medicines, open your browser and type in the following address: **www.dryoutnow.com** – click on the 'Treatment Guidelines' button on the left hand side of the page, and then download Section C of the Treatment Guidelines.

Of course, confidentiality may be an issue for you, and you will need to see a doctor to get these medicines prescribed. If you do not wish to see your GP about this, then the DryOutNow.com Immediate Response Service can give you details of your nearest private doctor who will be prepared to prescribe for you. Simply telephone 0800 160 1020 and ask for details of your nearest private doctor who specialises in addiction problems or go to **www.dryoutnow.com**

THE ACTION PHASE

OPTION 1: SLOW, BUT SURE CUT DOWN

To prepare to cut down your drinking slowly but surely to zero, there are four stages to go through:

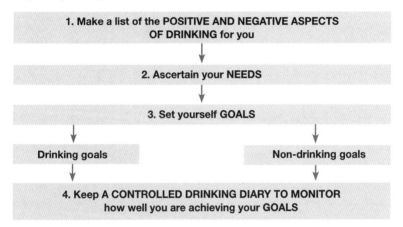

1. Make a list of the POSITIVE AND NEGATIVE ASPECTS OF DRINKING for you

↓

2. Ascertain your NEEDS

↓

3. Set yourself GOALS

↓   ↓

Drinking goals   **Non-drinking goals**

↓   ↓

4. Keep A CONTROLLED DRINKING DIARY TO MONITOR how well you are achieving your GOALS

1. MAKE A LIST OF THE POSITIVE AND NEGATIVE ASPECTS OF DRINKING FOR YOU

Making a list of the things you find both helpful and unhelpful about drinking, is the starting point of this process. You will find that if you write this list, you will be able to see quite clearly what you need in your life, that at the present time you are trying to get from alcohol. If you made these lists when you read Chapter Three, then refer back to them now.

Otherwise, continue right here. I've given some examples of the positive and negative reasons for drinking that people commonly write down. Cross these out if they don't apply to you, and then spend plenty of time thinking about the good and bad aspects of drinking for you – add to the list and make it your own.

Let's start by considering the possible reasons that you find drinking an enjoyable or helpful activity. Tick off those things on this list that apply to you, and add items of your own as you think of them. If you wish to record this for the future, I have included an empty table for you in the appendix of this book.

POSITIVE THINGS ABOUT DRINKING FOR YOU:

		Tick here
	Physical Health Reasons	
1	I enjoy the feeling of drinking and getting drunk.	
2	Drinking stops me getting withdrawal symptoms.	
3	I have trouble getting to sleep – without a drink I cannot sleep well.	
	Psychological Reasons	
4	I tend to get depressed and drinking improves my mood.	
5	Drinking makes me less anxious.	
6	I tend to get a bit paranoid about going out. If I have a drink I can get out the house without worrying.	
7	I'm usually tense and stressed - drinking helps me to relax.	
	Social Reasons	
8	I have a much better time going out if I have a drink.	
9	I can't imagine going out without having a drink.	
10	I tend to be anxious in the company of other people; when I have a drink inside me I can talk more easily and get on with people better.	
11	I've become a bit of a loner over the years - the only time I ever get into a conversation is at the pub.	
	PUT YOUR OWN REASONS in the spaces below:	

NEGATIVE THINGS ABOUT DRINKING FOR YOU:

		Tick here
	Physical Health Reasons	
1	I'm feeling generally un-well most of the time.	
2	I never eat anything these days.	
3	I'm increasingly worried that I'm permanently damaging my physical health.	
4	I wake up early in the morning covered in sweat.	
	Psychological Reasons	
5	I feel horribly depressed when I wake up in the morning after drinking.	
6	My memory seems terrible these days.	
7	I seem so much more nervous than I used to be.	
8	I'm sick and tired of having this thing called alcohol in control of me. I want to get back in control of myself.	
	Social Reasons	
9	I want to be a better parent to my children.	
10	My relationship is a mess and I know it's because of my drinking.	
11	I've just been arrested for my second drink-drive offence – I might go to prison this time – I know I've got to do something about it.	
12	I'm finding it difficult to get into work on time – someone is going to say something soon.	
13	Of late my temper has got increasingly worse. I'm worried what I might do next time someone annoys me.	
	PUT YOUR OWN REASONS in the spaces below:	

2. ASCERTAIN YOUR NEEDS

When you have completed making the two lists above, you will be in a position to write down what your needs are – and in particular those needs that you will need to meet if you are to successfully achieve abstinence from alcohol. Use the table below to do this. By writing in a positive or negative reason for drinking, you should then be able to work out what you need to do to resolve that – write it down in the space below the reason for drinking. I've started by giving you a few examples. If you run out of space, I have included a blank table for you in the appendix.

Reason	I enjoy the feeling of drinking and getting drunk.
NEED	I need to have enjoyable feelings.
Reason	I have trouble getting to sleep – without a drink I cannot sleep well.
NEED	I need to sleep well.
Reason	I'm usually tense and stressed - drinking helps me to relax.
NEED	I need to relax.
Reason	I never eat anything these days
NEED	I need to eat well
Reason	I feel horribly depressed when I wake up in the morning after drinking.
NEED	I need to improve my mood
Reason	My relationship is a mess and I know it's because of my drinking.
NEED	I need to improve my relationship
Reason	
NEED	
Reason	
NEED	
Reason	
NEED	
Reason	
NEED	
Reason	
NEED	

3. SET YOURSELF GOALS

You should set yourself two types of goals – 'drinking goals' and 'non-drinking goals'. 'Non-drinking goals' do not necessarily mean that you do not drink when you are trying to achieve these goals; it's just that they are not directly about drinking. E.g., a 'drinking goal' might be to drink 2 units and no more on a particular evening. A 'non-drinking goal' might be to cook a meal.

Your drinking goals will be what you plan to drink (how many units) on a particular day of the week. I advise you to take it slowly at first – do not plan to cut-down immediately to drinking 21 units weekly. Gradually get to these levels over a period of months.

Your 'non-drinking' goals will involve meeting the needs you have made a list of above. Now if you manage to achieve maintained abstinence from alcohol, some of these things will automatically sort themselves out for themselves (e.g. improved appetite). If you are lucky, other things like your relationship and your mood will also improve as a direct result of reduced drinking. However, many of the reasons you have used alcohol may have been there before you ever started drinking – these problems will not be resolved merely by a cessation of drinking (e.g. you may have started drinking heavily because of stress at work, or because your relationship was not working out). Equally, some of the problems caused by drinking may have become so difficult that they will take more than just stopping drinking to sort them out. These will need to be addressed by other means. If you fail to address them, they will put you at risk of a return to heavy drinking in due course.

And when you set your non-drinking goals in order to resolve these problems, you will also need to take into account your drinking goals.

Let's consider an example.

Example 'need': 'I need to have enjoyable feelings'

When considering how to achieve this without getting drunk, you will need to get away from the idea (which may have become a dominant one for you), that the only way you can experience pleasure is by drinking. You will need to think of other means of experiencing pleasure without drinking. Having done this, you will need to write these things down in the form of 'goals'. Here are some common themes that come out of this exercise when I run it by people in my clinic: socialising, sex and eating. Many people who have developed an alcohol problem will have forgotten how to socialise without the use of alcohol, will have poor sex lives (when they may well have had excellent sex lives in the past) and currently eat very little and are not particularly bothered by food (despite the fact that they used to enjoy food). Focus on similar things for you, and turn them into goals:

- **Goal – I will arrange to socialise with non-drinking friends on one evening this week.**

....

- **Goal – I will talk to my partner about our sex life on one evening this week.**

....

- **Goal – I will cook a lovely meal one night this week.**

....

Of vital importance is to link these goals up with your 'drinking goals'. Say this is your first week trying to cut down your alcohol consumption, and you have decided to drink on six nights of the week, and have one night without drinking. How will you tie this up with your 'non-drinking goals'. Here's an example of how you might do that:

Firstly, on the evening that you go out with non-drinking friends, there will be no need to drink alcohol – that could be your night completely without alcohol.

Secondly, on the night you decide to talk to your partner about your sex life, you may decide to make it a touch more relaxing and even romantic by opening a bottle of wine – why not have six units on that night? (Be prepared to re-cork the bottle if your partner does not drink).

Thirdly, why not have two glasses of wine on the night you cook the meal?

By doing things in such a manner, you may manage to **slightly enhance** the activities you have planned by the healthy, controlled use of alcohol. And, of course, that must be your aim if you are to successfully reduce your drinking without relapsing back to regular heavy drinking. **Your drinking should never again be about getting drunk, or forgetting unpleasant feelings.**

It must only be about slightly enhancing the pleasures you get from non-drinking activities. If you ever allow the idea of the main plan for the evening being about having a drink, then you will surely relapse to heavy, uncontrolled drinking again in good time.

Before you set your goals, there are some other important things to take into account:

Goals must be **realistic;** e.g. do not set a goal to stop drinking tomorrow; do not plan to run The Marathon; do not plan to read The Lord of the Rings in one week.

Goals must be **specific** and measurable; e.g. I will drink 2 units less of alcohol than usual on one day this week; I will go to the pub one time less than usual this week; I will see non-drinking friends once this week.

Goals must be **short-term** e.g. over the next week, or next day. While it is important to have a long-term objective in mind, this will not be reached overnight; if you are to achieve control over yourself, you must set short-term goals, and do your utmost to stick to them.

To achieve this, break your long-term goals down into smaller steps; e.g. as you plan to reduce your drinking to 0 units per week in due course, then plan to reduce drinking by 2 units on one day weekly, then every other day, then every day. Once you have achieved this, think about cutting down by another 2 units on one day weekly etc.etc..

Decide on the goals yourself – allow others to advise you, but make the decisions for yourself.

FINALLY: LEARN FROM YOUR FAILURES:

Doubtless, you will not achieve all your goals every day – that would not be human. The important thing is to question why you failed to achieve a particular goal, and then re-plan to make the goal more realistic. You should dwell on the positive more realistic plan and not berate yourself for failure. E.g.

- You planned to drink 2 glasses of wine withyour friends at a pub on Wednesday evening but ended up drinking 6 glasses:

- Why did this happen? Answer: you were offered another drink after the 2 glasses and did not find it in yourself to refuse.

- **Possible solutions:**

  - at the beginning of the next evening out, ask your friends not to offer you another drink after you have drunk two; OR

  - get up and leave half-way through the second drink, so that your friends are not given an opportunity to offer you another; OR

  - drink non-alcoholic drinks for the first half of the evening, and only start to drink alcohol one hour before closing time.

Repeat this re-planning process, as often as you feel like it; but at least once weekly. Set your goals for the next week and keep a 'drinking diary' (see below). Fill this in every day before your memory fades, and then review it weekly. This will help you pick up patterns that you might otherwise miss, e.g. a tendency to drink more if you had an argument that day; a tendency to drink less if you went walking that day etc. etc.

So here are some examples of a mixture of drinking and other goals:

Examples of goals include:

- **I will see my drinking friends once less each week at first.**

- **I will see my non-drinking friends at least once this week.**

- **I will spend one evening reading this week, and drink nothing.**

- **I will drink 2 units less than usual on Monday this week.**

- **I will spend all Tuesday looking at jobs advertised in the paper.**

- **On Thursday evening I will go to Relate with my partner.**

- **I will phone a dating agency on Wednesday.**

- **I will drink 2 units less on Friday evening.**

CONTROLED DRINKING DIARY

DAY OF THE WEEK

BEFORE
DRINKING GOAL 1:
Do you plan to drink?　　　　　Yes ☐　　No ☐
How much do you plan to drink?
AFTER
Did you keep to your drinking plan?　Yes ☐　　No ☐
If not, where did it go wrong?
How could you change it for the better?
What will you do the next time to make it work?

BEFORE
DRINKING GOAL 2:
Do you plan to drink? Yes ☐ No ☐
How much do you plan to drink?
AFTER
Did you keep to your drinking plan? Yes ☐ No ☐
If not, where did it go wrong?
How could you change it for the better?
What will you do the next time to make it work?

BEFORE
DRINKING GOAL 3:
Do you plan to drink? Yes ☐ No ☐
How much do you plan to drink?
AFTER
Did you keep to your drinking plan? Yes ☐ No ☐
If not, where did it go wrong?
How could you change it for the better?
What will you do the next time to make it work?

SO, IN SUMMARY:

- Identify the positive and negative aspects of drinking for you – I suggest you take at least a week over this – write them down, and add to the list over the week.

- Identify your needs, using the list of the positive and negative aspects of drinking – take another week over this.

- Set goals – take another week to plan your goals.

- Try to put into practice the goals you have set yourself, and start to keep the drinking diary.

- Continue, by learning from failures and reviewing your drinking diary on a weekly basis. Praise yourself for your successes, and plan how you will turn this week's failures into next week's successes.

- If after one year, you have not achieved your long-term goal of abstinence, consider whether another means (sudden stop or detox) of achieving abstinence is the only way forward, or whether you might benefit from a period of residential rehabilitation.

OPTION 2: STOPPING SUDDENLY:

If you decide to stop drinking suddenly, you should only implement this when:

- **You have prepared thoroughly as described above in 'the preparation phase'**

- **At a time of minimal stress**

BUT BEWARE – there is not likely to be any time in your life when there is no stress whatsoever. In planning the right time to stop drinking, you should have minimised the possibility of stress to lead to an immediate relapse to uncontrolled drinking; but you will never get rid of it completely.

Assuming you are not physically addicted to alcohol, then this should not lead to any permanent damage if you cease drinking suddenly – overnight. If you have any doubt over whether or not you are physically addicted to alcohol, then please re-read Chapter One of this book, or get individual advice by **phoning the DryOutNow.com Immediate Response Service on 0800 160 1020 or go to www.dryoutnow.com – click on 'Get Free Advice' on the left hand side of the page and send the email to get advice.**

OPTION 3: DETOXIFICATION

Most doctors will only consider detoxification necessary if you are physically addicted to alcohol. And they are right – from a medical perspective (i.e. making sure you remain well whilst giving up drinking). If you are physically addicted to alcohol, then on cessation of alcohol use you will experience, alcohol withdrawal symptoms such as tremor, sweating, nausea, vomiting, raised blood pressure and raised pulse. In severe alcohol withdrawal you may experience epileptic seizures, hallucinations, delusions and disorientation in time and place. In some cases, severe alcohol withdrawal can be fatal, and if not fatal may lead to permanent brain damage. All the symptoms of alcohol withdrawal are caused by what doctors call 'hyper-excitability of the central nervous system' - in other words the brain becomes massively overactive.

If you are not physically addicted to alcohol, none of these withdrawal effects should occur, and from a medical perspective, it is safe to cease drinking without detoxification. However, many people who attempt to cut their drinking down slowly to zero fail to achieve this, and many who make a plan to stop drinking suddenly, find themselves continuing to drink the next day, or within several days. If this is so in your case then you may wish to consider detoxification as a comfortable and practical way forward to achieving abstinence in the first place.

Equally, detoxification in a specialist unit offers more than just the medical side of things. There are three main reasons for this:

1. You will be in an alcohol-free environment, away from the temptation of readily available alcohol.

2. You will receive daily counselling from specialist alcohol counsellors, and get to witness and understand the difficulties others have had with alcohol.

3. You may be prescribed some medication on a short-term basis to keep you relaxed and to help you sleep – to take the edge of the first several days without alcohol.

All these things, may just make the difference for you this time around.

If you would like to know more about the technical side of alcohol detox, go to:

www.dryoutnow.com – click on the 'Treatment Guidelines' button on the left hand side of the page, and then download Section C of the Treatment Guidelines.

When you are planning detox there are several decisions that need to be made:

1. *Have you thought about the options of where detox may take place (home, psychiatric ward, hospital medical ward, specialist detoxification unit)?*

2. *Are you looking for a free detox or a self-pay service?*

3. *Have you decided whether or not you wish to continue to residential rehabilitation after detox?*

1. WHERE IS THE BEST PLACE FOR THE DETOX TO TAKE PLACE?

A. HOME

Detox at home may sound more appealing than having to be admitted to a hospital of some kind. However, it is a less safe and less effective means of undergoing detoxification on average. Approximately 50% of people who undergo detoxification at home will manage to complete the detox without starting to drink again, while over 90% will complete detoxification when admitted to a specialist detoxification unit. Equally, if anything does go wrong during detox, then being in hospital should mean that you get the right care immediately, whereas you may wait hours at home. In particular, home detox is generally agreed to be the wrong option if you have a history of epileptic fits when coming off alcohol, if you suffer from any serious medical condition, if you suffer from any serious psychiatric illness or feel suicidal, if you have a tendency to get disorientated, if you are unable to arrange for another adult to be with you at home for the detox, or if you live with others who drink.

B. PSYCHIATRIC WARD

Sometimes alcohol detox is arranged to take place on a psychiatric ward. From a doctor's perspective, the main problem here is that staff on psychiatric wards often have less experience of dealing with alcohol detoxification, than do those in a specialist unit. The psychological aspect of detoxification (preparing you to deal with life without drinking when you leave) is less likely to be addressed, and you are probably less likely overall to complete the detoxification without returning to drinking. Equally, you may not feel comfortable with the idea of admission to a psychiatric ward in view of the fact that most other patients there will be suffering from serious psychiatric illnesses.

C. HOSPITAL MEDICAL WARD

If you are seriously physically ill as a result of your drinking (e.g. jaundiced, having fits, bleeding from the rectum or vomiting blood, having hallucinations or delusions) or have another serious illness such as poorly controlled diabetes or active pancreatitis, then a hospital medical ward is probably the best place to receive detoxification. The reason I say this, is that if you are this ill, the absolute priority must be to place you where you will be provided with immediate attention from a doctor who is used to dealing with emergencies if things go wrong. There is a fine judgement to be made here, because you are unlikely to get the best overall treatment as far as completing the detox and staying dry afterwards. Some specialist detox units are very capable of dealing with all the common emergencies very effectively, and they will also be able to offer the 'full package' aimed at your drinking problem. On a hospital medical ward, you will probably be treated as just another patient who has to be kept alive until they are discharged.

D. SPECIALIST DETOX UNIT

Admission to a specialist unit for your detox is clearly the ideal in most cases. Such units have the most expertise in getting you through detox comfortably, and have the best chances of getting you through detox without relapsing to alcohol use before completion of the detox. Unless you are very ill indeed, they should also offer the safest option overall for detox. In addition to this, you will receive specialist counselling as part of the detox 'package'. This should improve your chances of staying dry after detox considerably, and unless you are seriously physically ill, that should be your main consideration. Remember that only around 25% of people who have detoxed from alcohol are still dry after one year. Any treatment you can get that will improve your chances of staying dry you should grab and soak up. Your main consideration must be to aim at that – 'The detox is the easy bit, staying dry is much harder.'

2. ARE YOU LOOKING FOR A FREE DETOX OR A SELF-PAY SERVICE?

2A. FREE ALCOHOL DETOXIFICATION

This can often be accessed through the NHS. If you wish to proceed along this route, the starting place is usually your local 'Community Alcohol Team' (sometimes 'Community Drug and Alcohol Team').

For details of your local Community Alcohol Team phone the DryOutNow. com Immediate Response Service on 0800 160 1020

Usually these days you can book in direct with your community alcohol team by giving them a call on the above number. However, in some cases they may require you to go to your GP first in order to be referred to them by your GP. When you have either referred yourself or been referred by your GP, you will be given an appointment for an assessment with the alcohol team. They will formulate a plan with you, which should include a detoxification if you are assessed as needing one. That's the theory and in some cases it will work exactly like this. In some cases you will get an excellent service from the NHS. In other cases you will not – it all depends on where you live. If you are lucky enough to live in an area where the treatment of alcoholism has been well funded over the last few years, then you are likely to experience few problems. However, the funding for alcohol treatment has been very poor in some areas for many years, and in some cases has got even worse over the last several years, as money has been diverted to treating illicit drug problems rather than alcohol problems. This is what is known as the 'postcode lottery'. There is no way of my predicting whether you will be lucky with the NHS or not. The problems you may experience are:

....

- **Long waits to be seen in the first place (many months).**

....

- **Long waits to access detoxification after you have been assessed (months to years).**

....

- **No detoxification available in practice whatsoever.**

....

- **Detoxification only available at home, (see above – home detoxification).**

....

- **Detoxification only available in the local psychiatric ward.**

....

Now, as I stated above, in some areas you will get an excellent service by going the NHS route – the only way to find out if this applies to you, is to give it a try.

2B. SELF-PAY ALCOHOL DETOX.

The large majority of self-pay detox units are dedicated, specialist units. In such units, you should receive good quality medical care and psychological support aimed at keeping you dry after completion of the detox.

....

- **The quality of the accommodation.**

....

- **The quality of the medical cover.**

....

- **How long you are prepared to wait.**

....

As a generalisation, the more you pay the better hotel services you will receive, and the quicker you will be admitted. The degree of medical cover in self-pay units ranges from non-specialist GPs available for telephone advice and to attend in an emergency only, to specialist consultants seeing you on a daily basis with a ward doctor on-site to attend to you 24 hours/day. The more expensive units will tend to have invested more in their medical cover than the less expensive units.

Deciding on the best self-pay unit to use depends on how ill you are, how long you are prepared to wait and what your needs are in terms of accommodation. Probably you will want to minimise the cost that you pay whilst making sure you get the best possible treatment for you. If you choose to seek detoxification privately, then the **DryOutNow.com Immediate Response Service** will arrange this for you. This is a free service and it is guaranteed that you will pay no more by using the booking service than by booking direct with the detox unit. In fact in some cases you will **pay less by booking through DryOutNow.com. DryOutNow. com** have a detailed knowledge of all the detox units in the UK and the kind of service they provide. Taking into account your needs, they will find you the cheapest detox suitable for you and the best detox suitable for you (safest and highest rates of completion). Some people will not wish to be referred by their GP, and for detox units that require a referral from a doctor, one of their doctors will be available to make that referral for you.

....

- **For details of detoxification units phone the DryOutNow.com Immediate Response Service on 0800 160 1020.**

....

3. HAVE YOU DECIDED WHETHER OR NOT YOU WISH TO CONTINUE TO RESIDENTIAL REHABILITATION AFTER DETOX?

Most specialist detoxification units will offer the option of staying on after completion of detoxification for a period of residential rehabilitation. However, there are also many residential rehabilitation units that do not provide a medical detox, and you may wish to consider attending one of these rather than staying on at the detox unit. Although it may seem the simplest option to stay on for residential rehabilitation at the same place you get detoxed, there are two reasons that you may wish to think otherwise: cost and quality. The unit that provides you with the best detox, may well not be the unit that offers the best rehabilitation for the price that you can afford.

The reason it is important to think about this now is that it is usually considered very important to continue straight to residential rehabilitation from detox. If you are planning a period of residential rehabilitation you will have to think about this well before admission for detox. If it is not the best option for you to stay at your detox unit for rehabilitation, then you will have to book admission to the 'rehab' unit before admission for detox.

If you have decided you would like to consider a period of residential rehabilitation to follow detox, then I advise you to discuss this with an expert at the DryOutNow. com Immediate Response Service making use of their free telephone advice service. They have details of all the UK residential rehabilitation units, and can help you plan in the most cost-effective way given your particular needs. Phone the DryOutNow.com Immediate Response Service on 0800 160 1020.

THE ABSTINENCE PHASE.

You have arrived! You've stopped drinking successfully, and are ready to face a new world – a world without alcohol. Now this is where the serious work begins – the work of staying dry for the next period of months at least. If you've implemented most of the steps I outlined in the 'preparation phase' then you will have a head start over all the new challenges that are going to face you:

....

• **Craving for alcohol**

....

• **Sleeplessness**

....

• **Agitation**

....

• **Boredom**

....

• **NO IMMEDIATE SOLUTION TO ALL THESE THINGS**

....

On the other side of the coin, you are likely to be:

- **Feeling well for the first time in a long time**

- **Eating well**

- **Feeling in a better mood if you have been depressed**

- **Feeling more confident in yourself, especially if you suffered with paranoia and anxiety while you were drinking**

However, you must remember this – most of the advantages of giving up drinking are long term advantages; they will not be apparent to you immediately, and they will require a sustained period of abstinence from alcohol to occur:

- **Improved relationships with the important people in your life**

- **Building new relationships with the future important people in your life**

- **Improved performance at work**

- **Finding and holding down employment if you are unemployed**

- **Enjoyment of leisure activities you could never have enjoyed while you were drinking**

- **Improved financial situation**

- **A sense of pride in yourself that had been forgotten during years of heavy drinking**

Maintaining abstinence will bring you rewards whether these are delivered by living longer, feeling better in yourself and with yourself, or having better relationships with others. All of these things can disappear in a moment if you relapse, and most of the truly rewarding things take months and years to start to occur. Only 25% of people who have ceased heavy drinking are still dry at the end of one year. How are you going to maximise your chances of being one of these 25%? For the first year (the highest risk time for relapse) you must implement your plan, and stick to it as much as is feasible for you. Let's re-cap:

1. If you have decided on a course of residential rehabilitation then you will learn more there about staying dry than anything I can tell you in this book. But remember this – the evidence shows that it is those that complete the course of rehabilitation that have the best chances of staying dry in the long term. Many people find residential rehabilitation hard going – it's not meant to be easy – it is

meant to prepare you for a life without alcohol. As it is very hard work, many people leave before they have completed the course. If you commit yourself to a period of residential rehabilitation, then do your utmost to stay the course – if you don't, then you have probably wasted your time.

2. If you are not carrying on to residential rehabilitation:

- Make sure you have some individual counselling in place to start immediately following cessation of drinking (ideally you will have attended at least several sessions of counselling before cessation of alcohol use). You should aim to continue with counselling on a weekly basis for the first year of abstinence.

- If you are up for AA meetings, then attend them as often as you can – ideally daily.

- See if you can be prescribed Campral (acamprosate) and/or Antabuse (disulfiram) – continue these medications for between six months and one year after detox. You have to stop taking Antabuse if you start drinking again, but you can continue to take Campral – this may work to limit your chances of starting to drink again at harmful levels.

- Use your weekly activity diary to keep your time full with planned activity. Make slow but sure progress with long term plans and objectives. In particular, always get active and focus on an activity that involves concentration if you start to crave for alcohol.

- Identify the positive and negative aspects of drinking for you – I suggest you take at least a week over this during the time you are abstinent – write them down, and add to the list over the week.

- Identify your needs, using the list of the positive and negative aspects of drinking – take another week over this.

- Set goals – take another week to plan your goals.

- Try to put into practice the goals you have set yourself, and start to keep the drinking diary.

- Continue, by learning from failures and reviewing your drinking diary on a weekly basis. Praise yourself for your successes, and plan how you will turn this week's failures into next week's successes.

- Whenever you experience craving, after it has calmed down, take some time to think how you have handled it without drinking, and how you will handle it more easily the next time it occurs. Think about the situation or feeling that triggered the craving – can you avoid this situation in the future? What did you do that enabled you to avoid drinking (e.g. walked away from the person that offered you a drink; started to do something you had planned in the diary)? Would there be a better way to deal with this same situation in the future that would make you even less likely to have a drink? If you can think of something, remember it and plan to behave in this way the next time you encounter a similar situation.

• Use telephone advice from the DryOutNow.com Immediate Response Service (0800 160 1020)

• If after one year, you have not achieved your goal of abstinence, reconsider the means by which you at trying to stop drinking (slow cut down or sudden stop or detox), and try an alternative method.

CONCLUSION

You should now be in a position to implement the best possible plan for you, in order to achieve abstinence in the long term. Everything I have advised you to do in this book is based on the research which demonstrates the best way 'on average' for someone to stay dry. This fits the majority of people, but not everyone, and different elements of the overall plan will be better suited to some individuals than to others. To arrive at the best possible plan for you as an individual, and to limit those odds of relapsing to the minimum you will need individual advice about your particular situation.

Phone the DryOutNow.com Immediate Response Service on 0800 160 1020

Now, at the point of reading this book you will most likely be in the 'planning phase' – getting ready for abstinence and the rest of your life without alcohol. Following is a check list of everything I advise you to have in place before you suddenly find yourself without a drink available to you. Continue straight to Part III, when you are satisfied that you have made all your decisions

PREPARATION PHASE CHECKLIST	Tick
1 Make absolutely sure you are ready to progress with planning for abstinence. If you have any doubts re-read Chapter 3, telephone the **DryOutNow.com Immediate Response Service on 0800 160 1020**	....
2 Arrange for some individual counselling to start as soon as possible – ideally before stopping drinking and continuing afterwards. Get details of your local counsellors by telephoning the **DryOutNow.com Immediate Response Service on 0800 160 1020**	....
3 If you are up for it, attend some AA meetings – ideally before stopping drinking, and continuing afterwards. Get details of your AA meetings by telephoning the **DryOutNow.com Immediate Response Service on 0800 160 1020**	....
4 Make a decision about whether or not you wish to go to residential rehabilitation. If you wish to clarify this or get advice about the best residential rehabilitation units for you, telephone the **DryOutNow.com Immediate Response Service on 0800 160 1020.**	....
5 Make a decision about how you are going to cease drinking – slow but sure cut-down, sudden stop or detox.	....
6 If you are unsure, then either start with an attempt at slow but sure cut down, or telephone the **DryOutNow.com Immediate Response Service on 0800 160 1020 to discuss the options.**	....
7 If you choose detoxification and are considering the self-pay option, telephone the **DryOutNow.com Immediate Response Service (0800 160 1020)** to get advice on the unit that will best suit your needs and to make use of the free booking, medical advice and support service. In most circumstances you should leave a period of weeks before admission for detox, in order to complete your planning	....
8 Start to write your weekly activity diary. Make use of the various tables in this chapter to assess your needs and replace drinking with other activities that have the potential to lead to fulfillment.	....
9 Speak to those you live with about drinking in the house while you are trying to cut down your drinking and after you have achieved abstinence.	....

www.dryoutnow.com
IMMEDIATE RESPONSE SERVICE: CALL 0800 160 1020 NOW

PREPARATION PHASE CHECKLIST	Tick
10 If you have difficulties at work, then make a plan about how you are going to minimise these difficulties. If you would like confidential advice around these issues, then phone the **DryOutNow.com Immediate Response Service on 0800 160 1020.**	
11 If you have difficulties in your relationship with your partner, telephone Relate on **0845 130 4016**, to book relationship counselling.	
12 Get expert medical advice about whether or not you can be prescribed medication to prevent relapse – either visit your GP or phone the **DryOutNow.com Immediate Response Service (0800 160 1020)** to get free telephone advice and/or details of your nearest private doctor who can advise on this.	

CHAPTER NINE

YOU ARE NOT PHYSICALLY ADDICTED TO
ALCOHOL AND YOU PLAN TO CONTINUE
TO DRINK WITHIN HEALTHY LIMITS
YOU DRINK HEAVILY ON A REGULAR BASIS

If at any time you require urgent access to treatment, or need an
immediate response for any other reason, do not hesitate to telephone
the DryOutNow.com Immediate Response Service (IRS) on:

0800 160 1020
(8am-9pm, seven days weekly)

CHAPTER NINE

YOU ARE NOT PHYSICALLY ADDICTED TO ALCOHOL AND YOU PLAN TO CONTINUE TO DRINK WITHIN HEALTHY LIMITS. YOU DRINK HEAVILY ON A REGULAR BASIS

There are 3 stages though which you will need to progress, along your route to achieving and maintaining controlled drinking.

PREPARATION PHASE
▼

ACTION PHASE
▼

CONTROLLED DRINKING PHASE

THE PREPARATION PHASE

The preparation phase mainly involves planning/booking the help you will need and getting ready to start to control your drinking in the long term.

So what does preparing for controlled drinking involve? There are three things to do:

1. *Prepare yourself psychologically, and also seek out professional psychological support (various forms of counselling).*

2. *Prepare yourself socially, and seek out the available professional support.*

3. *Consider the possibility of medication to help you control your drinking.*

TO PREPARE YOURSELF PSYCHOLOGICALLY:

a. Make absolutely sure that you are fully committed to doing this, and that you are 100% realistic about how hard it's going to be. Re-read Chapter Three to help you to do this.

b. Book some specialist individual (1-to-1) alcohol counselling as soon as possible to start BEFORE you start to cut down drinking.

c. Consider attending some Alcoholics Anonymous (AA) meetings before you start to cut down drinking.

Specialist 1-to-1 counselling can help in one of two ways: firstly by giving you the skills to avoid relapse to heavy alcohol use, and secondly by helping you to understand any underlying emotional issues which are leading you to drink heavily. For detailed information on how counselling works, go to:

....

- **www.dryoutnow.com – and download Section E of the professional treatment guidelines.**

....

Specialist counselling is available from the NHS/charitable services for free. Or you can book with a private counsellor. In terms of the quality of service you will receive, there is probably little difference between NHS and private counsellors. However, in the NHS you may have to wait a long time (months or years in some cases) before you can access counselling. This varies between areas and depends on where you live. So, overall, I suggest contacting your local NHS/charitable specialist alcohol counselling service first. If the waiting time seems unsatisfactory, or other things don't seem right, then try the self-pay route.

....

- **For details of your local counselling services phone DryOutNow.com Immediate Response Service on 0800 160 1020.**

....

Private counsellors who specialise in alcohol problems are not so many in number. There are probably in the region of 400 in the country. If your nearest counsellor seems too far away, then a general counsellor may still be able to help. Many problems that lead to heavy drinking are general in nature (e.g. stress, relationship difficulties etc.) and a general counsellor will still be able to help with these. So, if your nearest specialist alcohol counsellor is too far away, a general counsellor may still be of help to you:

....

- **For details of your nearest private general counsellors phone the DryOutNow.com Immediate Response Service on 0800 160 1020.**

....

SPECIALIST TELEPHONE Counselling

Alternatively, you can access specialist private alcohol counselling by telephone. You may wish to use this service if your nearest specialist counsellor is too far away, or if you would prefer the privacy and convenience of receiving counselling in your own home. This service is provided via DryOutNow.com. Call 0800 160 1020 to request details of the specialist telephone counselling service.

Alcoholics Anonymous meetings: People are often nervous about attending these meetings, but those who attend have been shown to have **better long term outcomes.** There is no requirement to have stopped drinking in order to attend – just to be relatively sober at the time of attendance. There is no requirement to speak at a meeting – just to say 'pass' if asked to speak. The theme of the meetings is religious and requires a belief in a 'higher power', but there is no requirement to believe in God as such, or in any particular God. Some people think of the 'higher power' as the 'sober part' of themselves. There is no need to book in advance – just turn up to a meeting and sit alone just to observe at first. People will probably come to talk to you after the meeting – one of the main beliefs of Alcoholics Anonymous is that alcoholics need other alcoholics to help them to get sober – so people will be keen to help you. For more information on 'AA' meetings and how they work, open your browser and type in the following address:

- **www.DryOutNow.com and download section E of the professional treatment guidelines**

- **For details of your nearest Alcoholics Anonymous meetings phone the DryOutNow.com Immediate Response Service on 0800 160 1020.**

TO PREPARE YOURSELF SOCIALLY:

Probably the single most important part of planning for controlled drinking is to **write out your weekly diary.**

Your weekly diary should provide you with the kind of activities that have a good chance of giving you some kind of sense of fulfillment or pleasure – that are rewarding. The aim here is to start to build up activities that will replace your need for alcohol in the longer term. As discussed in Chapter Three – don't expect anything to replace alcohol totally – there are very few activities that can result in you brain experiencing the reward that use of an addictive substance brings, and probably no healthy activities that produce that reward as easily and as immediately as does alcohol. You will need to re-think your objectives and search more for a sense of satisfaction and fulfillment in life than for the experience of immediate pleasure or immediate relief from unpleasant feelings which is delivered by alcohol.

You should think this through in great detail starting now. It must be ready to implement the very day you start to cut down your drinking. You should try to think of activities that are purposeful, and have the potential to lead to some sense of satisfaction; this will depend very much on personal taste. Some examples might include: socialising with non-drinking friends, reading, gym, gardening, walking. In particular, if you are able to devote yourself to any kind of long-term project that involves dedication and a great deal of work, this might start to act to replace the psychological need for alcohol.

In summary, you should create a diary ideally providing several options of activity for all times of every day of the week. This is not to say that you must or will complete every such activity – the important thing is that the diary is always there to turn to if you find yourself sitting and starting to dwell on the idea of having a drink when you have planned not to have one. When that thought enters your head (and it will), you should immediately pick up the diary and implement one of the activities that are listed for that time of that day.

Following is an empty diary covering seven days of the week from 6 in the morning to 12 midnight. It also allows for you to enter two alternative activities for any two hour period. Now you may think that an 18 hour day is a long period of time to plan to fill, but bear the following in mind. The idea of the diary is not that you necessarily do every thing on it at the specified time, although you may choose to, and there will be no harm in this unless you get stressed thinking that you have to do everything on it. The idea of the diary IS that when you feel yourself starting to crave alcohol, you have something to occupy yourself with immediately, and which is already planned so that you can implement that activity immediately. If you wait until you start to crave before trying to think of something to occupy your mind, you may well not be able to do what you wish to immediately, and you may not even be able to concentrate effectively in order to think of something else to do. If you have your diary ready, you've got a great head-start over the craving.

Secondly, remember that your sleep may be disturbed for a period after you cut down your drinking. It is thus important to have planned activities from early in the morning to late at night – again you will not necessarily carry out all these activities, but if you are awake for long hours, you must make sure you have something to do. Poor sleep is a major cause of relapse to drinking. Be prepared to have something to do if you cannot get to sleep – if you enjoyed reading in the past get some good books in. If you enjoyed film, get in a stack of videos or sign up for satellite channels (probably less expensive than your total alcohol costs). Poor sleep will improve as your brain gets used to a world free of alcohol – but you may have to be prepared to persevere for a good while.

Finally, if you are having difficulty thinking of the type of activities you should include in the diary the following questions may give you some ideas:

- What did you used to enjoy doing before alcohol started to replace other things in your life?

- What are the enjoyable things about drinking for you? Can you replace these with activities that result in a similar reward? (E.g. you may drink after work to relax; can you arrange for a massage on some nights as an alternative form of relaxation?) If you completed the table in Chapter 3, Question 4, then refer to that now.

- What would you like to achieve from life? What would you need to do to achieve these things? Is there something you could dedicate yourself to achieving?

- How is your physical health? Could you improve it by eating well and healthily? Could you improve it by exercising regularly? What kinds of exercise would you enjoy?

- How is your social life? Do you have any non-drinking friends you could get in touch with? Can you think of a variety of social activities that don't involve drinking that you may enjoy?

- Do you need to search for work? What do you need to do to search for work?

	MONDAY	TUESDAY	WEDNESDAY	THURSDAY	FRIDAY	SATURDAY	SUNDAY
Activity 1: 6-8							
Activity 2: 6-8							
Activity 1: 8-10							
Activity 2: 8-10							
Activity 1: 10-12							
Activity 2: 10-12							
Activity 1: 12-2							
Activity 2: 12-2							
Activity 1: 2-4							
Activity 2: 2-4							
Activity 1: 4-6							
Activity 2: 4-6							
Activity 1: 6-8							
Activity 2: 6-8							
Activity 1: 8-10							
Activity 2: 8-10							
Activity 1: 10-12							
Activity 2: 10-12							
NIGHT-TIME 1							
NIGHT-TIME 2							

OTHER THINGS TO PREPARE FOR SOCIALLY:

1. ACCOMMODATION.

Is your accommodation situation stable and are you living with others who drink?

At the point of stopping drinking you will wish for the amount of stress in your life to be as minimal as is possible; stress is a major reason for starting to drink heavily and it is also a major reason for relapse. If you do not have permanent accommodation, or you are at risk of losing permanent accommodation for whatever reason, do your best to sort this out in advance of starting to cut down your drinking. Lack of a stable environment in which to re-start your life will greatly increase your chances of relapse.

If you are living with others who drink heavily, then you should very seriously consider either asking them to leave or leaving yourself. The odds of you managing to remain sober when there is someone living with you who drinks heavily on a regular basis are limited. Of course, if that person is also planning to seek help for an alcohol problem, then ideally this should be planned so that you start to cut down and seek professional help at the same time as each other.

If you live with other(s) who do drink, but do not drink heavily, you should see if they will agree to avoid drinking in the house.

2. WORK.

Is your working situation stable?
Are you unemployed?
Are you facing some kind of disciplinary action?
Are you on sick leave?

If you are in work and have no problems there, then this is usually the ideal situation.

If you are on sick leave due to your alcohol problem, again you should try to arrange to return to work, possibly on a part-time basis initially. Of course, there is a fine balance here between too much stress at work, and too much time on your hands if you do not return to work. If work-related stress is a problem for you, then your return to work should be a graded one.

If you are facing some kind of disciplinary action at work as a direct or indirect result of your drinking, do your best to get this resolved before stopping drinking. Remember the aim is to limit the amount of stress you will have to deal with in those vital first few months when you are cutting down and working at maintaining controlled drinking. Of course, there's a bit of a catch 22 about this; while you are

drinking heavily you may not feel up to sorting these kind of things out. Overall, do your best to sort out what you can before you start to cut down; what you cannot do, you just cannot do.

If you are unemployed at the moment, then make some initial plans for a return to work as soon as possible. Of course this may well not be practical for you – if it is not, spend some time before you start to cut down thinking about what kinds of employment you may wish to get, and how you may go about searching for this. Build this into your weekly diary (see above).

3. RELATIONSHIPS

If you are in a relationship with a person who has a drinking problem, then the ideal is that you should both deal with this at the same time – it's highly unlikely to work for either of you if one person stops drinking while the other continues to drink. If you are in a relationship with someone who does not drink heavily, then you may well be experiencing problems in your relationship. You may find that your relationship improves dramatically when you control your drinking, but sometimes this will not be the case. Whatever, if you are having relationship problems at the moment, consider whether to book some relationship counselling with RELATE. This organization often has waiting lists of several months – if you book now, then the counselling will probably have started by the time you are getting towards controlled drinking.

Here is the central contact telephone number for RELATE: **0845 130 4016**

MEDICATION THAT CAN HELP PREVENT RELAPSE TO DRINKING.

1. Acamprosate, also known as Campral.

Acamprosate works to reduce the feeling of craving for alcohol. It is very effective for a few patients, quite effective for some, and simply doesn't work for others. As it is a relatively safe medicine to prescribe, in my NHS practice I prescribe it for most patients who decide to cease drinking. Equally, it can be useful for those who are trying to control their drinking without stopping completely – there is good evidence that it reduces the total amount of alcohol that people consume, for the duration that they are using acamprosate.

For more information on acamprosate, open your browser and type in the following address:

....

- **www.dryoutnow.com and then download Section C of the Treatment Guidelines.**

....

Of course, confidentiality may be an issue for you, and you will need to see a doctor to get these medicines prescribed. If you do not wish to see your GP about this, then the DryOutNow.com Immediate Response Service can give you details of your nearest private doctor who will be prepared to prescribe for you. Simply telephone 0800 160 1020 and ask for details of your nearest private doctor who specialises in addiction problems.

THE CUT-DOWN PHASE

To prepare to control your drinking, and keep it within healthy limits there are four stages to go through:

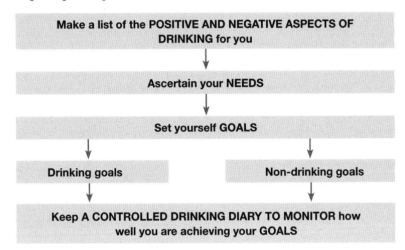

1. MAKE A LIST OF THE POSITIVE AND NEGATIVE ASPECTS OF DRINKING FOR YOU

Making a list of the things you find both helpful and unhelpful about drinking, is the starting point of this process. You will find that if you write this list, you will be able to see quite clearly what you need in your life, that at the present time you are trying to get from alcohol. If you made these lists when you read Chapter Three, then refer back to them now. Otherwise, continue right here. I've given some examples of the positive and negative reasons for drinking that people commonly write down. Cross these out if they don't apply to you, and then spend plenty of time thinking about the good and bad aspects of drinking for you – add to the list and make it your own.

Let's start by considering the possible reasons that you find drinking an enjoyable or helpful activity. Tick off those things on this list that apply to you, and add items of your own as you think of them. If you wish to record this for the future, I have included an empty table for you in the appendix of this book.

POSITIVE THINGS ABOUT DRINKING FOR YOU:

		Tick here
	Physical Health Reasons	
1	I enjoy the feeling of drinking and getting drunk.	
2	Drinking stops me getting withdrawal symptoms.	
3	I have trouble getting to sleep – without a drink I cannot sleep well.	
	Psychological Reasons	
4	I tend to get depressed and drinking improves my mood.	
5	Drinking makes me less anxious.	
6	I tend to get a bit paranoid about going out. If I have a drink I can get out the house without worrying.	
7	I'm usually tense and stressed - drinking helps me to relax.	
	Social Reasons	
8	I have a much better time going out if I have a drink.	
9	I can't imagine going out without having a drink.	
10	I tend to be anxious in the company of other people; when I have a drink inside me I can talk more easily and get on with people better.	
11	I've become a bit of a loner over the years - the only time I ever get into a conversation is at the pub.	
	PUT YOUR OWN REASONS in the spaces below:	

NEGATIVE THINGS ABOUT DRINKING FOR YOU:

		Tick here
	Physical Health Reasons	
1	I'm feeling generally un-well most of the time.	
2	I never eat anything these days.	
3	I'm increasingly worried that I'm permanently damaging my physical health.	
4	I wake up early in the morning covered in sweat.	
	Psychological Reasons	
5	I feel horribly depressed when I wake up in the morning after drinking.	
6	My memory seems terrible these days.	
7	I seem so much more nervous than I used to be.	
8	I'm sick and tired of having this thing called alcohol in control of me. I want to get back in control of myself.	
	Social Reasons	
9	I want to be a better parent to my children.	
10	My relationship is a mess and I know it's because of my drinking.	
11	I've just been arrested for my second drink-drive offence – I might go to prison this time – I know I've got to do something about it.	
12	I'm finding it difficult to get into work on time – someone is going to say something soon.	
13	Of late my temper has got increasingly worse. I'm worried what I might do next time someone annoys me.	
	PUT YOUR OWN REASONS in the spaces below:	

2. ASCERTAIN YOUR NEEDS

When you have completed making the two lists above, you will be in a position to write down what your needs are – and in particular those needs that you will need to meet if you are to successfully control your drinking.

Use the table below to do this. By writing in a positive or negative reason for drinking, you should then be able to work out what you need to do to resolve that – write it down in the space below the reason for drinking. I've started by giving you a few examples. If you run out of space, I have included a blank table for you in the appendix.

Reason	I enjoy the feeling of drinking and getting drunk.
NEED	I need to have enjoyable feelings.
Reason	I have trouble getting to sleep – without a drink I cannot sleep well.
NEED	I need to sleep well.
Reason	I'm usually tense and stressed - drinking helps me to relax.
NEED	I need to relax.
Reason	I never eat anything these days
NEED	I need to eat well
Reason	I feel horribly depressed when I wake up in the morning after drinking.
NEED	I need to improve my mood
Reason	My relationship is a mess and I know it's because of my drinking.
NEED	I need to improve my relationship
Reason	
NEED	
Reason	
NEED	
Reason	
NEED	
Reason	
NEED	
Reason	
NEED	

3. SET YOURSELF GOALS

You should set yourself two types of goals – 'drinking goals' and 'non-drinking goals'. 'Non-drinking goals' do not necessarily mean that you do not drink when you are trying to achieve these goals; it's just that they are not directly about drinking. E.g., a 'drinking goal' might be to drink 2 units and no more on a particular evening. A 'non-drinking goal' might be to cook a meal.

Your drinking goals will be what you plan to drink (how many units) on a particular day of the week. If you are to attempt to return to controlled drinking, then I advise you to take it slowly at first – do not plan to cut-down immediately to drinking 21 units weekly, or as much as 3 units in one night. Gradually get to these levels over a period of months.

Your 'non-drinking' goals will involve meeting the needs you have made a list of above. Now if you manage to successfully control your drinking, some of these things will automatically sort themselves out for themselves. If you are lucky, things like your relationship and your mood will improve as a direct result of reduced drinking. However, many of the reasons you have used alcohol, may have been there before you ever started drinking – these problems will not be resolved merely by a cessation of drinking (e.g. you may have started drinking heavily because of stress at work, or because your relationship was not working out). Equally, some of the problems caused by drinking may have become so difficult that they will take more than just stopping drinking to sort them out. These will need to be addressed by other means. If you fail to address them, they will put you at risk of a return to heavy drinking in due course.

And when you set your non-drinking goals in order to resolve these problems, you will also need to take into account your drinking goals.

Let's consider an example.

Example 'need': 'I need to have enjoyable feelings'.

When considering how to achieve this without getting drunk, you will need to get away from the idea (which may have become a dominant one for you), that the only way you can experience pleasure is by drinking. You will need to think of other means of experiencing pleasure without drinking. Having done this, you will need to write these things down in the form of 'goals'. Here are some common themes that come out of this exercise when I run it by people in my clinic: socialising without getting drunk, sex and eating. Many people who have developed an alcohol problem will have forgotten how to socialise without the use of alcohol, will have poor sex lives (when they may well have had excellent sex lives in the past) and currently eat very little and are not particularly bothered by food (despite the fact that they used to enjoy food). Focus on similar things for you, and turn them into goals:

- **Goal – I will arrange to socialise with nondrinking friends on one evening this week.**

....

- **Goal – I will talk to my partner about our sex life on one evening this week.**

....

- **Goal – I will cook a lovely meal one night this week.**

....

Of vital importance is to link these goals up with your 'drinking goals'. Say this is your first week trying to cut down your alcohol consumption, and you have decided to drink on six nights of the week, and have one night without drinking. How will you tie this up with your 'non-drinking goals'. Here's an example of how you might do that:

Firstly, on the evening that you go out with non-drinking friends, there will be no need to drink alcohol – that could be your night completely without alcohol.

Secondly, on the night you decide to talk to your partner about your sex life, you may decide to make it a touch more relaxing and even romantic by opening a bottle of wine – why not have six units on that night? (Be prepared to re-cork the bottle if your partner does not drink).

Thirdly, why not have two glass of wine on the night you cook the meal?

By doing things in such a manner, you may manage to **slightly enhance** the activities you have planned by the healthy, controlled use of alcohol. And, of course, that must be your aim if you are planning to return to controlled drinking. **Your drinking should never again be about getting drunk, or forgetting unpleasant feelings. It must only be about slightly enhancing the pleasures you get from non-drinking activities.** If you ever allow the idea of the main plan for the evening being about having a drink, then you will surely relapse to heavy, uncontrolled drinking again in good time. As someone who has had a drink problem in the past, this is going to be difficult to get your head around. Really, the safest option is to aim for abstinence in the long term – for life. If you cannot imagine yourself having only a small amount to drink, with the aim of just **slightly enhancing** the pleasure you take from **another activity,** then you should probably think twice before starting to drink again. If you see no point in drinking like this, then you are probably best not drinking at all.

Before you set your goals, there are some other important things to take into account:

Goals must be **realistic**; e.g. do not set a goal to stop drinking tomorrow; do not plan to run The Marathon; do not plan to read The Lord of the Rings in one week.

Goals must be **specific** and measurable; e.g. I will drink 2 units less of alcohol than usual on one day this week; I will go to the pub one time less than usual this week; I will see non-drinking friends once this week.

Goals must be **short-term** e.g. over the next week, or next day. While it is important to have a long-term objective in mind, this will not be reached overnight; if you are to achieve control over yourself, you must set short-term goals, and do your utmost to stick to them.

To achieve this, break your long-term goals down into **smaller steps;** e.g. plan to reduce drinking by 2 units on one day weekly, then every other day, then every day. Once you have achieved this, think about cutting down by another 2 units on one day weekly etc.etc..

Decide on the goals yourself – allow others to advise you, but make the decisions for yourself.

FINALLY: LEARN FROM YOUR FAILURES:

Doubtless, you will not achieve all your goals every day – that would not be human. The important thing is to question why you failed to achieve a particular goal, and then re-plan to make the goal more realistic. You should dwell on the positive more realistic plan and not **berate yourself for failure. E.g.**

- **You planned to drink 2 glasses of wine with your friends at a pub on Wednesday evening but ended up drinking 6 glasses:**

- **Why did this happen? Answer: you were offered another drink after the 2 glasses and did not find it in yourself to refuse.**

- **Possible solutions:**

  - at the beginning of the next evening out, ask your friends not to offer you another drink after you have drunk two; OR

  - get up and leave half-way through the second drink, so that your friends are not given an opportunity to offer you another; OR

  - drink non-alcoholic drinks for the first half of the evening, and only start to drink alcohol one hour before closing time.

Repeat this re-planning process, as often as you feel like it; but at least once weekly. Set your goals for the next week and keep a **'drinking diary'** (see below). Fill this in every day before your memory fades, and then **review it weekly.** This will help you pick up patterns that you might otherwise miss, e.g. a tendency to drink more if you had an argument that day; a ,tendency to drink less if you went walking that day etc. etc.

So here are some examples of a mixture of drinking and other goals:

Examples of goals include:

....

• **I will see my drinking friends once less each week at first.**

....

• **I will see my non-drinking friends at least once this week.**

....

• **I will spend one evening reading this week, and drink nothing.**

....

• **I will drink 2 units less than usual on Monday this week.**

....

• **I will spend all Tuesday looking at jobs advertised in the paper.**

....

• **On Thursday evening I will go to Relate with my partner.**

....

• **I will phone a dating agency on Wednesday.**

....

• **I will drink 2 units less on Friday evening.**

....

CONTROLLED DRINKING DIARY

DAY OF WEEK

BEFORE

DRINKING GOAL 1:

Do you plan to drink?   Yes ☐   No ☐

How much do you plan to drink?

AFTER

Did you keep to your drinking plan?   Yes ☐   No ☐

If not, where did it go wrong?

How could you change it for the better?

What will you do the next time to make it work?

BEFORE

DRINKING GOAL 2:

Do you plan to drink?   Yes ☐   No ☐

How much do you plan to drink?

AFTER

Did you keep to your drinking plan?   Yes ☐   No ☐

If not, where did it go wrong?

How could you change it for the better?

What will you do the next time to make it work?

BEFORE

DRINKING GOAL 3:

Do you plan to drink?   Yes ☐   No ☐

How much do you plan to drink?

AFTER

Did you keep to your drinking plan?   Yes ☐   No ☐

If not, where did it go wrong?

How could you change it for the better?

What will you do the next time to make it work?

SO, IN SUMMARY:

- Identify the positive and negative aspects of drinking for you – I suggest you take at least a week over this – write them down, and add to the list over the week.

- Identify your needs, using the list of the positive and negative aspects of drinking – take another week over this.

- Set goals – take another week to plan your goals.

- Try to put into practice the goals you have set yourself, and start to keep the drinking diary.

- Continue, by learning from failures and reviewing your drinking diary on a weekly basis. Praise yourself for your successes, and plan how you will turn this week's failures into next week's successes.

- If after one year, you have not achieved your longterm goal of controlled drinking within healthy limits, re-consider whether this is a realistic alternative for you, or whether complete abstinence is the only way forward.

THE CONTROLLED DRINKING PHASE

You have arrived! You have finally controlled your drinking within healthy limits, and are feeling all the better for it. Now this is where the serious work begins – the work of keeping it controlled for the rest of your life. If you've implemented most of the steps I outlined in the 'preparation phase' then you will have a head start over all the challenges that have been facing you since you started to cut down your drinking:

- **Craving for alcohol**

- **Sleeplessness**

- **Agitation**

- **Boredom**

- **NO IMMEDIATE SOLUTION TO ALL THESE THINGS**

On the other side of the coin, you are likely to be:

- **Feeling well for the first time in a long time**

- **Eating well**

- **Feeling in a better mood if you have been depressed**

- **Feeling more confident in yourself, especially if you suffered with paranoia and anxiety while you were drinking heavily**

However, you must remember this – most of the advantages of controlling your drinking are long term advantages; they will not be apparent to you immediately:

- **Improved relationships with the important people in your life**

- **Building new relationships with the future important people in your life**

- **Improved performance at work**

- **Finding and holding down employment if you are unemployed**

- **Enjoyment of leisure activities you could never have enjoyed while you were drinking heavily**

- **Improved financial situation**

- **A sense of pride in yourself that had been forgotten during years of heavy drinking**

Keeping your drinking controlled will bring you rewards whether these are delivered by living longer, feeling better in yourself and with yourself, or having better relationships with others. All of these things can disappear in a moment if you relapse to uncontrolled heavy drinking, and most of the truly rewarding things take months and years to start to occur.

The risks of relapsing to uncontrolled drinking are ever present, and many of those who get this far will find themselves back at square one in due course. How are you going to maximise your chances of maintaining controlled drinking? For the first year (the highest risk time for relapse) you must implement your plan, and stick to it as much as is feasible for you.

Let's re-cap:

- Make sure you have some individual counselling in place to continue for well after you have achieved controlled drinking.

- If you are up for AA meetings, then attend them as often as you can – ideally daily.

- See if you can be prescribed Campral (acamprosate) and continue with this for between six months and one year in total.

- Use your weekly diary to keep your time full with planned activity. Make slow but sure progress with long term plans and objectives. In particular, always get active and focus on an activity that involves concentration if you start to crave for alcohol.

- Identify the positive and negative aspects of drinking for you – I suggest you take at least a week over this.

- Identify your needs, using the list of the positive and negative aspects of drinking – take another week over this).

- Set goals – take another week to plan your goals.

- Try to put into practice the goals you have set yourself, and start to keep the drinking diary.

- Continue, by learning from failures and reviewing your drinking diary on a weekly basis. Praise yourself for your successes, and plan how you will turn this week's failures into next week's successes.

- Whenever you experience craving, after it has calmed down, take some time to think how you have handled it without drinking, and how you will handle it more easily the next time it occurs. Think about the situation or feeling that triggered the craving – can you avoid this situation in the future? What did you do that enabled you to avoid drinking, or drinking more than you had planned to (e.g. walked away from the person that offered you a drink; started to do something you had planned in the diary)? Would there be a better way to deal with this same situation in the future that would make you even less likely to have a drink? If you can think of something, remember it and plan to behave in this way the next time you encounter a similar situation.

- Use telephone advice from the DryOutNow.com Immediate Response Service (0800 160 1020) if you have any specific questions, or just need to speak to someone to help you on in the right direction or go to www.dryoutnow.com – click on 'Get Free Advice' on the left hand side of the page and send the email to receive advice.

CONCLUSION

You should now be in a position to implement the best possible plan for you, in order to achieve controlled drinking in the long term. Everything I have advised you to do in this book is based on the research which demonstrates the best way 'on average' for someone to stay dry or achieve controlled drinking. This fits the majority of people, but not everyone, and different elements of the overall plan will be better suited to some individuals than to others. To arrive at the best possible plan for you as an individual, and to limit those odds of relapsing to the minimum you will need individual advice about your particular situation.

Phone the DryOutNow.com Immediate Response Service on 0800 160 1020

Now, at the point of reading this book you will most likely be in the 'planning phase' – getting ready for abstinence and the rest of your life without alcohol. Following is a check list of everything I advise you to have in place before you suddenly find yourself without a drink available to you. Continue straight to Part III, when you are satisfied that you have made all your decisions.

PREPARATION PHASE CHECKLIST	Tick
1 Make absolutely sure you are ready to progress with planning for controlled drinking. If you have any doubts re-read Chapter 3, telephone the **DryOutNow.com Immediate Response Service on 0800 160 1020**.	
2 Arrange for some individual counselling to start as soon as possible – ideally before starting to control your drinking and continuing during and after you have achieved this. Get details of your local counsellors by telephoning the **DryOutNow.com Immediate Response Service on 0800 160 1020**.	
3 IIf you are up for it, attend some AA – ideally before starting to control your drinking and continuing during and after you have achieved this. Get details of your AA meetings by telephoning the **DryOutNow.com Immediate Response Service on 0800 160 1020**.	
4 Start to write your weekly activity diary. Make use of the various tables in this chapter to assess your needs and replace drinking with other activities that have the potential to lead to fulfillment..	
5 Speak to those you live with about drinking in the house.	
6 If you have difficulties at work, then make a plan about how you are going to minimize these difficulties. If you would like confidential advice around these issues, then phone the **DryOutNow.com Immediate Response Service on 0800 160 1020**.	
7 If you have difficulties in your relationship with your partner, telephone Relate on 0845 130 4016, to book relationship counselling.	
8 Get expert medical advice about whether or not you can be prescribed medication to prevent relapse to heavy drinking – either visit your GP or phone the **DryOutNow.com Immediate Response Service (0800 160 1020)** to get free telephone advice and/or details of your nearest private doctor who can advise on this.	

www.dryoutnow.com
IMMEDIATE RESPONSE SERVICE
CALL 0800 160 1020 NOW

CHAPTER TEN

YOU ARE NOT PHYSICALLY ADDICTED TO ALCOHOL AND YOUR DRINKING IS IN A MIXED HEAVY REGULAR/BINGE PATTERN

If at any time you require urgent access to treatment, or need an immediate response for any other reason, do not hesitate to telephone the DryOutNow.com Immediate Response Service (IRS) on:

0800 160 1020
(8am-9pm, seven days weekly)

CHAPTER TEN

YOU ARE NOT PHYSICALLY ADDICTED TO ALCOHOL AND YOUR DRINKING IS IN A MIXED HEAVY REGULAR/BINGE PATTERN

In the case of someone who is binge drinking, they will usually have periods of drinking nothing (or at least very little), and as such the only realistic option is to prepare to cease drinking suddenly during one of these periods. Of course, there are binge drinkers who drink heavily on most days, and then especially heavily on other days. If your pattern of drinking is like this, then this is the chapter for you (unless you are physically addicted to alcohol – in which case refer to Chapter 4 or 5).

There are either 3 or 4 stages though which you will need to progress, along your route to achieving a life that is not controlled by alcohol.

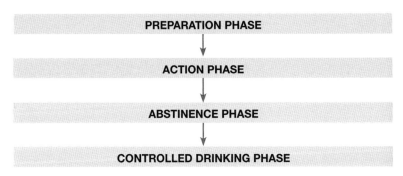

PREPARATION PHASE

ACTION PHASE

ABSTINENCE PHASE

CONTROLLED DRINKING PHASE

It may be the case that you are looking for good advice about how to re-start drinking again immediately after ceasing mixed heavy regular/binge drinking. As far as I am aware, there is no such advice to give. Anyone who is going through periods of binge drinking, will need to give themselves a good period without any drinking whatsoever, if they are to restart drinking within healthy limits and keep it there.

Why is this? In Chapter Three I explained how the brain takes a long time to readjust to a world without alcohol – drinking before significant readjustment has occurred will only trigger the brain into telling you to drink more and more ...and more. It is also likely to take many months before you have started to replace the habit of drinking with alternative activities that fill the times when you used to drink. If you have not made progress on developing alternative activities by the time you start to drink again, you will probably find yourself drinking more and more…and more. For these reasons, I must advise you to aim to remain completely abstinent from alcohol for at least six months following cessation of alcohol use. And having said that, the only way to make sure that you will not return to damaging levels of drinking in the future, is to commit yourself to never drinking again.

Of course, you may prove me wrong, and I congratulate you if you do – you will be one of the few people to have beaten the odds and recommenced drinking quickly in a way that enhances your life rather than diminishes it. However, if you would prefer to minimise your chances of returning quickly to the old pattern of heavy binge drinking rather than take the risk of a quick relapse, then read on.

THE PREPARATION PHASE.

The preparation phase mainly involves planning/booking the help you will need and getting ready to stay dry in the medium term. So what does preparing for staying dry involve? There are three things to do:

1. Prepare yourself psychologically, and also seek out professional psychological support (various forms of counselling).

2. Prepare yourself socially, and seek out the available professional support.

3. Consider the possibility of medication to help you stay dry.

TO PREPARE YOURSELF PSYCHOLOGICALLY:

a. Make absolutely sure that you are fully committed to doing this, and that you are 100% realistic about how hard it's going to be. Re-read Chapter Three to help you to do this.

b. Book some specialist individual (1-to-1) alcohol counselling as soon as possible to start BEFORE you stop drinking.

c. Consider attending some Alcoholics Anonymous (AA) meetings BEFORE you stop drinking. Specialist 1-to-1 counselling can help in one of two ways: firstly by giving you the skills to control your drinking, and secondly by helping you to understand any underlying emotional issues which are leading you to drink heavily. For detailed information on how counselling works, go to:

. . . .

• **www.dryoutnow.com – and download Section E of the professional treatment guidelines**

. . . .

Specialist counselling is available from the NHS/charitable services for free. Or you can book with a private counsellor. In terms of the quality of service you will receive, there is probably little difference between NHS and private counsellors. However, in the NHS you may have to wait a long time (months or years in some cases) before you can access counselling. This varies between areas and depends on where you live. So, overall, I suggest contacting your local NHS/charitable specialist alcohol counselling service first. If the waiting time seems unsatisfactory, or other things don't seem right, then try the self-pay route.

....

- **For details of your local counselling services phone DryOutNow.com Immediate Response Service on 0800 160 1020.**

....

Private counsellors who specialise in alcohol problems are not so many in number. There are probably in the region of 400 in the country. Many problems that lead to heavy drinking are general in nature (e.g. stress, relationship difficulties etc.). So, if your nearest specialist alcohol counsellor is too far away, a general counsellor may still be of help to you:

....

- **For details of your nearest private general counselors phone the DryOutNow.com Immediate Response Service on 0800 160 1020.**

....

SPECIALIST TELEPHONE COUNSELLING

Alternatively, you can access specialist private alcohol counselling by telephone. You may wish to use this service if your nearest specialist counsellor is too far away, or if you would prefer the privacy and convenience of receiving counselling in your own home.

This service is provided via DryOutNow.com. Call 0800 160 1020 to request details of the specialist telephone counselling service.

Alcoholics Anonymous meetings: People are often nervous about attending these meetings, but those who attend have been shown to have **better long term outcomes**. There is no requirement to have stopped drinking in order to attend – just to be relatively sober at the time of attendance. There is no requirement to speak at a meeting – just to say 'pass' if asked to speak. The theme of the meetings is religious and requires a belief in a 'higher power', but there is no requirement to believe in God as such, or in any particular God. Some people think of the 'higher power' as the 'sober part' of themselves. There is no need to book in advance – just turn up to a meeting and sit alone just to observe at first. People will probably come to talk to you after the meeting – one of the main beliefs of Alcoholics Anonymous is that alcoholics need other alcoholics to help them to get sober – so people will be keen to help you. For more information on 'AA' meetings and how they work, go to:

- **www.DryOutNow.com and download section E of the professional treatment guidelines**

- **For details of your nearest Alcoholics Anonymous meetings phone the DryOutNow.com Immediate Response Service on 0800 160 1020**

TO PREPARE YOURSELF SOCIALLY:

Firstly you should make a decision about whether you are going to stay in a residential rehabilitation unit for a period of time, or whether you plan to deal with this at home.

Residential rehabilitation. This is a very intense form of treatment, and many people will not wish to go through it, or just cannot for practical reasons. Residential rehabilitation involves staying in a specialist psychological unit for a period of time (durations of stay range from 2 weeks to 9 months). The advantages of a period of residential rehabilitation include i) an alcohol-free environment so there is minimal risk of relapse ii) the person is living and learning from others with alcohol problems iii) as a generalisation, this is the best form of counselling available, as it is so intense, and because people are confronted every time they try to deny they have a problem. Most people will decide this is not for them, especially if it is your first attempt at staying dry. However – bear this in mind – the evidence clearly shows that those who go to a residential rehabilitation unit and complete the course without leaving early, are more likely to remain dry from alcohol in the long term than those who do not go to residential rehabilitation. For more information on how residential rehabilitation works, go to:

- **www.dryoutnow.com – and download section E of the professional treatment guidelines**

Most residential rehabilitation units are not in the NHS. However, the NHS will sometimes pay for you to go to one if they think you need it. If you want to plan for a period of residential rehabilitation, and wish the NHS to pay for it, then **you will need to contact your local NHS Community Alcohol Team.** They will arrange for you to be assessed, and if they think you meet their criteria for paying, will then arrange for your admission. Waits may be long for assessment and admission (many months in some cases), but the treatment you get at the end of the day will be of the same quality as going privately to one of the cheaper units.

- **For details of your local NHS Community Alcohol Team phone the DryOutNow.com Immediate Response Service on 0800 160 1020.**

ACHIEVING AND MAINTAINING ABSTINENCE AT HOME:

If you plan to stay at home, probably the single most important part of planning for this is to write out your **weekly activity diary.**

There are two aims of the weekly diary. Firstly it should enable you fill your time completely from the day you cease drinking, onwards. Your time should be full for the simple reason that this will leave you less time to think about alcohol. The nature of craving is such that if you give it a chance to build up, it will end up filling your head with repetitive thoughts: "Just one drink won't hurt – how could it? Just one drink won't hurt – how could it?" You must do your utmost to divert your attention from any such thoughts at all times. Being active and having to concentrate on a task of some kind is much more likely to result in the feeling of craving subsiding, than is sitting in a chair doing nothing. The vital element here is having to concentrate on something. This is very important if you are back in your usual routine, and not in specialist care.

Secondly it should provide you with the kind of activities that have a good chance of giving you some kind of sense of fulfillment or pleasure – that are rewarding. The aim here is to start to build up activities that will replace your need for alcohol in the longer term. As discussed in Chapter Three – don't expect anything to replace alcohol totally – there are very few activities that can result in your brain experiencing the reward that use of an addictive substance brings, and probably no healthy activities that produce that reward as easily and as immediately as does alcohol. You will need to re-think your objectives and search more for a sense of satisfaction and fulfillment in life than for the experience of immediate pleasure or immediate relief from unpleasant feelings which is delivered by alcohol.

You should think this through in great detail starting now. It must be ready to implement the very day you stop drinking. You should try to think of activities that are purposeful, and have the potential to lead to some sense of satisfaction; this will depend very much on personal taste. Some examples might include: socialising with non-drinking friends, reading, gym, gardening, walking. You may well have found that your appetite has been terrible for as long as you can remember; when you have stopped drinking for a week or so, it is very likely that your appetite will start to improve, and by the time you have finished detox you will be enjoying food again. As such, one activity you plan may involve food, such as developing your culinary skills. Or more simply, what about planning to sit down to lunch and dinner every day – you probably haven't done that in a while. (Don't worry about weight gain – alcohol is much more fattening than many foods). If it's possible to devote yourself to some kind of work project with a long-term goal in mind this could be useful.

In particular, if you are able to devote yourself to any kind of long-term project that involves dedication and a great deal of work, this might start to act to replace the psychological need for alcohol. (This kind of approach would be disagreed with by many professionals, especially those from a theoretical counselling background – they would argue that the addictive behaviour is merely being transferred from one object – drink – to another – work. However, if you are not considering residential rehabilitation, I think this is exactly what you should aim to do – replace the alcohol with healthy activity rather than destructive activity.)

In summary, you should create a diary ideally providing several options of activity for all times of every day of the week. This is not to say that you must or will complete every such activity – the important thing is that the diary is always there to turn to if you find yourself sitting and starting to dwell on the idea of having a drink. When that thought enters your head (and it will), you should immediately pick up the diary and implement one of the activities that are listed for that time of that day.

Following is an empty diary covering seven days of the week from 6 in the morning to 12 midnight. It also allows for you to enter two alternative activities for any two hour period. Now you may think that an 18 hour day is a long period of time to plan to fill, but bear the following in mind. The idea of the diary is not that you necessarily do every thing on it at the specified time, although you may chose to, and there will be no harm in this unless you get stressed thinking that you have to do everything on it. The idea of the diary IS that when you feel yourself starting to crave alcohol, you have something to occupy yourself with immediately, and which is already planned so that you can implement that activity immediately. If you wait until you start to crave before trying to think of something to occupy your mind, you may well not be able to do what you wish to immediately, and you may not even be able to concentrate effectively in order to think of something else to do. If you have your diary ready, you've got a great head-start over the craving.

Secondly, remember that your sleep may be disturbed for a period after cessation of drinking. It is thus important to have planned activities from early in the morning to late at night – again you will not necessarily carry out all these activities, but if you are awake for long hours, you must make sure you have something to do. Poor sleep is a major cause of relapse to drinking. Be prepared to have something to do if you cannot get to sleep – if you enjoyed reading in the past get some good books in. If you enjoyed film, get in a stack of videos or sign up for satellite channels (probably less expensive than your total alcohol costs). Poor sleep will improve as your brain gets used to a world free of alcohol – but you may have to be prepared to persevere for a good while.

Finally, if you are having difficulty thinking of the type of activities you should include in the diary the following questions may give you some ideas:

- What did you used to enjoy doing before alcohol started to replace other things in your life?

- What are the enjoyable things about drinking for you? Can you replace these with activities that result in a similar reward? (E.g. you may drink after work to relax; can you arrange for a massage on some nights as an alternative form of relaxation?) If you completed the tables in Chapter 3, Question 4, then you may wish to use these now.

- What would you like to achieve from life? What would you need to do to achieve these things? Is there something you could dedicate yourself to achieving?

- How is your physical health? Could you improve it by eating well and healthily? Could you improve it by exercising regularly? What kinds of exercise would you enjoy?

- How is your social life? Do you have any non-drinking friends you could get in touch with? Can you think of a variety of social activities that don't involve drinking that you may enjoy?

- Do you need to search for work? What do you need to do to search for work?

	MONDAY	TUESDAY	WEDNESDAY	THURSDAY	FRIDAY	SATURDAY	SUNDAY
Activity 1: 6-8							
Activity 2: 6-8							
Activity 1: 8-10							
Activity 2: 8-10							
Activity 1: 10-12							
Activity 2: 10-12							
Activity 1: 12-2							
Activity 2: 12-2							
Activity 1: 2-4							
Activity 2: 2-4							
Activity 1: 4-6							
Activity 2: 4-6							
Activity 1: 6-8							
Activity 2: 6-8							
Activity 1: 8-10							
Activity 2: 8-10							
Activity 1: 10-12							
Activity 2: 10-12							
NIGHT-TIME 1							
NIGHT-TIME 2							

OTHER THINGS TO PREPARE FOR SOCIALLY:

1. Accommodation.

Is your accommodation situation stable and are you living with others who drink?

At the point of stopping drinking you will wish for the amount of stress in your life to be as minimal as is possible; stress is a major reason for starting to drink heavily and it is also a major reason for relapse. If you do not have permanent accommodation, or you are at risk of losing permanent accommodation for whatever reason, do your best to sort this out in advance of stopping drinking. Lack of a stable environment in which to re-start your life will greatly increase your chances of relapse.

If you are living with others who drink heavily, then you should very seriously consider either asking them to leave or leaving yourself. The odds of you managing to remain sober when there is someone living with you who drinks on a regular basis are very small indeed. Of course, if that person is also planning to seek help for an alcohol problem, then ideally this should be planned so that neither of you are living together at the time that one of you is still drinking. This will probably mean either planning to cease drinking at the same time as each other, or at least one of you arranging for admission to a residential rehabilitation unit.

If you live with other(s) who do drink, but do not drink heavily, you should see if they will agree to avoid drinking in the house. Ideally, the house should be completely empty of alcohol at the point you stop drinking, and it should stay that way for the foreseeable future.

2. Work.

Is your working situation stable? Are you unemployed? Are you facing some kind of disciplinary action? Are you on sick leave?

If you are in work and have no problems there, then this is usually the ideal situation.

If you are on sick leave due to your alcohol problem, again you should try to arrange to return to work, possibly on a part-time basis initially. Of course, there is a fine balance here between too much stress at work, and too much time on your hands if you do not return to work.

If work-related stress is a problem for you, then your return to work should be a graded one. If you are facing some kind of disciplinary action at work as a direct or indirect result of your drinking, do your best to get this resolved before stopping drinking. Remember the aim is to limit the amount of stress you will have to deal with in those vital first few months when you may be battling to stay dry. Of course, there's a bit of a catch 22 about this; while you are drinking heavily you may not feel up to sorting these kind of things out. Overall, do your best to sort out what you can before you stop drinking; what you cannot do, you just cannot do.

If you are unemployed at the moment, then make some initial plans for a return to work following cessation of drinking. Ideally, arrange for a return to employment as soon as you have stopped drinking. Of course this may well not be practical for you – if it is not, spend some time before you stop drinking thinking about what kinds of employment you may wish to get, and how you may go about searching for this. Build this into your weekly diary (see above).

3. Relationships

If you are in a relationship with a person who has a drinking problem, then the ideal is that you should both deal with this at the same time – it's highly unlikely to work for either of you if one person stops ,drinking while the other continues to drink. If you are unable to convince your partner of this, then if you are committed to aiming for a period of abstinence from alcohol, you should seriously consider whether or not to continue with the relationship.

If you are in a relationship with someone who does not drink heavily, then you may well be experiencing problems in your relationship. You may find that your relationship improves dramatically when you cease drinking, but sometimes this will not be the case. Whatever, if you are having relationship problems at the moment, consider whether to book some relationship counselling with RELATE. This organization often has waiting lists of several months – if you book now, then the counselling will probably have started by the time you have ceased to drink. Here is the central contact telephone number for RELATE: **0845 130 4016**

MEDICATION THAT CAN HELP PREVENT RELAPSE TO DRINKING.

There are two medications commonly use in the UKto help prevent a return to drinking.

1. Acamprosate, also known as Campral.

Acamprosate works to reduce the feeling of craving for alcohol. It is very effective for a few patients, quite effective for some, and simply doesn't work for others. As it is a relatively safe medicine to prescribe, in my NHS practice I prescribe it for most patients who decide to cease drinking. It is usually safe to continue to take it, even if you temporarily lapse to drinking again.

2. Disulfiram, also known as Antabuse.

Disulfiram blocks the complete breakdown of alcohol by the liver. This causes you to feel absolutely terrible if you have a drink. Disulfiram can work well for people who are likely to relapse to drinking on the spur of the moment – you simply can't do this if you are taking disulfiram. However, it's no magic cure, as you can decide to stop taking it, and within several days you are likely to be able to drink again without feeling ill. I prescribe disulfiram less often than acamprosate as it has the potential to cause some quite nasty side-effects in some people. In particular, it should generally be avoided in people who have a history of blood vessel problems (e.g. high blood pressure, history of stroke or heart attack), who have liver disease, or who have suffered serious psychiatric illness in the past.

For more information on both these medicines, open your browser and type in the following address:

www.dryoutnow.com and then download Section C of the Treatment Guidelines. Pages 41-44 are the relevant ones.

Of course, confidentiality may be an issue for you, and you will need to see a doctor to get these medicines prescribed. If you do not wish to see your GP about this, then the DryOutNow.com Immediate Response Service can give you details of your nearest private doctor who will be prepared to prescribe for you. **Simply telephone 0800 160 1020 and ask for details of your nearest private doctor who specialises in addiction problems.**

THE ACTION PHASE.

There are two ways of stopping drinking if you are have a mixed heavy regular/ binge pattern of drinking:

OPTION 1: STOPPING SUDDENLY:

If you decide to stop drinking suddenly, you should only implement this when:

- **You have prepared thoroughly as described above in 'the preparation phase'**

- **At a time of minimal stress**

BUT BEWARE – there is not likely to be any time in your life when there is no stress whatsoever. In planning the right time to stop drinking, you should have minimised the possibility of stress to lead to an immediate relapse to uncontrolled drinking; but you will never get rid of it completely.

Assuming you are not physically addicted to alcohol, then this should not lead to any permanent damage if you cease drinking suddenly – overnight. Having

said this, some people who binge drink, drink heavily enough to drink to induce physical addiction to alcohol for periods of time. If you think this might apply to you, then read Chapter One of this book to establish this. If you find that it does apply to you, then you should not be reading this chapter – rather, you should follow the advice in Chapter Four or Chapter Five.

If you have any doubts about this, then get individual advice by telephoning **the DryOutNow.com Immediate Response Service on 0800 160 1020.**

OPTION 2: DETOXIFICATION

Most doctors will only consider detoxification necessary if you are physically addicted to alcohol. And they are right – from a medical perspective (i.e. making sure you remain well whilst giving up drinking). If you are physically addicted to alcohol, then on cessation of alcohol use you will experience alcohol withdrawal symptoms such as tremor, sweating, nausea, vomiting, raised blood pressure and raised pulse. In severe alcohol withdrawal you may experience epileptic seizures, hallucinations, delusions and disorientation in time and place. In some cases, severe alcohol withdrawal can be fatal, and if not fatal may lead to permanent brain damage. All the symptoms of alcohol withdrawal are caused by what doctors call 'hyper-excitability of the central nervous system' - in other words the brain becomes massively overactive.

In order to control this over-activity of the brain, sedative medication is prescribed – detox. Quite large doses of sedative medication are prescribed at first, and then the dosage gradually reduced down to zero over a number of days. If the detox is performed professionally, the risk of epileptic seizures occurring is very small indeed, and no other complications of alcohol withdrawal are likely to occur. Equally, you should expect to feel quite comfortable during detox, and by the time it's completed, you will probably feel the best you have in years. Don't get confused between sedative medication and sleeping tablets – although they are similar, you will not be sent to sleep for the detox. The medication you are prescribed (usually a medicine called chlordiazepoxide (Librium) or diazepam (Valium)) is not aimed at sending you to sleep, rather just to calm you and prevent the brain over-activity that occurs during alcohol withdrawal.

But detoxification in a specialist unit offers more than just the medical side of things. In short, although you are not physically addicted to alcohol, it may still be the case that you have tried and failed to cease drinking on several occasions in the past. Psychological addiction to alcohol, although not a thing that places you at physical risk, nevertheless often stops people achieving abstinence. If this is so in your case, then admission for a week or so to a specialist detoxification unit may just make the difference, leading to a successful result this time around.

There are three main reasons for this:

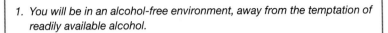

1. *You will be in an alcohol-free environment, away from the temptation of readily available alcohol.*

2. *You will receive daily counselling from specialist alcohol counsellors, and get to witness and understand the difficulties others have had with alcohol.*

3. *You may be prescribed some medication on a short-term basis to keep you relaxed and to help you sleep.*

All these things, may just make the difference for you this time around. If you would like to know more about the technical side of alcohol detox, go to:

www.dryoutnow.com – click on the 'Treatment Guidelines' button on the left hand side of the page, and then download Section C of the Treatment Guidelines.

When you are planning detox there are several decisions that need to be made:

1. *Have you thought about the options of where detox may take place (home, psychiatric ward, hospital medical ward, specialist detoxification unit)?*

2. *Are you looking for a free detox or a self-pay service?*

3. *Have you decided whether or not you wish to continue to residential rehabilitation after detox?*

1. WHERE IS THE BEST PLACE FOR THE DETOX TO TAKE PLACE.

A. HOME.

Detox at home may sound more appealing than having to be admitted to a hospital of some kind. However, it is a less safe and less effective means of undergoing detoxification on average. Approximately 50% of people who undergo detoxification at home will manage to complete the detox without starting to drink again, while over 90% will complete detoxification when admitted to a specialist detoxification unit. Equally, if anything does go wrong during detox, then being in hospital should mean that you get the right care immediately, whereas you may wait hours at home. In particular, home detox is generally agreed to be the wrong option if you have a history of epileptic fits when coming off alcohol, if you suffer from any serious medical condition, if you suffer from any serious psychiatric illness or feel suicidal, if you have a tendency to get disorientated, if you are unable to arrange for another adult to be with you at home for the detox, or if you live with others who drink.

B. PSYCHIATRIC WARD.

Sometimes alcohol detox is arranged to take place on a psychiatric ward. From a doctor's perspective, the main problem here is that staff on psychiatric wards often have less experience of dealing with alcohol detoxification, than do those in a specialist unit. The psychological aspect of detoxification (preparing you to deal with life without drinking when you leave) is less likely to be addressed, and you are probably less likely overall to complete the detoxification without returning to drinking. Equally, you may not feel comfortable with the idea of admission to a psychiatric ward in view of the fact that most other patients there, will be suffering from serious psychiatric illnesses.

C. HOSPITAL MEDICAL WARD.

If you are seriously physically ill as a result of your drinking (e.g. jaundiced, having fits, bleeding from the rectum or vomiting blood, having hallucinations or delusions) or have another serious illness such as poorly controlled diabetes or pancreatitis, then a hospital medical ward is probably the best place to receive detoxification. The reason I say this, is that if you are this ill, the absolute priority must be to place you where you will be provided with immediate attention from a doctor who is used to dealing with emergencies if things go wrong. There is a fine judgement to be made here, because you are unlikely to get the best overall treatment as far as completing the detox and staying dry afterwards. Some specialist detox units are very capable of dealing with all the common emergencies very effectively, and they will also be able to offer the 'full package' aimed at your drinking problem. On a hospital medical ward, you will probably be treated as just another patient who has to be kept alive until they are discharged.

D. SPECIALIST DETOX UNIT.

Admission to a specialist unit for your detox is clearly the ideal in most cases. Such units have the most expertise in getting you through detox comfortably, and have the best chances of getting you through detox without relapsing to alcohol use before completion of the detox. Unless you are very ill indeed, they should also offer the safest option overall for detox. In addition to this, you will receive specialist counselling as part of the detox 'package'. This should improve your chances of staying dry after detox considerably, and unless you are seriously physically ill, that should be your main consideration. Remember that only around 25% of people who have detoxed from alcohol are still dry after one year. Any treatment you can get that will improve your chances of staying dry you should grab and soak up. Your main consideration must be to aim at that – 'The detox is the easy bit, staying dry is much harder.'

2. ARE YOU LOOKING FOR A FREE DETOX OR A SELF-PAY SERVICE?

2A. FREE ALCOHOL DETOXIFICATION.

This can often be accessed through the NHS. If you wish to proceed along this route, the starting place is usually your local 'Community Alcohol Team' (sometimes 'Community Drug and Alcohol Team').

For details of your local Community Alcohol Team **phone the DryOutNow.com Immediate Response Service on 0800 160 1020**

Usually these days you can book in direct with your community alcohol team by giving them a call on the above number. However, in some cases they may require you to go to your GP first in order to be referred to them by your GP. When you have either referred yourself or been referred by your GP, you will be given an appointment for an assessment with the alcohol team. They will formulate a plan with you, which should include a detoxification if you are assessed as needing one. That's the theory and in some cases it will work exactly like this. In some cases you will get an excellent service from the NHS. In other cases you will not – it all depends on where you live. If you are lucky enough to live in an area where the treatment of alcoholism has been well funded over the last few years, then you are likely to experience few problems. However, the funding for alcohol treatment has been very poor in some areas for many years, and in some case has got even worse over the last several years, as money has been diverted to treating illicit drug problems rather than alcohol problems. This is what is known as the 'postcode lottery'. There is no way of my predicting whether you will be lucky with the NHS or not. The problems you may experience are:

- Long waits to be seen in the first place (many months).

- Long waits to access detoxification after you have been assessed (months to years).

- No detoxification available in practice whatsoever.

- Detoxification only available at home, (see above – home detoxification).

- Detoxification only available in the local psychiatric ward.

Now, as I stated above, in some areas you will get an excellent service by going the NHS route – the only way to find out if this applies to you, is to give it a try.

2B. SELF-PAY ALCOHOL DETOX.

The large majority of self-pay detox units are dedicated, specialist units. In such units, you should receive good quality medical care and psychological support aimed at keeping you dry after completion of the detox. The main differences in price are accounted for by:

....

- **The quality of the accommodation.**

....

- **The quality of the medical cover.**

....

- **How long you are prepared to wait.**

....

As a generalisation, the more you pay the better hotel services you will receive, and the quicker you will be admitted. The degree of medical cover in self-pay units ranges from non-specialist GPs available for telephone advice and to attend in an emergency only, to specialist consultants seeing you on a daily basis with a ward doctor on-site to attend to you 24 hours/day. The more expensive units will tend to have invested more in their medical cover than the less expensive units.

Deciding on the best self-pay unit to use depends on how ill you are, how long you are prepared to wait and what your needs are in terms of accommodation. Probably you will want to minimise the cost that you pay whilst making sure you get the best possible treatment for you. If you choose to seek detoxification privately, then DryOutNow.com will arrange this for you. This is a free service and **it is guaranteed that you will pay no more** by using the booking service than by booking direct with the detox unit. In fact in some cases you will **pay less by booking through DryOutNow.com.** DryOutNow.com have a detailed knowledge of all the detox units in the UK and the kind of service they provide. Taking into account your needs, they will find you the cheapest detox suitable for you and the best detox suitable for you (safest and highest rates of completion). Some people will not wish to be referred by their GP, and for detox units that require a referral from a doctor, one of their doctors will be available to make that referral for you.

....

- **For details of detoxification units phone the DryOutNow.com Immediate Response Service on 0800 160 1020.**

....

3. HAVE YOU DECIDED WHETHER OR NOT YOU WISH TO CONTINUE TO RESIDENTIAL REHABILITATION AFTER DETOX?

Most specialist detoxification units will offer the option of staying on after completion of detoxification for a period of residential rehabilitation. However, there are also many residential rehabilitation units that do not provide a medical detox, and you may wish to consider attending one of these rather than staying on at the detox unit. Although it may seem the simplest option to stay on for residential rehabilitation at the same place you get detoxed, there are two reasons that you may wish to think otherwise: cost and quality. The unit that provides you with the best detox, may well not be the unit that offers the best rehabilitation for the price that you can afford.

The reason it is important to think about this now is that it is usually considered very important to continue straight to residential rehabilitation from detox. If you are planning a period of residential rehabilitation you will have to think about this well before admission for detox. If it is not the best option for you to stay at your detox unit for rehabilitation, then you will have to book admission to the 'rehab' unit before admission for detox.

If you have decided you would like to consider a period of residential rehabilitation to follow detox, then I advise you to discuss this with an expert at the DryOutNow. com Immediate Response Service making use of their free telephone advice service (0800 160 1020). They have details of all the UK residential rehabilitation units, and can help you plan in the most cost-effective way given your particular needs.

THE ABSTINENCE PHASE.

You have arrived! You've stopped drinking successfully, and are ready to face a new world – a world without alcohol in control of you. Now this is where the serious work begins – the work of staying dry, either permanently or before a return to controlled drinking within healthy limits. If you've implemented most of the steps I outlined in the 'preparation phase' then you will have a head start over all the new challenges that are going to face you:

....

- **Craving for alcohol**

....

- **Sleeplessness**

....

- **Agitation**

....

- **Boredom**

....

- **NO IMMEDIATE SOLUTION TO ALL THESE THINGS**

....

On the other side of the coin, you are likely to be:

- **Feeling well**

- **Eating well**

- **Feeling in a better mood if you have been depressed**

- **Feeling more confident in yourself, especially if you suffered with paranoia and anxiety while you were drinking**

However, you must remember this – most of the advantages of giving up uncontrolled drinking are long term advantages; they will not be apparent to you immediately, and they will require a sustained period of abstinence from alcohol to occur:

- **Improved relationships with the important people in your life**

- **Building new relationships with the future important people in your life**

- **Improved performance at work**

- **Finding and holding down employment if you are unemployed**

- **Enjoyment of leisure activities you could never have enjoyed while you were drinking**

- **Improved financial situation**

- **A sense of pride in yourself that had been forgotten during years of heavy drinking**

Controlling your drinking will bring you rewards whether these are delivered by living longer, feeling better in yourself and with yourself, or having better relationships with others. All of these things can disappear in a moment if you relapse, and most of the truly rewarding things take months and years to start to occur.

Probably only 25% of people who decide to stop drinking in a damaging way are actually achieving this at the end of one year. How are you going to maximise your chances of being one of these 25%? For the first year (the highest risk time for relapse) you must implement your plan, and stick to it as much as is feasible for you. Let's re-cap:

1. If you have decided on a course of residential rehabilitation then you will learn more there about staying dry than anything I can tell you in this book. But remember this – the evidence shows that it is those that complete the course of

rehabilitation that have the best chances of staying dry in the long term. Many people find residential rehabilitation hard going – it's not meant to be easy – it is meant to prepare you for a life without alcohol. As it is very hard work, many people leave before they have completed the course. If you commit yourself to a period of residential rehabilitation, then do your utmost to stay the course – if you don't, then you have probably wasted your time.

2. If you are staying at home having stopped drinking:

- Make sure you have some individual counselling in place to start before you stop drinking, and to continue afterwards. You should aim to continue with counselling on a weekly basis for the first year of abstinence.

- If you are up for AA meetings, then attend them as often as you can – ideally daily.

- See if you can be prescribed Campral (acamprosate) and/or Antabuse (disulfiram) – continue these medications for between six months and one year after you stop drinking. You have to stop taking Antabuse if you decide to start drinking again, but you can continue to take Campral – this may work to limit your chances of starting to drink again at harmful levels.

- Use your weekly diary to keep your time full with planned activity. Make slow but sure progress with long term plans and objectives. In particular, always get active and focus on an activity that involves concentration if you start to crave for alcohol.

- Use your weekly activity diary to keep your time full with planned activity. Make slow but sure progress with long term plans and objectives. In particular, always get active and focus on an activity that involves concentration if you start to crave for alcohol.

- Identify the positive and negative aspects of drinking for you – I suggest you take at least a week over this during the time you are abstinent – write them down, and add to the list over the week.

- Identify your needs, using the list of the positive and negative aspects of drinking – take another week over this.

- Set goals – take another week to plan your goals.

- Try to put into practice the goals you have set yourself, and start to keep the drinking diary.

- Continue, by learning from failures and reviewing your drinking diary on a weekly basis. Praise yourself for your successes, and plan how you will turn this week's failures into next week's successes.

- Whenever you experience craving, after it has calmed down, take some time to think how you have handled it without drinking, and how you will handle it more easily the next time it occurs. Think about the situation or feeling that triggered the craving – can you avoid this situation in the future? What did you do that enabled you to avoid drinking, or drinking more than you had planned to (e.g. walked away from the person that offered you a drink; started to do something you had planned in the diary)? Would there be a better way to deal with this same situation in the future that would make you even less likely to have a drink? If you can think of something, remember it and plan to behave in this way the next time you encounter a similar situation.

- Use telephone advice from the DryOutNow.com Immediate Response Service (0800 160 1020) if you have any specific questions, or just need to speak to someone to help you on in the right direction.

THE CONTROLLED DRINKING PHASE.

This phase is only relevant to you if you are sure that you want to try drinking again at some point in the future. Overall, I advise you against trying to drink again – that's not to say that you will not manage to achieve controlled drinking within healthy limits at some point in the future – it is to say that you are more likely to beat the odds against a return to alcoholic drinking if you decide on complete abstinence.

If you are not ready to commit to complete abstinence then read on. But if you do read on then please remember this: I make no guarantees that you will not find yourself back at square one in several months time.

First of all, what is controlled drinking? Very simply, most doctors will consider it to be drinking within healthy limits as defined by the World Health Organization. These are as follows:

FOR MALES:

- A maximum of 21 units should be consumed in any one week.

- Within a period of one week there should be at least two drink-free days.

- No more than 4 units should be consumed in any one day.

Effectively this means the following:

- You should drink no more than 2 pints of 3-4% lager/ beer or 1½ pints of 5% lager/beer or 1/3bottle of wine or 1/9th bottle of spirits on any onenight.

- You should have at least two days in the week when you drink no alcohol at all.

- You should drink no more than 9 pints of 3-4% lager/beer per week or no more than 7 pints of 5% lager/beer per week or no more than 2 bottles wine per week or no more than 2/3 bottle spirits per week.

FOR FEMALES:

- A maximum of 14 units should be consumed in any one week.

- Within a period of one week there should be at least two drink-free days.

- No more than 3 units should be consumed in any one day.

Effectively this means the following:

- You should drink no more than 1.5 pints of 3-4% lager/beer or 1 pint of 5% lager/beer (like Stella/Kronenberg) or ¼ bottle of wine or 1/10th bottle ofspirits on any one night.

- You should have at least two days in the week when you drink no alcohol at all.

- You should drink no more than 6 pints of 3-4% lager/beer per week or no more than 4½ pints of 5% lager/beer per week or no more than 1½ bottles wine per week or no more than ½ bottle of spirits per week.

So if your aim is to start drinking again and control your drinking, then you should keep your dinking within these limits. If you do relapse to heavy drinking when trying to keep drinking at safe amounts (controlled drinking), you will then know that complete abstinence is the only way forward for you in the long term. People will often need to demonstrate this to themselves before coming to a decision to aim for complete abstinence from alcohol. And that's not necessarily a bad thing. In order to have a good chance of staying off alcohol for ever, your mind will have to be completely made-up that this is the way you have to do it. If you have any doubt about this, then you are likely to relapse in time anyway.

To prepare to control your drinking, and keep it within healthy limits there are four stages to go through:

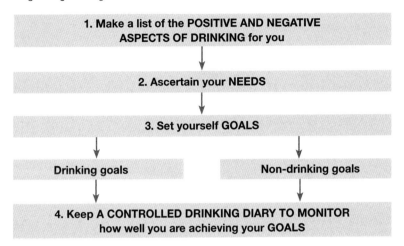

1. MAKE A LIST OF THE POSITIVE AND NEGATIVE ASPECTS OF DRINKING FOR YOU

Making a list of the things you find both helpful and unhelpful about drinking, is the starting point of this process. You will find that if you write this list, you will be able to see quite clearly what you need in your life, that at the present time you are trying to get from alcohol. If you made these lists when you read Chapter Three, then refer back to them now. Otherwise, continue right here. I've given some examples of the positive and negative reasons for drinking that people commonly write down. Cross these out if they don't apply to you, and then spend plenty of time thinking about the good and bad aspects of drinking for you – add to the list and make it your own.

Let's start by considering the possible reasons that you find drinking an enjoyable or helpful activity. Tick off those things on this list that apply to you, and add items of your own as you think of them. If you wish to record this for the future, I have included an empty table for you in the appendix of this book.

POSITIVE THINGS ABOUT DRINKING FOR YOU:

		Tick here
	Physical Health Reasons	
1	I enjoy the feeling of drinking and getting drunk.	
2	Drinking stops me getting withdrawal symptoms.	
3	I have trouble getting to sleep – without a drink I cannot sleep well.	
	Psychological Reasons	
4	I tend to get depressed and drinking improves my mood.	
5	Drinking makes me less anxious.	
6	I tend to get a bit paranoid about going out. If I have a drink I can get out the house without worrying.	
7	I'm usually tense and stressed - drinking helps me to relax.	
	Social Reasons	
8	I have a much better time going out if I have a drink.	
9	I can't imagine going out without having a drink.	
10	I tend to be anxious in the company of other people; when I have a drink inside me I can talk more easily and get on with people better.	
11	Iv'e become a bit of a loner over the years - the only time I ever get into a conversation is at the pub.	
	PUT YOUR OWN REASONS in the spaces below:	

NEGATIVE THINGS ABOUT DRINKING FOR YOU:

		Tick here
	Physical Health Reasons	
1	I'm feeling generally un-well most of the time.	
2	I never eat anything these days.	
3	I'm increasingly worried that I'm permanently damaging my physical health.	
4	I wake up early in the morning covered in sweat.	
	Psychological Reasons	
5	I feel horribly depressed when I wake up in the morning after drinking.	
6	My memory seems terrible these days.	
7	I seem so much more nervous than I used to be.	
8	I'm sick and tired of having this thing called alcohol in control of me. I want to get back in control of myself.	
	Social Reasons	
9	I want to be a better parent to my children.	
10	My relationship is a mess and I know it's because of my drinking.	
11	I've just been arrested for my second drink-drive offence – I might go to prison this time – I know I've got to do something about it.	
12	I'm finding it difficult to get into work on time – someone is going to say something soon.	
13	Of late my temper has got increasingly worse. I'm worried what I might do next time someone annoys me.	
	PUT YOUR OWN REASONS in the spaces below:	

2. ASCERTAIN YOUR NEEDS

When you have completed making the two lists above, you will be in a position to write down what your needs are – and in particular those needs that you will need to meet if you are to successfully control your drinking.

Use the table below to do this. By writing in a positive or negative reason for drinking, you should then be able to work out what you need to do to resolve that – write it down in the space below the reason for drinking. I've started by giving you a few examples. If you run out of space, I have included a blank table for you in the appendix.

Reason	I enjoy the feeling of drinking and getting drunk.
NEED	I need to have enjoyable feelings.
Reason	I have trouble getting to sleep – without a drink I cannot sleep well.
NEED	I need to sleep well.
Reason	I'm usually tense and stressed - drinking helps me to relax.
NEED	I need to relax.
Reason	I never eat anything these days
NEED	I need to eat well
Reason	I feel horribly depressed when I wake up in the morning after drinking.
NEED	I need to improve my mood
Reason	My relationship is a mess and I know it's because of my drinking.
NEED	I need to improve my relationship
Reason	
NEED	
Reason	
NEED	
Reason	
NEED	
Reason	
NEED	
Reason	
NEED	

3. SET YOURSELF GOALS

You should set yourself two types of goals – 'drinking goals' and 'non-drinking goals'. 'Non-drinking goals' do not necessarily mean that you do not drink when you are trying to achieve these goals; it's just that they are not directly about drinking. E.g., a 'drinking goal' might be to drink 2 units and no more on a particular evening. A 'non-drinking goal' might be to cook a meal. Your drinking goals will be what you plan to drink (how many units) on a particular day of the week. If you are to attempt to return to controlled drinking, then I advise you to take it slowly at first – do not plan to return immediately to drinking 21 units weekly, or as much as 3 units in one night. Gradually get to these levels over a period of months, or settle for drinking less than this in the long term.

Your 'non-drinking' goals will involve meeting the needs you have made a list of above. Now if you manage to successfully control your drinking, some of these things will automatically sort themselves out for themselves (e.g. morning sweats and withdrawal symptoms will not return). If you are lucky, other things like your relationship and your mood will also improve as a direct result of reduced drinking. However, many of the reasons you have used alcohol may have been there before you ever started drinking – these problems will not be resolved merely by a cessation of drinking (e.g. you may have started drinking heavily because of stress at work). Equally, some of the problems caused by drinking may have become so difficult that they will take more than just stopping drinking to sort them out. These will need to be addressed by other means. If you fail to address them, they will put you at risk of a return to heavy drinking in due course.

And when you set your non-drinking goals in order to resolve these problems, you will also need to take into account your drinking goals.

Let's consider an example.

Example 'need': 'I need to have enjoyable feelings'

When considering how to achieve this without getting drunk, you will need to get away from the idea (which may have become a dominant one for you), that the only way you can experience pleasure is by drinking. You will need to think of other means of experiencing pleasure without drinking. Having done this, you will need to write these things down in the form of 'goals'. Here are some common themes that come out of this exercise when I run it by people in my clinic: socialising, sex and eating. Many people who have developed an alcohol problem will have forgotten how to socialise without the use of alcohol, will have poor sex lives (when they may well have had excellent sex lives in the past) and currently eat very little and are not particularly bothered by food (despite the fact that they used to enjoy food). Focus on similar things for you, and turn them into goals:

- **Goal – I will arrange to socialise with non-drinking friends on one evening this week.**

....

- **Goal – I will talk to my partner about our sex life on one evening this week.**

....

- **Goal – I will cook a lovely meal one night this week.**

....

Of vital importance is to link these goals up with your 'drinking goals'. Say this is your first week back drinking after a period of abstinence, and you have decided to drink on two nights of the week, and have one unit on one night, and two units on the other night. How will you tie this up with your 'non-drinking goals'. Here's an example of how you might do that:

Firstly, on the evening that you go out with non-drinking friends, there will be no need to drink alcohol.

Secondly, on the night you decide to talk to your partner about your sex life, you may decide to make it a touch more relaxing and even romantic by opening a half-bottle of wine – why not have the two units on that night? (Be prepared to re-cork the bottle if your partner does not drink).

Thirdly, why not have a single glass of wine on the night you cook the meal?

By doing things in such a manner, you may manage to **slightly enhance** the activities you have planned by the healthy, controlled use of alcohol. And, of course, that must be your aim if you are planning to return to controlled drinking. **Your drinking should never again be about getting drunk, or forgetting unpleasant feelings. It must only be about slightly enhancing the pleasures you get from non-drinking activities.** If you ever allow the idea of the main plan for the evening being about having a drink, then you will surely relapse to heavy, uncontrolled drinking again in good time. As someone who has had a drink problem in the past, this is going to be difficult to get your head around. Really, the safest option is to aim for abstinence in the long term – for life. If you cannot imagine yourself having only a small amount to drink, with the aim of just **slightly enhancing** the pleasure you take from **another activity,** then you should probably think twice before starting to drink again. If you see no point in drinking like this, then you are probably best not drinking at all.

Before you set your goals, there are some other important things to take into account:

Goals must be **realistic**; e.g. do not plan to drink 21 units on Saturday and nothing for the rest of the week. Spread your planned drinking out over the week, allowing for at least 2 days without drinking at all. When you start to drink again, aim at first to keep it well below the total units 'allowed in a week'.

Goals must be **specific** and measurable; e.g. I will drink 2 units of alcohol on two days this week; I will go to the pub only once this week; I will see non-drinking friends once this week.

Goals must be **short-term** e.g. over the next week, or next day. While it is important to have a long-term objective in mind, this will not be reached overnight; if you are to achieve control over yourself, you must set short-term goals, and do your utmost to stick to them.

To achieve this, **break your long-term goals down into smaller steps**; e.g. if you plan to end up drinking 21 units per week, then plan to start by drinking 2 units on one day weekly, then every other day, then on five days weekly. Once you have achieved this, think about increasing by another unit on one day weekly etc.etc..

Decide on the goals yourself – allow others to advise you, but make the decisions for yourself.

FINALLY: LEARN FROM YOUR FAILURES:

Doubtless, you will not achieve all your goals every day – that would not be human. The important thing is to question why you failed to achieve a particular goal, and then re-plan to make the goal more realistic. You should dwell on the positive more realistic plan and **not berate yourself for failure**. E.g.

- **You planned to drink 2 glasses of wine with your friends at a pub on Wednesday evening but ended up drinking 6 glasses:**

- **Why did this happen? Answer: you were offered another drink after the 2 glasses and did not find it in yourself to refuse.**

- **Possible solutions:**

  - at the beginning of the next evening out, ask your friends not to offer you another drink after you have drunk two; OR

  - get up and leave half-way through the second drink, so that your friends are not given an opportunity to offer you another; OR

  - drink non-alcoholic drinks for the first half of the evening, and only start to drink alcohol one hour before closing time.

Repeat this re-planning process, as often as you feel like it; but at least once weekly. Set your goals for the next week and keep a **'drinking diary'** (see below). Fill this in every day before your memory fades, and then **review it weekly.** This will help you pick up patterns that you might otherwise miss, e.g. a tendency to drink more if you had an argument that day; a tendency to drink less if you went walking that day etc. etc.

So here are some examples of a mixture of drinking and other goals:

Examples of goals include:

- **I will see my drinking friends only once weekly at first.**

- **I will see my non-drinking friends at least once this week.**

- **I will spend two evenings reading this week, and drink nothing.**

- **I will drink a maximum of 2 units on Monday this week.**

- **I will spend all Tuesday looking at jobs advertised in the paper.**

- **On Thursday evening I will go to Relate with my partner.**

- **I will phone a dating agency on Wednesday.**

- **I will drink a maximum of 1 unit on Friday evening.**

CONTROLLED DRINKING DIARY

DAY OF WEEK

BEFORE		
DRINKING GOAL 1:		
Do you plan to drink?	Yes ☐	No ☐
How much do you plan to drink?		
AFTER		
Did you keep to your drinking plan?	Yes ☐	No ☐
If not, where did it go wrong?		
How could you change it for the better?		
What will you do the next time to make it work?		

BEFORE
DRINKING GOAL 2:
Do you plan to drink? Yes ☐ No ☐
How much do you plan to drink?
AFTER
Did you keep to your drinking plan? Yes ☐ No ☐
If not, where did it go wrong?
How could you change it for the better?
What will you do the next time to make it work?

BEFORE
DRINKING GOAL 3:
Do you plan to drink? Yes ☐ No ☐
How much do you plan to drink?
AFTER
Did you keep to your drinking plan? Yes ☐ No ☐
If not, where did it go wrong?
How could you change it for the better?
What will you do the next time to make it work?

SO, IN SUMMARY:

- Identify the positive and negative aspects of drinking for you – I suggest you take at least a week over this during the time you are abstinent – write them down, and add to the list over the week.

- Identify your needs, using the list of the positive and negative aspects of drinking – take another week over this.

- Set goals – take another week to plan your goals.

- Try to put into practice the goals you have set yourself, and start to keep the drinking diary.

- Continue, by learning from failures and reviewing your drinking diary on a weekly basis. Praise yourself for your successes, and plan how you will turn this week's failures into next week's successes.

- If in time you find yourself starting to drink more and more heavily above healthy limits, but have not yet become physically addicted, then stop all drinking immediately if you can. Leave it a couple of months, and then try again to restart drinking, minimally at first, and increasing only as far as the World Health Organization guidelines.

- If after one year, you have not achieved your longterm goal of controlled drinking within healthy limits, re-consider whether this is a realistic alternative for you, or whether complete abstinence is the only way forward.

CONCLUSION

You should now be in a position to implement the best possible plan for you, in order to achieve abstinence and then control your drinking in the long term. Everything I have advised you to do in this book is based on the research which demonstrates the best way 'on average' for someone to stay dry. This fits the majority of people, but not everyone, and different elements of the overall plan will be better suited to some individuals than to others. To arrive at the best possible plan for you as an individual, and to limit those odds of relapsing to the minimum you will need individual advice about your particular situation.

You can get this for free by telephoning the DryOutNow.com Immediate Response Service on 0800 160 1020.

Now, at the point of reading this book you will most likely be in the 'planning phase' – getting ready for abstinence and the rest of your life without alcohol or with controlled drinking. Following is a check list of everything I advise you to have in place before you suddenly find yourself without a drink available to you. Continue straight to Part III, when you are satisfied that you have made all your decisions.

PREPARATION PHASE CHECKLIST	Tick
1 Make absolutely sure you are ready to progress with planning for abstinence from controlled drinking. If you have any doubts re-read Chapter 3, telephone the **DryOutNow.com Immediate Response Service on 0800 160 1020**.	
2 Arrange for some individual counselling to start as soon as possible – ideally before starting to control your drinking and continuing during and after you have achieved this. Get details of your local counsellors by telephoning the **DryOutNow.com Immediate Response Service on 0800 160 1020**.	
3 IIf you are up for it, attend some AA – ideally before starting to control or stop your drinking and continuing during and after you have achieved this. Get details of your AA meetings by telephoning the **DryOutNow.com Immediate Response Service on 0800 160 1020**.	
4 Make a decision about whether or not you wish to go to residential rehabilitation.If you wish to clarify this or get advice about the best residential rehabilitation units for you, telephone the **DryOutNow.com Immediate Response Service on 0800 160 1020**.	
5 Make a decision about how you are going to cease drinking – sudden stop or detox. If you wish to take advice regarding this telephone the **DryOutNow.com Immediate Response Service on 0800 160 1020** to discuss the options.	
6 If you choose detoxification and are considering the self-pay option, telephone the **DryOutNow.com Immediate Response Service (0800 160 1020)** to get advice on the unit that will best suit your needs and to make use of the free booking, medical advice and support service. In most circumstances you should leave a period of weeks before admission for detox, in order to complete your planning.	
7 Start to write your weekly activity diary. Make use of the various tables in this chapter to assess your needs and replace drinking with other activities that have the potential to lead to fulfillment.	

PREPARATION PHASE CHECKLIST	Tick
8 Speak to those you live with about drinking in the house while you are trying to cut down your drinking and after you have achieved abstinence.	
9 If you have difficulties at work, then make a plan about how you are going to minimise these difficulties. If you would like confidential advice around these issues, then phone the **DryOutNow.com Immediate Response Service on 0800 160 1020**.	
10 If you have difficulties in your relationship with your partner, telephone Relate on 0845 1304016, to book relationship counselling	
11 Get expert medical advice about whether or not you can be prescribed medication to prevent relapse – either visit your GP or phone the **DryOutNow.com Immediate Response Service (0800 160 1020)** to get free telephone advice and/or details of your nearest private doctor who can advise on this.	

PART THREE

HOW TO MAXIMISE THE ODDS OF
SUCCESS FOR YOU AS AN INDIVIDUAL

If at any time you require urgent access to treatment, or need an immediate response for any other reason, do not hesitate to telephone the DryOutNow.com Immediate Response Service (IRS) on:

0800 160 1020
(8am-9pm, seven days weekly)

PART THREE

Now you have completed reading the other sections of this book, you should be in a good position to make decisions about the kind of help you need, find and get that help, and remain abstinent or drinking within healthy limits for the rest of your life.

However, at this point, I need to throw just a small spanner in the works.

- The advice I have given in this book is based on the research evidence which demonstrates which treatments work best. This means that if you follow the advice, the odds are that you will do better than if you don't follow the advice.

- However, that is a very different thing to saying that you will do the best it's possible for you to do simply by following the advice in this book.

Research evidence is provided by studying **groups** of people over time, and seeing how they do **on average.** For example, if I gave a sleeping pill to 10 people and 7 of them slept well, but 3 had a terrible night, the research results would show that on average the pill worked well to send people to sleep. That is, the odds of getting a good night's sleep would be in your favour if you took the pill.

But what if you were one of the 3 people who had a terrible night's sleep? The pill certainly didn't work for you. Might there be a way of predicting this, and therefore coming up with a better way for you as an individual to get a good night's sleep than taking the pill?

The answer is yes – **there is a better way to do that.**

- To make the most out of this book, and to maximise your chances of achieving abstinence or controlled drinking, **you should seek individual expert advice.**

- You can get this for free and in complete confidence by telephoning the DryOutNow.com Immediate Response Service on 0800 160 1020. There are two reasons I suggest you do this: There are two reasons I suggest you do this:

The first reason: people differ – no one is 'average' – everyone is an individual.

People vary so much as individuals that what is right for one person will not necessarily be right for another. To iron out the best possible way forward for you as an individual, you will need to actually talk to someone – and that someone should have expertise in the treatment of people with alcohol problems.

One obvious example of a way in which people with alcohol problems differ from each other is the experience of craving. The things that trigger craving for some people are completely different from the things that trigger craving for others. Some people start to crave for drink heavily when they get excited and in a particularly good mood; others only experience craving when they get depressed. Most people will have to completely avoid going in to a pub ever again if they are to avoid relapsing to alcoholism. A few will successfully return to the pub on a regular basis, drink orange and lemonade, and do this happily for the rest of their life.

In this book, it is impossible for me to tell you whether you are likely to experience craving when you get excited, or whether you will only crave when you get depressed. Equally, in this book, it is impossible for me to tell you whether you could be one of those people who could safely return to the pub after detox. However, by speaking to a professional advisor, that person may well be able to make a judgement on these kind of things. How could they do that? Simply because over the years people who work regularly in the field have built up what doctors refer to as 'clinical experience'. Probably the best example of the importance of long experience in a job comes from the classic army scenario – a new junior officer arrives fresh from training and well up on all the latest military theories and practice - however, when the battle arrives he makes mistakes and puts the platoon in danger – it is the old sergeant with 20 years of experience under his belt who saves the day.

The second reason you should seek individual expert advice is that you may suffer from what doctors call 'complicating factors':

A variety of physical, psychological and social complications may have an impact on the best way forward in treatment for you. The possible examples are too numerous to list – the only way to really make sure that these are taken into account is by seeking individual expert advice. Here is just one example of how your individual circumstances could radically alter what is the best way forward for you:

- In most of the Chapters on Your Route Through Treatment (Chapters 4 to 10), and also in Chapter 3: 'Are You Ready?' I gave routine advice about not rushing things. I emphasised the importance of both making sure you really wanted to do this, and also spending at least a period of weeks preparing before you were admitted for detox. This advice is based on evidence that has demonstrated that on average, people who form an 'aftercare plan' before going into detox are more likely to succeed in staying dry in the longer term. However, in certain circumstances, to delay things could make things worse rather than better. If you are suffering from some complications of liver failure such as difficulty with blood clotting, or episodes of confusion, then you really should be admitted to hospital as an emergency – to wait for a period of weeks in such an instance may even be fatal.

There are many other potential complicating factors such as depression, other psychiatric illness, elements of brain damage, serious physical illness of various kinds, pregnancy etc.etc. – the presence of any of these difficulties will alter the detail of the kind of help you need, and will also impact on your choice of detox unit. For example, some detox units cater very well for people with severe liver disease; but while these units excel in their medical cover, there are other units that offer a better all round service for a cheaper price. The unit you should choose will depend on your particular circumstances.

My message here is that ascertaining the best treatment plan for you as an individual depends on two things:

A: Taking into account the research evidence that says what the best way forward is 'on average' (that's largely covered by this book).

AND in addition

B: Getting individual advice by telephone or face-to-face, from an expert who can advise you how to maximise the odds in your favour taking into account your individual needs.

To get advice on any aspect of your difficulty with alcohol call the DryOutNow.com Immediate Response Service on 0800 160 1020.

CONCLUSION

You have now reached the end of this book. My main aim in this book has been to give you the knowledge to maximise your chances of beating the disease of alcoholism, according to the research evidence available, and by giving you details of all your local help contacts. To improve your chances further, and to take advice on the best way forward for you as an individual, then I advise you to make use of the contacts for free, confidential advice provided above.

I wish you luck.

Best wishes,

Dr Bruce Trathen

APPENDICES

If at any time you require urgent access to treatment, or need an immediate response for any other reason, do not hesitate to telephone the DryOutNow.com Immediate Response Service (IRS) on:

0800 160 1020
(8am-9pm, seven days weekly)

	MONDAY	TUESDAY	WEDNESDAY	THURSDAY	FRIDAY	SATURDAY	SUNDAY
Activity 1: 6-8							
Activity 2: 6-8							
Activity 1: 8-10							
Activity 2: 8-10							
Activity 1: 10-12							
Activity 2: 10-12							
Activity 1: 12-2							
Activity 2: 12-2							
Activity 1: 2-4							
Activity 2: 2-4							
Activity 1: 4-6							
Activity 2: 4-6							
Activity 1: 6-8							
Activity 2: 6-8							
Activity 1: 8-10							
Activity 2: 8-10							
Activity 1: 10-12							
Activity 2: 10-12							
NIGHT-TIME 1							
NIGHT-TIME 2							

	MONDAY	TUESDAY	WEDNESDAY	THURSDAY	FRIDAY	SATURDAY	SUNDAY
Activity 1: 6-8							
Activity 2: 6-8							
Activity 1: 8-10							
Activity 2: 8-10							
Activity 1: 10-12							
Activity 2: 10-12							
Activity 1: 12-2							
Activity 2: 12-2							
Activity 1: 2-4							
Activity 2: 2-4							
Activity 1: 4-6							
Activity 2: 4-6							
Activity 1: 6-8							
Activity 2: 6-8							
Activity 1: 8-10							
Activity 2: 8-10							
Activity 1: 10-12							
Activity 2: 10-12							
NIGHT-TIME 1							
NIGHT-TIME 2							

	MONDAY	TUESDAY	WEDNESDAY	THURSDAY	FRIDAY	SATURDAY	SUNDAY
Activity 1: 6-8							
Activity 2: 6-8							
Activity 1: 8-10							
Activity 2: 8-10							
Activity 1: 10-12							
Activity 2: 10-12							
Activity 1: 12-2							
Activity 2: 12-2							
Activity 1: 2-4							
Activity 2: 2-4							
Activity 1: 4-6							
Activity 2: 4-6							
Activity 1: 6-8							
Activity 2: 6-8							
Activity 1: 8-10							
Activity 2: 8-10							
Activity 1: 10-12							
Activity 2: 10-12							
NIGHT-TIME 1							
NIGHT-TIME 2							

www.dryoutnow.com
IMMEDIATE RESPONSE SERVICE: CALL 0800 160 1020 NOW

	MONDAY	TUESDAY	WEDNESDAY	THURSDAY	FRIDAY	SATURDAY	SUNDAY
Activity 1: 6-8							
Activity 2: 6-8							
Activity 1: 8-10							
Activity 2: 8-10							
Activity 1: 10-12							
Activity 2: 10-12							
Activity 1: 12-2							
Activity 2: 12-2							
Activity 1: 2-4							
Activity 2: 2-4							
Activity 1: 4-6							
Activity 2: 4-6							
Activity 1: 6-8							
Activity 2: 6-8							
Activity 1: 8-10							
Activity 2: 8-10							
Activity 1: 10-12							
Activity 2: 10-12							
NIGHT-TIME 1							
NIGHT-TIME 2							

www.dryoutnow.com
IMMEDIATE RESPONSE SERVICE:
CALL 0800 160 1020 NOW

Appendices - 269

	MONDAY	TUESDAY	WEDNESDAY	THURSDAY	FRIDAY	SATURDAY	SUNDAY
Activity 1: 6-8							
Activity 2: 6-8							
Activity 1: 8-10							
Activity 2: 8-10							
Activity 1: 10-12							
Activity 2: 10-12							
Activity 1: 12-2							
Activity 2: 12-2							
Activity 1: 2-4							
Activity 2: 2-4							
Activity 1: 4-6							
Activity 2: 4-6							
Activity 1: 6-8							
Activity 2: 6-8							
Activity 1: 8-10							
Activity 2: 8-10							
Activity 1: 10-12							
Activity 2: 10-12							
NIGHT-TIME 1							
NIGHT-TIME 2							

POSITIVE THINGS ABOUT DRINKING FOR YOU:

		Tick here
	Physical Health Reasons	
1	I enjoy the feeling of drinking and getting drunk.	
2	Drinking stops me getting withdrawal symptoms.	
3	I have trouble getting to sleep – without a drink I cannot sleep well.	
	Psychological Reasons	
4	I tend to get depressed and drinking improves my mood.	
5	Drinking makes me less anxious.	
6	I tend to get a bit paranoid about going out. If I have a drink I can get out the house without worrying.	
7	I'm usually tense and stressed - drinking helps me to relax.	
	Social Reasons	
8	I have a much better time going out if I have a drink.	
9	I can't imagine going out without having a drink.	
10	I tend to be anxious in the company of other people; when I have a drink inside me I can talk more easily and get on with people better.	
11	I've become a bit of a loner over the years - the only time I ever get into a conversation is at the pub.	
	PUT YOUR OWN REASONS in the spaces below:	

POSITIVE THINGS ABOUT DRINKING FOR YOU:

		Tick here
	Physical Health Reasons	
1	I enjoy the feeling of drinking and getting drunk.	
2	Drinking stops me getting withdrawal symptoms.	
3	I have trouble getting to sleep – without a drink I cannot sleep well.	
	Psychological Reasons	
4	I tend to get depressed and drinking improves my mood.	
5	Drinking makes me less anxious.	
6	I tend to get a bit paranoid about going out. If I have a drink I can get out the house without worrying.	
7	I'm usually tense and stressed - drinking helps me to relax.	
	Social Reasons	
8	I have a much better time going out if I have a drink.	
9	I can't imagine going out without having a drink.	
10	I tend to be anxious in the company of other people; when I have a drink inside me I can talk more easily and get on with people better.	
11	I've become a bit of a loner over the years - the only time I ever get into a conversation is at the pub.	
	PUT YOUR OWN REASONS in the spaces below:	

POSITIVE THINGS ABOUT DRINKING FOR YOU:

		Tick here
	Physical Health Reasons	
1	I enjoy the feeling of drinking and getting drunk.	
2	Drinking stops me getting withdrawal symptoms.	
3	I have trouble getting to sleep – without a drink I cannot sleep well.	
	Psychological Reasons	
4	I tend to get depressed and drinking improves my mood.	
5	Drinking makes me less anxious.	
6	I tend to get a bit paranoid about going out. If I have a drink I can get out the house without worrying.	
7	I'm usually tense and stressed - drinking helps me to relax.	
	Social Reasons	
8	I have a much better time going out if I have a drink.	
9	I can't imagine going out without having a drink.	
10	I tend to be anxious in the company of other people; when I have a drink inside me I can talk more easily and get on with people better.	
11	I've become a bit of a loner over the years - the only time I ever get into a conversation is at the pub.	
	PUT YOUR OWN REASONS in the spaces below:	

POSITIVE THINGS ABOUT DRINKING FOR YOU:

		Tick here
	Physical Health Reasons	
1	I enjoy the feeling of drinking and getting drunk.	
2	Drinking stops me getting withdrawal symptoms.	
3	I have trouble getting to sleep – without a drink I cannot sleep well.	
	Psychological Reasons	
4	I tend to get depressed and drinking improves my mood.	
5	Drinking makes me less anxious.	
6	I tend to get a bit paranoid about going out. If I have a drink I can get out the house without worrying.	
7	I'm usually tense and stressed - drinking helps me to relax.	
	Social Reasons	
8	I have a much better time going out if I have a drink.	
9	I can't imagine going out without having a drink.	
10	I tend to be anxious in the company of other people; when I have a drink inside me I can talk more easily and get on with people better.	
11	I've become a bit of a loner over the years - the only time I ever get into a conversation is at the pub.	
	PUT YOUR OWN REASONS in the spaces below:	

POSITIVE THINGS ABOUT DRINKING FOR YOU:

		Tick here
	Physical Health Reasons	
1	I enjoy the feeling of drinking and getting drunk.	
2	Drinking stops me getting withdrawal symptoms.	
3	I have trouble getting to sleep – without a drink I cannot sleep well.	
	Psychological Reasons	
4	I tend to get depressed and drinking improves my mood.	
5	Drinking makes me less anxious.	
6	I tend to get a bit paranoid about going out. If I have a drink I can get out the house without worrying.	
7	I'm usually tense and stressed - drinking helps me to relax.	
	Social Reasons	
8	I have a much better time going out if I have a drink.	
9	I can't imagine going out without having a drink.	
10	I tend to be anxious in the company of other people; when I have a drink inside me I can talk more easily and get on with people better.	
11	I've become a bit of a loner over the years - the only time I ever get into a conversation is at the pub.	
	PUT YOUR OWN REASONS in the spaces below:	

NEGATIVE THINGS ABOUT DRINKING FOR YOU:

		Tick here
	Physical Health Reasons	
1	I'm feeling generally un-well most of the time.	
2	I never eat anything these days.	
3	I'm increasingly worried that I'm permanently damaging my physical health.	
4	I wake up early in the morning covered in sweat.	
	Psychological Reasons	
5	I feel horribly depressed when I wake up in the morning after drinking.	
6	My memory seems terrible these days.	
7	I seem so much more nervous than I used to be.	
8	I'm sick and tired of having this thing called alcohol in control of me. I want to get back in control of myself.	
	Social Reasons	
9	I want to be a better parent to my children.	
10	My relationship is a mess and I know it's because of my drinking.	
11	I've just been arrested for my second drink-drive offence – I might go to prison this time – I know I've got to do something about it.	
12	I'm finding it difficult to get into work on time – someone is going to say something soon.	
13	Of late my temper has got increasingly worse. I'm worried what I might do next time someone annoys me.	
	PUT YOUR OWN REASONS in the spaces below:	

NEGATIVE THINGS ABOUT DRINKING FOR YOU:

		Tick here
	Physical Health Reasons	
1	I'm feeling generally un-well most of the time.	
2	I never eat anything these days.	
3	I'm increasingly worried that I'm permanently damaging my physical health.	
4	I wake up early in the morning covered in sweat.	
	Psychological Reasons	
5	I feel horribly depressed when I wake up in the morning after drinking.	
6	My memory seems terrible these days.	
7	I seem so much more nervous than I used to be.	
8	I'm sick and tired of having this thing called alcohol in control of me. I want to get back in control of myself.	
	Social Reasons	
9	I want to be a better parent to my children.	
10	My relationship is a mess and I know it's because of my drinking.	
11	I've just been arrested for my second drink-drive offence – I might go to prison this time – I know I've got to do something about it.	
12	I'm finding it difficult to get into work on time – someone is going to say something soon.	
13	Of late my temper has got increasingly worse. I'm worried what I might do next time someone annoys me.	
	PUT YOUR OWN REASONS in the spaces below:	

NEGATIVE THINGS ABOUT DRINKING FOR YOU:

		Tick here
	Physical Health Reasons	
1	I'm feeling generally un-well most of the time.	
2	I never eat anything these days.	
3	I'm increasingly worried that I'm permanently damaging my physical health.	
4	I wake up early in the morning covered in sweat.	
	Psychological Reasons	
5	I feel horribly depressed when I wake up in the morning after drinking.	
6	My memory seems terrible these days.	
7	I seem so much more nervous than I used to be.	
8	I'm sick and tired of having this thing called alcohol in control of me. I want to get back in control of myself.	
	Social Reasons	
9	I want to be a better parent to my children.	
10	My relationship is a mess and I know it's because of my drinking.	
11	I've just been arrested for my second drink-drive offence – I might go to prison this time – I know I've got to do something about it.	
12	I'm finding it difficult to get into work on time – someone is going to say something soon.	
13	Of late my temper has got increasingly worse. I'm worried what I might do next time someone annoys me.	
	PUT YOUR OWN REASONS in the spaces below:	

NEGATIVE THINGS ABOUT DRINKING FOR YOU:

		Tick here
	Physical Health Reasons	
1	I'm feeling generally un-well most of the time.	
2	I never eat anything these days.	
3	I'm increasingly worried that I'm permanently damaging my physical health.	
4	I wake up early in the morning covered in sweat.	
	Psychological Reasons	
5	I feel horribly depressed when I wake up in the morning after drinking.	
6	My memory seems terrible these days.	
7	I seem so much more nervous than I used to be.	
8	I'm sick and tired of having this thing called alcohol in control of me. I want to get back in control of myself.	
	Social Reasons	
9	I want to be a better parent to my children.	
10	My relationship is a mess and I know it's because of my drinking.	
11	I've just been arrested for my second drink-drive offence – I might go to prison this time – I know I've got to do something about it.	
12	I'm finding it difficult to get into work on time – someone is going to say something soon.	
13	Of late my temper has got increasingly worse. I'm worried what I might do next time someone annoys me.	
	PUT YOUR OWN REASONS in the spaces below:	

NEGATIVE THINGS ABOUT DRINKING FOR YOU:

		Tick here
	Physical Health Reasons	
1	I'm feeling generally un-well most of the time.	
2	I never eat anything these days.	
3	I'm increasingly worried that I'm permanently damaging my physical health.	
4	I wake up early in the morning covered in sweat.	
	Psychological Reasons	
5	I feel horribly depressed when I wake up in the morning after drinking.	
6	My memory seems terrible these days.	
7	I seem so much more nervous than I used to be.	
8	I'm sick and tired of having this thing called alcohol in control of me. I want to get back in control of myself.	
	Social Reasons	
9	I want to be a better parent to my children.	
10	My relationship is a mess and I know it's because of my drinking.	
11	I've just been arrested for my second drink-drive offence – I might go to prison this time – I know I've got to do something about it.	
12	I'm finding it difficult to get into work on time – someone is going to say something soon.	
13	Of late my temper has got increasingly worse. I'm worried what I might do next time someone annoys me.	
	PUT YOUR OWN REASONS in the spaces below:	

Reason	I enjoy the feeling of drinking and getting drunk.
NEED	I need to have enjoyable feelings.
Reason	I have trouble getting to sleep – without a drink I cannot sleep well.
NEED	I need to sleep well.
Reason	I'm usually tense and stressed - drinking helps me to relax.
NEED	I need to relax.
Reason	I never eat anything these days
NEED	I need to eat well
Reason	I feel horribly depressed when I wake up in the morning after drinking.
NEED	I need to improve my mood
Reason	My relationship is a mess and I know it's because of my drinking.
NEED	I need to improve my relationship
Reason	
NEED	
Reason	
NEED	
Reason	
NEED	
Reason	
NEED	
Reason	
NEED	
Reason	
NEED	
Reason	
NEED	
Reason	
NEED	
Reason	
NEED	

Reason	I enjoy the feeling of drinking and getting drunk.
NEED	I need to have enjoyable feelings.
Reason	I have trouble getting to sleep – without a drink I cannot sleep well.
NEED	I need to sleep well.
Reason	I'm usually tense and stressed - drinking helps me to relax.
NEED	I need to relax.
Reason	I never eat anything these days
NEED	I need to eat well
Reason	I feel horribly depressed when I wake up in the morning after drinking.
NEED	I need to improve my mood
Reason	My relationship is a mess and I know it's because of my drinking.
NEED	I need to improve my relationship
Reason	
NEED	
Reason	
NEED	
Reason	
NEED	
Reason	
NEED	
Reason	
NEED	
Reason	
NEED	
Reason	
NEED	
Reason	
NEED	

Reason	I enjoy the feeling of drinking and getting drunk.
NEED	I need to have enjoyable feelings.
Reason	I have trouble getting to sleep – without a drink I cannot sleep well.
NEED	I need to sleep well.
Reason	I'm usually tense and stressed - drinking helps me to relax.
NEED	I need to relax.
Reason	I never eat anything these days
NEED	I need to eat well
Reason	I feel horribly depressed when I wake up in the morning after drinking.
NEED	I need to improve my mood
Reason	My relationship is a mess and I know it's because of my drinking.
NEED	I need to improve my relationship
Reason	
NEED	
Reason	
NEED	
Reason	
NEED	
Reason	
NEED	
Reason	
NEED	
Reason	
NEED	
Reason	
NEED	
Reason	
NEED	

Reason	I enjoy the feeling of drinking and getting drunk.
NEED	I need to have enjoyable feelings.
Reason	I have trouble getting to sleep – without a drink I cannot sleep well.
NEED	I need to sleep well.
Reason	I'm usually tense and stressed - drinking helps me to relax.
NEED	I need to relax.
Reason	I never eat anything these days
NEED	I need to eat well
Reason	I feel horribly depressed when I wake up in the morning after drinking.
NEED	I need to improve my mood
Reason	My relationship is a mess and I know it's because of my drinking.
NEED	I need to improve my relationship
Reason	
NEED	
Reason	
NEED	
Reason	
NEED	
Reason	
NEED	
Reason	
NEED	
Reason	
NEED	
Reason	
NEED	
Reason	
NEED	

Reason	I enjoy the feeling of drinking and getting drunk.
NEED	I need to have enjoyable feelings.
Reason	I have trouble getting to sleep – without a drink I cannot sleep well.
NEED	I need to sleep well.
Reason	I'm usually tense and stressed - drinking helps me to relax.
NEED	I need to relax.
Reason	I never eat anything these days
NEED	I need to eat well
Reason	I feel horribly depressed when I wake up in the morning after drinking.
NEED	I need to improve my mood
Reason	My relationship is a mess and I know it's because of my drinking.
NEED	I need to improve my relationship
Reason	
NEED	
Reason	
NEED	
Reason	
NEED	
Reason	
NEED	
Reason	
NEED	
Reason	
NEED	
Reason	
NEED	
Reason	
NEED	

CONTROLLED DRINKING DIARY

DAY OF WEEK

BEFORE

DRINKING GOAL 1:

Do you plan to drink?   Yes ☐   No ☐

How much do you plan to drink?

AFTER

Did you keep to your drinking plan?   Yes ☐   No ☐

If not, where did it go wrong?

How could you change it for the better?

What will you do the next time to make it work?

BEFORE

DRINKING GOAL 2:

Do you plan to drink?   Yes ☐   No ☐

How much do you plan to drink?

AFTER

Did you keep to your drinking plan?   Yes ☐   No ☐

If not, where did it go wrong?

How could you change it for the better?

What will you do the next time to make it work?

BEFORE

DRINKING GOAL 3:

Do you plan to drink?   Yes ☐   No ☐

How much do you plan to drink?

AFTER

Did you keep to your drinking plan?   Yes ☐   No ☐

If not, where did it go wrong?

How could you change it for the better?

What will you do the next time to make it work?

CONTROLLED DRINKING DIARY

DAY OF WEEK

BEFORE
....
DRINKING GOAL 1:
....
Do you plan to drink?　　　　　　　Yes ☐　　　No ☐
....
How much do you plan to drink?
....
AFTER
....
Did you keep to your drinking plan?　Yes ☐　　　No ☐
....
If not, where did it go wrong?
....
How could you change it for the better?
....
What will you do the next time to make it work?

BEFORE
....
DRINKING GOAL 2:
....
Do you plan to drink?　　　　　　　Yes ☐　　　No ☐
....
How much do you plan to drink?
....
AFTER
....
Did you keep to your drinking plan?　Yes ☐　　　No ☐
....
If not, where did it go wrong?
....
How could you change it for the better?
....
What will you do the next time to make it work?

BEFORE
....
DRINKING GOAL 3:
....
Do you plan to drink?　　　　　　　Yes ☐　　　No ☐
....
How much do you plan to drink?
....
AFTER
....
Did you keep to your drinking plan?　Yes ☐　　　No ☐
....
If not, where did it go wrong?
....
How could you change it for the better?
....
What will you do the next time to make it work?

CONTROLLED DRINKING DIARY

DAY OF WEEK

BEFORE

DRINKING GOAL 1:

Do you plan to drink?   Yes ☐   No ☐

How much do you plan to drink?

AFTER

Did you keep to your drinking plan?   Yes ☐   No ☐

If not, where did it go wrong?

How could you change it for the better?

What will you do the next time to make it work?

BEFORE

DRINKING GOAL 2:

Do you plan to drink?   Yes ☐   No ☐

How much do you plan to drink?

AFTER

Did you keep to your drinking plan?   Yes ☐   No ☐

If not, where did it go wrong?

How could you change it for the better?

What will you do the next time to make it work?

BEFORE

DRINKING GOAL 3:

Do you plan to drink?   Yes ☐   No ☐

How much do you plan to drink?

AFTER

Did you keep to your drinking plan?   Yes ☐   No ☐

If not, where did it go wrong?

How could you change it for the better?

What will you do the next time to make it work?

CONTROLLED DRINKING DIARY

DAY OF WEEK

BEFORE

DRINKING GOAL 1:

Do you plan to drink?   Yes ☐   No ☐

How much do you plan to drink?

AFTER

Did you keep to your drinking plan?   Yes ☐   No ☐

If not, where did it go wrong?

How could you change it for the better?

What will you do the next time to make it work?

BEFORE

DRINKING GOAL 2:

Do you plan to drink?   Yes ☐   No ☐

How much do you plan to drink?

AFTER

Did you keep to your drinking plan?   Yes ☐   No ☐

If not, where did it go wrong?

How could you change it for the better?

What will you do the next time to make it work?

BEFORE

DRINKING GOAL 3:

Do you plan to drink?   Yes ☐   No ☐

How much do you plan to drink?

AFTER

Did you keep to your drinking plan?   Yes ☐   No ☐

If not, where did it go wrong?

How could you change it for the better?

What will you do the next time to make it work?

CONTROLLED DRINKING DIARY

DAY OF WEEK

BEFORE

DRINKING GOAL 1:

Do you plan to drink?   Yes ☐   No ☐

How much do you plan to drink?

AFTER

Did you keep to your drinking plan?   Yes ☐   No ☐

If not, where did it go wrong?

How could you change it for the better?

What will you do the next time to make it work?

BEFORE

DRINKING GOAL 2:

Do you plan to drink?   Yes ☐   No ☐

How much do you plan to drink?

AFTER

Did you keep to your drinking plan?   Yes ☐   No ☐

If not, where did it go wrong?

How could you change it for the better?

What will you do the next time to make it work?

BEFORE

DRINKING GOAL 3:

Do you plan to drink?   Yes ☐   No ☐

How much do you plan to drink?

AFTER

Did you keep to your drinking plan?   Yes ☐   No ☐

If not, where did it go wrong?

How could you change it for the better?

What will you do the next time to make it work?

NON-DRINKING GOALS DIARY

DAY OF WEEK

NON-DRINKING GOAL 1:

Did you achieve your goal?   Yes ☐   No ☐

If not, where did it go wrong?

How could you change it for the better?

What will you do the next time to make it work?

NON-DRINKING GOAL 2:

Did you achieve your goal?   Yes ☐   No ☐

If not, where did it go wrong?

How could you change it for the better?

What will you do the next time to make it work?

NON-DRINKING GOAL 3:

Did you achieve your goal?   Yes ☐   No ☐

If not, where did it go wrong?

How could you change it for the better?

What will you do the next time to make it work?

NON-DRINKING GOALS DIARY

DAY OF WEEK

NON-DRINKING GOAL 1:

Did you achieve your goal?   Yes ☐   No ☐

If not, where did it go wrong?

How could you change it for the better?

What will you do the next time to make it work?

NON-DRINKING GOAL 2:

Did you achieve your goal?   Yes ☐   No ☐

If not, where did it go wrong?

How could you change it for the better?

What will you do the next time to make it work?

NON-DRINKING GOAL 3:

Did you achieve your goal?   Yes ☐   No ☐

If not, where did it go wrong?

How could you change it for the better?

What will you do the next time to make it work?

NON-DRINKING GOALS DIARY

DAY OF WEEK

NON-DRINKING GOAL 1:

Did you achieve your goal?   Yes ☐   No ☐

If not, where did it go wrong?

How could you change it for the better?

What will you do the next time to make it work?

NON-DRINKING GOAL 2:

Did you achieve your goal?   Yes ☐   No ☐

If not, where did it go wrong?

How could you change it for the better?

What will you do the next time to make it work?

NON-DRINKING GOAL 3:

Did you achieve your goal?   Yes ☐   No ☐

If not, where did it go wrong?

How could you change it for the better?

What will you do the next time to make it work?

NON-DRINKING GOALS DIARY

DAY OF WEEK

NON-DRINKING GOAL 1:

Did you achieve your goal?   Yes ☐   No ☐

If not, where did it go wrong?

How could you change it for the better?

What will you do the next time to make it work?

NON-DRINKING GOAL 2:

Did you achieve your goal?   Yes ☐   No ☐

If not, where did it go wrong?

How could you change it for the better?

What will you do the next time to make it work?

NON-DRINKING GOAL 3:

Did you achieve your goal?   Yes ☐   No ☐

If not, where did it go wrong?

How could you change it for the better?

What will you do the next time to make it work?

NON-DRINKING GOALS DIARY

DAY OF WEEK

NON-DRINKING GOAL 1:

Did you achieve your goal?   Yes ☐   No ☐

If not, where did it go wrong?

How could you change it for the better?

What will you do the next time to make it work?

NON-DRINKING GOAL 2:

Did you achieve your goal?   Yes ☐   No ☐

If not, where did it go wrong?

How could you change it for the better?

What will you do the next time to make it work?

NON-DRINKING GOAL 3:

Did you achieve your goal?   Yes ☐   No ☐

If not, where did it go wrong?

How could you change it for the better?

What will you do the next time to make it work?

....

....

....

....

....

....

....

....

....

....

....

....

....

....

....

....

....

....

....

....

....

....

....

....

....

....

....

....

....

....

....

....

....

....

....

....

....

....

....

....

....

....

....

....

....

....

www.dryoutnow.com
IMMEDIATE RESPONSE SERVICE: CALL 0800 160 1020 NOW

....
....
....
....
....
....
....
....
....
....
....
....
....
....
....
....
....
....
....
....
....
....

www.dryoutnow.com
IMMEDIATE RESPONSE SERVICE:
CALL 0800 160 1020 NOW

....

....

....

....

....

....

....

....

....

....

....

....

....

....

....

....

....

....

....

....

....

....

....

....

....

....

....

....

....

....

....

....

....

....

....

....

....

....

....

....

....

....

....

....

....

....

....

....

....

....

....

....

....

....

....

....

....

....

....

....

....

....

....

....

....

....

....

....

....

....

....

....

....

....

....

....

....

....

....

....

....

....

....

....

....

....

....

....

....

....

....

....

....

....

....

....